PRAEGER INTRODUCTORY GEOGRAPHIES

Germany

Praeger Introductory Geographies

ITALY
J. P. Cole

FRANCE
E. Estyn Evans

SPAIN
W. B. Fisher and H. Bowen-Jones

HUMAN GEOGRAPHY
Emrys Jones

EAST-CENTRAL EUROPE
R. H. Osborne

GERMANY

An Introductory Geography

by

T. H. ELKINS

FREDERICK A. PRAEGER, *Publishers*
New York · Washington

BOOKS THAT MATTER

Published in the United States of America in 1968
by Frederick A. Praeger, Inc., Publishers
111 Fourth Avenue, New York, N.Y. 10003

The original edition of this book
was published in 1960
by Chatto & Windus, London,
and a revised edition was issued in 1968.

Library of Congress Catalog Card Number: 68-55931

Printed in the United States of America

PREFACE

This book is intended to meet the needs of students of geography in high schools and in colleges and universities for a treatment of Germany intermediate in length between that found in the normal textbook on Europe and in the advanced university text. The opportunity has been taken to give a picture of Germany which goes a little beyond the narrowly geographical. It is hoped that this will enable the student of geography to deepen his understanding of the life and history of the country he is studying, and also render the book useful to others who are seeking a background knowledge of the land of Germany, its evolution, and its problems.

Certain explanations are necessary on the controversial question of Germany's eastern frontiers. The frontier on the Oder-Neisse line is not at the date of writing recognized by all nations, least of all by the inhabitants of West Germany. The fact remains that since 1945 the German population has been expelled from all territory east of the line, and replaced by a continuous Soviet and Polish population under effective Soviet and Polish rule. This has been recognized by excluding territory east of Oder-Neisse line from the regional, but not from the historical, sections of the book. It is realized that this attempt to deal realistically with Germany's present eastern frontier will cause pain to many friends in West Germany; nevertheless, even unrecognized frontiers are major facts of geography, and it is impossible to ignore their existence.

The term 'West Germany' is to be taken as meaning the territory of the 'German Federal Republic', while 'western Germany' implies the territory west of the Elbe and Saale rivers in a more general sense. Correspondingly, 'eastern Germany' refers to all land continuously settled by Germans east of the Elbe and Saale. The term 'East Germany' is taken in its current English sense to mean the territory of the 'German Democratic Republic', formed from the Soviet zone of military occupation. This territory was at the time of writing officially referred to in West Germany as 'Central Germany' (*Mitteldeutschland*). In West German official language 'East Germany' (*Ostdeutschland*) means the territory lost to Poland and the U.S.S.R. in 1945, sometimes known as the 'Separated Territories'.

There is also a danger of criticism from many sides on the forms of place-name chosen. Where there is a commonly accepted English form, it is used in the text that follows: Cologne is preferred to Köln, and Black Forest to Schwarzwald. Place-names beyond Germany's present frontiers for which there is no common English form are given in the language of their present owners, even if the names are of German origin: Strasbourg is preferred to Strassburg.

Throughout the book, the population of towns is given in thousands for 1965, as in Stuttgart (633). All heights, distances, areas, etc., are given in both metric and British units, except in the case of weights since the metric ton (2,205 lb) is almost the same as the British, or long, ton (2,240 lb).

Since the first edition of this book was published, in 1960, there have been profound changes in the structure of German industry and in its supplies of energy, which have greatly changed the economic geography of the country. It is now much easier than ten years ago to distinguish what is a reaction to new economic forces from what was merely a restoration of an old pattern. In particular, attention has become focused on the significance of the *Verdichtungsgebiete*, the great agglomerations of industry, services and population.

To give some account of all these changes it has been necessary to revise and substantially to rewrite the chapters dealing with modern Germany and its economy, as well as all the regional chapters. The opportunity has also been taken to revise the treatment of some sections where scholarly opinion has now changed, notably with regard to the origins of rural settlement.

T. H. Elkins

Acknowledgement Note

The publishers would like to thank the German Tourist Information Bureau and Foto-Gräf Düsseldorf for permission to reproduce the photographs on the cover and jacket.

CONTENTS

MAPS AND DIAGRAMS

TABLES

Chapter 1

INTRODUCTION

THE LAND OF GERMANY AND ITS FRONTIERS

At the heart of the triangular peninsula that is Europe outside the U.S.S.R. lies Germany, centrally placed and uncertainly poised between east and west. The chapters that follow will, it is hoped, reveal something of the richness and variety of the German land as it has been developed by man over the centuries. First, however, it would be well to notice the broader relationships between Germany and its geographical environment. Three major facts emerge: Germany lacks physical unity and clearly marked frontiers; as a state it has notably failed to include all German-speaking peoples; and finally, in spite of being unified under one rule from 1871 to 1945, it still shows strong contrasts of interest and outlook between its various regions.

The European peninsula is divided physically into a number of major belts of country running from east to west (Fig. 1). The most prominent belt consists of the great arc of the Alpine fold mountains, which shut off to the south the Mediterranean world in which Germany, unlike her neighbour France, has no part. To the north, the Alps look down on a lower country of hills and included basins, the Central Uplands. Beyond that again lies the Northern Lowland of Europe, broadening eastwards to merge in the vast plains of Poland and Russia. The German land is made up of these three major elements, Alps, Central Uplands, Northern Lowland. Linking the three is the slender thread of the Rhine, the historical axis of the German people.

Yet Germany does not embrace the whole of any one of these belts; it is merely a section cut across them, running from the Alps across the Central Uplands and Northern Lowland to the Baltic. Only in the south and north is the boundary reasonably clear; to east and west the major belts of terrain pass without break into the territory of neighbouring states. Here the borders of the German realm are tragically vague, and have fluctuated throughout history.

The boundary is most definite in the north, where it is provided by the waters of the North Sea and the Baltic, with only a few land miles across the base of the Jutland peninsula.

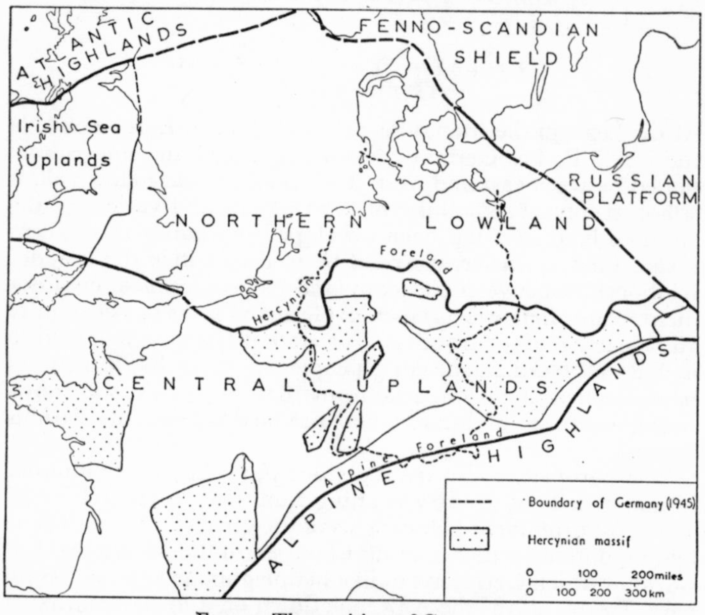

FIG. 1. The position of Germany.
(Structural divisions after Linton.)

Yet even this line is of comparatively recent origin; the Swedes held land on the southern shore of the Baltic until the Napoleonic era, while the present Schleswig-Holstein frontier with Denmark was established only in 1920.

In the south, the Alps once again provide a fairly definite barrier, but in no sense a sharp 'natural frontier'. The Alps are not a line but a major region; the people who live there have developed states of their own, so that German territory does not extend beyond the extreme northern fringe of the mountains.

In the west, the story of Germany's frontier is of centuries of retreat, and of conflict between the German view of the Rhine as the traditional axis of the German lands, and the French striving for the river as a 'natural' eastern frontier. In medieval times the German Empire stretched westwards beyond the Meuse and Saône rivers, yet today Burgundy, Lorraine, Luxemburg and Alsace have all been lost, and for over 100 miles the Rhine, that once lay at the heart of Germany, is now its western frontier.

The great permanent French gains had all been made by the eve of the French Revolution; the really catastrophic recent changes have been in the east. No natural feature on which a stable frontier can be based crosses the Northern Lowland; the open plain stretches from Berlin to Warsaw, even to Moscow, without substantial break. In 1914, German territory stretched eastwards to Memel on the Baltic, and to industrial Upper Silesia. Yet by 1945 the effective frontier of Germany had been thrust back to the Oder and Neisse rivers, and millions of Germans had been expelled by the Poles and Russians from land that their forefathers had occupied since the Middle Ages. In view of the bitterness left by these enforced movements, it would be rash indeed to prophesy that the question of Germany's eastern frontier will not again disturb the peace of Europe.

GERMANY AND THE GERMAN-SPEAKING PEOPLES

The second characteristic of the modern German state is that its boundaries have never, even at their greatest extent in 1941–4, expanded to include all German-speaking peoples. In Switzerland, men of German speech have separated themselves to join with their French-speaking mountain neighbours, while the neighbouring Austrians were forcibly expelled from Germany, first by a rising Prussia, then by the victors of 1918. In the west, the reasons are rather different; German-speaking peoples lie outside German state territory in Alsace, Lorraine and Luxemburg because they have been forcibly detached in the course of the long advance of France towards the 'natural frontier' of the Rhine.

In the east, conditions vary again. In medieval times, groups of German settlers had pushed deep into eastern and south-eastern Europe, far beyond the limits even of the Germany of

1871–1914. Their descendants remained until the present century, carefully preserving their German identity, so that their relations with other nationalities became more and more explosive as modern nationalism set in. After the defeat of Germany in 1945, the terrible decision was taken to expel them, and millions of Germans were sent back to the homeland that their forefathers had left centuries before. In this most tragic way the eastern boundary of the German-speaking peoples has now come to coincide with the *de facto* eastern frontier of the state of Germany.

THE DIVISIONS OF GERMANY

Perhaps the most important thing to remember about Germany as a country is that from the 13th to the 19th centuries it was only a group of states, lacking any effective central leadership. This fragmentation has enabled the various regions of Germany to preserve their individuality to a degree unimaginable in France or Britain. The dividing lines within the country were sharpened by the outcome of the Reformation and Counter-Reformation, which split the country into a substantially Roman Catholic south and west, a predominantly Protestant north and east. These regional contrasts were sufficiently deep-rooted to survive the effects of three-quarters of a century of rigid Prussian centralization.

The Rhinelands are pulled by ties of religion, culture and commerce westwards towards France, southwards to the Alps and beyond them, Italy. From the Rhinelands Frankish missionaries carried Christianity to the heathen Hessians and Saxons further east, and through the Rhinelands spread the French culture that dominated the intellectual life of Germany in the 17th and 18th centuries. After strong discouragement in the period 1871–1945, this feeling of internationalism and of common interest with the adjoining Catholic countries emerged once more in the support given by the postwar West German government to the various projects for European Union.

In the southeast, Bavaria has a very marked individuality as the largest of the former German states to retain a degree of independence from Prussia. Little affected until recently by the growth of modern industry, Bavaria has remained strongly agricultural, strongly Catholic, strongly conservative, opposed alike to centralization and to liberalism in the German government. Naturally Bavaria has strong links with Austria, and with the Danube lands as a whole.

The ports of the northern coast stand in striking contrast; they have naturally cosmopolitan interests, looking out across the oceans of the world, and a long tradition of liberalism and independent government. Then there is colonial Germany, carved in the Middle Ages from the Slav lands beyond the Elbe and Saale rivers. The states that developed here, Saxony and, above all, Brandenburg-Prussia, were always preoccupied with the poorly defined frontier on the wide lowland to the east. They tended to be larger and more efficient than the states of western Germany. Prussia in particular, under rulers like Frederick the Great and Bismarck, developed the rigid centralization and consistent purpose that led eventually to dominance over all Germany.

This long-continued political fragmentation is in many ways a key to the understanding of German affairs today. It was the fundamental weakness which led alike to the failure to establish firm frontiers and to the failure of the German state to unite all German peoples. Fragmentation also explains in part the rigidity of German centralization and the violence of German nationalism; the separatist tendencies of the various regions were so strong that they had to be crushed by violence, and held in check by nationalism. The same weakness led to long cultural subordination to France. The strong traditions of regional self-interest explain, too, why the postwar division of Germany, although officially deplored, was long accepted calmly by the people of western Germany; it was easy to slip into the older, more local, allegiances.

So Germany remains geographically, and in many ways culturally, a shifting scene, full of contradictions. Frontiers change, people are displaced in millions, armies pass, cities are ruined and rise again. It is a country at once devoted to regional independence and to rigid control from the centre, at once endowed with many individual links with neighbouring countries and yet subject to periodic indulgence in intense nationalism. Fortunately the postwar settlement, which might be regarded as rendered inherently unstable by the division of Germany and of Berlin, surprisingly survived without major conflict for a longer period than did the Versailles settlement that closed the First World War.

SOME STANDARD WORKS ON GERMANY

R. E. DICKINSON, *Germany: A general and regional geography* (Methuen), 2nd ed., 1961.

P. GEORGE and J. TRICART, *L'Europe centrale*, 2 vols. (Presses Universitaires de France), Paris, 1954.

F. KLUTE (ed.), *Das Deutsche Reich*, Potsdam, 1936 and 1940 (vols. 1 & 2 of Handbuch der geographischen Wissenschaft).

E. DE MARTONNE, *Europe centrale* (A. Colin), Paris, 1930 (vol. 4, pt. 1 of the *Géographie Universelle*).

K. A. SINNHUBER, *Germany, its geography and growth* (John Murray), 1961 (Chester Springs, Pa: Dufour, 1961).

Statistisches Jahrbuch für die Bundesrepublik Deutschland (Kohlhammer-Verlag), Stuttgart, annual, 1952 ff.

Statistisches Jahrbuch der Deutschen Demokratischen Republik (V.E.B. Deutscher Zentralverlag), Berlin, annual, 1955 ff.

Die Bundesrepublik Deutschland in Karten (Kohlhammer-Verlag), Mainz, 1965, etc. (The 'National Atlas' of the Federal Republic).

A valuable aid to teaching is the collection of annotated maps known as *Deutsche Landschaften: geographische-landeskundliche Erläuterungen zur Topographischer Karte 1:50,000*. Bad Godesberg (Bundesanstalt für Landeskunde und Raumforschung), 1963, etc.

PART ONE
THE LAND

Chapter 2
THE PHYSICAL BASIS

THE BUILDING OF THE CENTRAL UPLANDS

Most people have some kind of picture in their minds of the typical German countryside. Generally there is a ruined castle, from which vineyards slope steeply to a river. On a fertile plain near by is a village of irregular, half-timbered houses, and the whole scene is backed by mountains covered with a dark and menacing forest. Rather surprisingly, this romantic Grimms' fairy-tale landscape is in fact typical of the Central Uplands, the first of the three major regions, Alps, Central Uplands and Northern Lowland, into which Germany is divided. The Central Uplands are not only the most varied and characteristically German of the three, but were the first to assert their identity in the process of the building of the land.

For the beginnings of the story we must look back to the Primary or Palaeozoic era of geological time, when a vast mass of sediments was accumulated in a great sea that lay over what is now Germany. In the course of the mountain-building movements to which we give the name Hercynian,[1] the Primary sediments were driven against the edge of the rigid Fenno-Scandian Shield to the north. They were crumpled into a mountain chain, running in a series of great arcs from east to west across Europe. Immense deltaic swamps developed as the mountains began to rise, and have left us Europe's greatest mineral treasure, the coal of Carboniferous age. The seams are preserved today in small basins within the Uplands (Saar) and in larger fields dipping off their northern edge (Aachen, Ruhr).

By the end of Primary times these once mighty mountains

[1] From *Hercynia Silva*, the classical name for the forest which, at the beginning of our era, covered the remains of these mountains in Germany.

SYSTEM		CHARACTERISTIC ROCKS	PRINCIPAL AREAS OF OCCURRENCE	ASSOCIATED ECONOMIC MINERALS
TERTIARY	Pliocene Miocene Oligocene Eocene	gravel sandstone clay limestone	Rhine Rift Valley, Basins of Hesse, Lower Rhine & Saxon 'Bays'	gravel, limestone for cement, salt & potash of Rhine Rift Valley, brown coal, ceramic clays
CRETACEOUS	Upper	clay, limestone, sandstone	Lower Saxon Hills, Westphalian Basin, Dresden Basin	limestone for cement
	Lower	clay, sandstone	Lower Saxon Hills, Upper Palatinate, Lowland	iron ore of Harz Foreland & Upper Palatinate, Wealden coal of Lower Saxon Hills
JURASSIC	Malm	limestone, clay	South German Scarplands & Lower Saxon Hills	limestone for cement, lithographic stone, iron ore in Northern Lowland
	Dogger	sandstone, clay		brown iron ore of South German Scarplands, oolithic iron ore of Northern Lowland
	Lias	clay, some limestone		
TRIASSIC	Keuper	sandstone, clay	South German Scarplands, Thuringian Basin	
	Muschelkalk	limestone	Weser Hills	limestone for cement, salt in Baden-Württemberg & Thuringia
	Bunter	sandstone, clay	South German Scarplands & Hesse	building stone, lead in Rh. Uplands, salt in Northern Lowland
PERMIAN	Zechstein	clay, limestone, salt, conglomerate	Thuringia, Harz Foreland	major salt and potash deposits, anhydrite, gypsum, dolomite copper of Harz
	Rotliegendes	sandstone, conglomerate	Saar-Nahe Hills, Saxony, Thuringia	Coal of Saxony & Thuringia

The sedimentary rocks of the basins of the Central Uplands, with their economic minerals had been laid low by erosion, and their stumps were covered by the seas of the succeeding Secondary or Mesozoic era, which deposited another series of sedimentary rocks, ranging in age from Triassic to Cretaceous. The Secondary rocks were fairly thin where they covered the roots of the old Hercynian mountains in Germany, but miles thick in the great trough or Alpine geosyncline that lay to the south.

Just as the Primary rocks had been driven northwards to form the Hercynian mountains, so in the Alpine mountain-building period the secondary rocks of the geosyncline were in their turn driven north against the Hercynian remnants, piling up great folds in the process. Under the impact, the resistant Hercynian rocks, too rigid to fold, shattered into a number of independent blocks. Some blocks were forced upwards by the pressure, and remain today as Hercynian massifs, their Secondary cover stripped away by erosion. In the intervening basins, the Secondary rocks were preserved with only gentle flexuring, since really violent folding was prevented by the resistance of the Hercynian rocks beneath. Finally, there were a few areas of subsidence so great that, as in the Rhine Rift Valley, Tertiary seas and lakes left deposits hundreds, even thousands of feet in thickness (Fig. 2).

The shattering of the remains of the Hercynian mountains did not take place haphazardly, but along diagonal lines of weakness which dominate the pattern of relief in the Central Uplands to this day. One set of lines runs from southeast to northwest, the most prominent forming the strikingly sharp southwestern edge of the Bohemian Massif and its continuation, the Thuringian Forest. Intersecting these at right angles are southwest to northeast faults and flexures which continue the Hercynian trends of eastern France.[1] These can best be seen in the Rhenish Uplands.

The diamond-mesh pattern of the major trend lines is reflected in the shape of hill masses and in the course of rivers throughout the Central Uplands, as a glance at Figure 2 will show. Yet cleft right across this orderly arrangement is the great downfaulted trough of the Rhine Rift Valley, following a direction a little to the east of north, and providing an immensely important water, road and rail routeway through the hills of southern Germany. It should be carefully noted that the Rift Valley is continued northwards, not by the gorge of

[1] See E. Estyn Evans, *France* (Frederick A. Praeger), p. 10, Fig. 4.

the Rhine through the Rhenish Uplands, but through the downfaulted basins of Hesse further east. This is another vital land route, although almost hidden on the map because it is

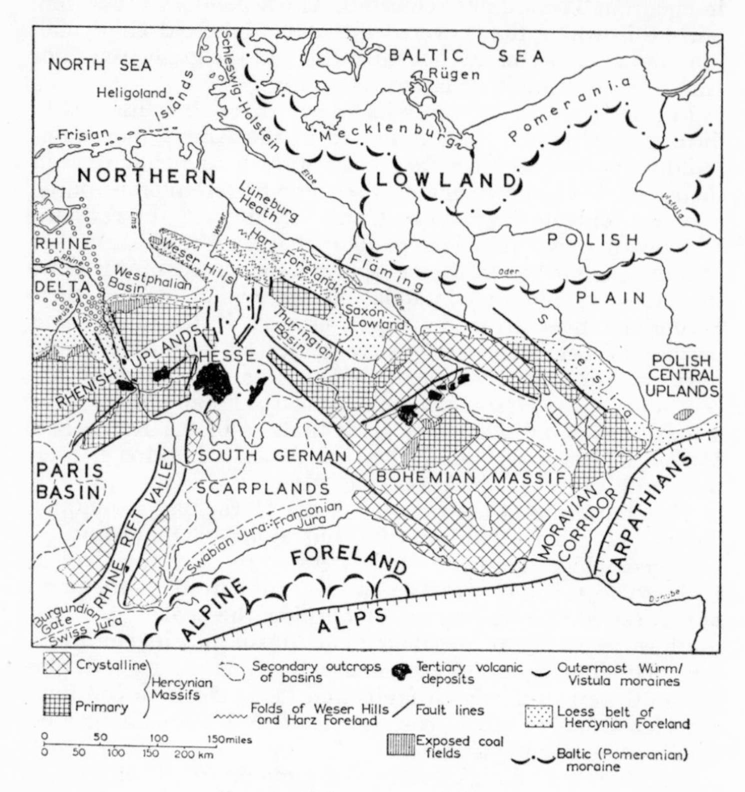

FIG. 2. Major structural features.

nearly blocked by the volcanic Volgelsberg massif. Such volcanic outpourings were frequently associated with Tertiary faulting, and contribute to the variety of the German landscape.

As a result of the earth history that has been outlined, there are two major types of country in the Central Uplands, the

Hercynian massifs, and their intervening scarpland basins. In addition, variety is introduced by two less widespread types, the downfaulted Tertiary basins, and the volcanic districts.

REGIONS OF THE CENTRAL UPLANDS

Lowlands and Massifs of South Germany. The Central Uplands can be divided into three main parts: the lowlands of southern Germany proper, a forested upland barrier which stretches from the Rhine to Bohemia, and lastly the fringe regions bordering the Northern Lowland.

In southern Germany, lowlands predominate; rather small and isolated Hercynian blocks appear only on either side of the Upper Rhine. Originally, the Vosges and *Black Forest* (Schwarzwald) must have been linked to form one of the major massifs of the Central Uplands, but they have been broken apart through the sinking of a central strip, about 40 km/25 miles wide, to form the *Rhine Rift Valley*. This has a total length of about 300 km/180 miles, and is filled with hundreds of feet of Tertiary rocks, topped by a skin of Rhine terrace gravels.

The greatest heights of both Vosges and Black Forest are in the south, where the thrust of the Alpine folding was greatest. Northwards their crystalline rocks dip beneath a cover of Secondary sediments, but on both sides of the Rhine the massif rises again still further north to underlie the sandstone hills of the *Haardt* to the west and of the *Odenwald* to the east. All of these highlands have steep, fault-line escarpments facing inwards to the Rift Valley. On the outer side, the descent is much more gentle, to the scarplands of Lorraine and of the Paris Basin in the west, and of southern Germany in the east (Fig. 41).

In contrast to the predominantly Jurassic and Cretaceous scarplands of England and France, the *Scarplands of Southern Germany* are mainly composed of Triassic rocks. The work of erosion on the eastward-dipping strata has left the sandstones standing out as wooded west or northwest-facing scarps, overlooking vales or low plateaus on the clays or flaggy Muschelkalk limestones. The sequence of Triassic rocks ends in the south and east against the great scarps of the Swabian and Franconian Juras, built of resistant Jurassic Limestone, and rising to over 1,000 m/3,000 ft (Figs 40 and 42).

The Northern Barrier Arc. This open and climatically favoured land of southern Germany is cut off to the north by a barrier composed of Hercynian massifs and forested sandstone plateaus. The eastern buttress of the arc is formed by the *Bohemian Massif*, the borders of which are clearly marked by the Sudetes, rising to 1,600 m/5,000 ft in the northeast, the long ridge of the Ore Mountains (Erzgebirge) in the northwest, and by the Bohemian Forest in the southwest. These highlands shelter an interior basin, in which Secondary rocks are preserved, and into which the drainage of the massif converges before escaping northwards by the single exit of the river Elbe. The favourable loam and loess soils of the basin were occupied by a Slav people, the Czechs; only the mountain borders were later occupied by Germans and so remain, in part, within the boundaries of Germany today.

The western part of the barrier is provided by another Hercynian massif, the *Rhenish Uplands* (Rheinische Schiefergebirge). This great block of contorted slates is tilted generally northwestwards towards the Northern Lowland (Fig. 47). Erosion surfaces cut across the slates give the surface of the massif a rather monotonous appearance, broken only by occasional quartzite ridges, rising to 850 m/2,800 ft.

Into the massif is sawn the spectacular gorge of the Rhine, providing the most important of the rare routeways through the barrier arc. The Rhine and its deeply incised tributary valleys are all that most people, travelling through by rail, road or water, ever see of the Rhenish Uplands; the plateau surfaces themselves are lonely and thinly peopled. Some variety is given to the scene by volcanic activity, responsible for the eroded volcanic necks of the Siebengebirge, the flooded craters and cinder cones of the Eifel, or the sombre basalt flows of the Westerwald. On the fringes of the massif are vitally important coalfields, the Saar in the south and the Aachen and Ruhr fields to the north.

The last link in the barrier is provided by the uplands of *Hesse*. The rocks are mainly Triassic, as in southern Germany, but they are not tilted and dissected into scarps. Instead they lie almost horizontally, forming sterile, forested plateaus of Bunter Sandstone. Volcanic activity in Tertiary times added the great Vogelsberg and Rhön (950 m/3,117 ft) massifs, as well as scores of minor volcanic necks, nearly all crowned by a castle in this military barrier zone. Fortunately the accident of geological history which created the Rhine Rift Valley and its northward prolongation has provided a way through the hills. By means of a series of faulted Tertiary basins, the traveller can penetrate the barrier arc, and emerge onto the Northern Lowland (Fig. 46).

The Northern Fringe of the Central Uplands. Beyond the upland barrier there are four transitional regions, in which the lively and changing relief of the Central Uplands begins to give place to the monotony of the Northern Lowland. First of all, there are two gentle scarpland basins, balanced on either side of the plateaus of Hesse, the *Thuringian Basin* (Fig. 57) in the east and the *Westphalian Basin* (Fig. 51) in the west. In each, the subdued relief has been partially invaded by glacial outwash sands from further north.

Hesse and the Westphalian Basin are then barred off from the Northern Lowland by the *Weser and Lower Saxon Hills*. Here the structure of the Secondary rocks takes yet another form, differing alike from southern Germany and from Hesse. This time they are rather tightly folded into a number of roughly east–west trending anticlines and synclines, very reminiscent of southern England. Erosion has carved the folded rocks into escarpments and vales, breaching the anticlines to form 'Wealden' country, with scarps facing inwards over an interior lowland. The most prominent of these breached anticlines, the Weser Hills, pushes far out to the northwest, separating the Westphalian Basin from the Northern Lowland (Figs 51 and 53).

North of the Harz, in the *Harz Foreland*, the Secondary rocks of the Lower Saxon Hills gradually disappear beneath later deposits. The wooded escarpments stand like islands, half buried in a 'sea' of glacial deposits and loess, in this transitional region between Central Uplands and Northern Lowland.

ALPS AND ALPINE FORELAND

The Alps. The great arc of the Alps lies almost entirely outside Germany. The frontier includes only limited sections of the outer limestone Alps and, especially in the west, sandstone foothills. The ranges are broken by south–north valleys, their sides steepened by the glaciers which once emerged from them onto the Foreland to the north.

The Alpine Foreland. While the Alps were being uplifted, a profound furrow developed along the outer side of the mountain arc, which was filled by sandstones, conglomerates and clays swept down by torrents from the peaks. By the end of the Tertiary period the furrow had become the plain known as the Alpine Foreland, which is at its widest in Germany (Fig. 43).

The surface detail of the Foreland today is mainly the result of the Pleistocene Ice Age. There were four or five major advances and retreats of the ice, which geologists have named in alphabetical order after rivers of the Foreland (see Table below). Only the deposits of the last advance, the Würm, remain fresh today. In this glaciation, the ice emerged from the major Alpine valleys to form piedmont glaciers, semi-

ALPS	NORTHERN LOWLAND	REMARKS
Würm	Vistula (Weichsel)	The younger drifts of the N. Lowland E. of Elbe. Geologists distinguish six or seven groups of terminal moraines, of which the most prominent are: (North) Pomeranian (Centre) Frankfurt (South) Brandenburg.
Riss	Saale	Leached drifts W. of Elbe. The eroded Warthe terminal moraine (Lüneburg Heath—Fläming—Lusatian Heath) belongs here geographically, although many geologists regard it as the outermost stage of the Vistula glaciation.
Mindel	Elster	Scattered erratics of northern fringe of Central Uplands.
Günz	?	No certain equivalent in N.
? Danube	?	No certain equivalent in N.

The glaciations of the Northern Lowland, with their probable Alpine equivalents.

circular lobes stretching some 30–60 km/20–35 miles into the plain. Where the ice came to a halt, terminal moraines were built up, which remain today as crescentic hills, looping across the plain. Beyond the edge of the ice, flood water laid down sheets of outwash gravel, while within the terminal moraines the retreating ice left irregular deposits of boulder clay, and many lakes. Only in the northeast, where the Foreland is at its widest, do the Tertiary clays and sandstones emerge from beneath the glacial drifts to form a low hill country.

THE NORTHERN LOWLAND

Less than 150 km/90 miles broad in the west, the Lowland widens eastwards across the whole of northern Germany to merge without a break into the plains of Poland and Russia. It is bounded on the south by the Central Uplands, on the north by the waters of the North Sea and Baltic. Like the Alpine Foreland, it is an area where Tertiary rocks have been deposited. Like the Foreland also, its surface detail is almost entirely due to glacial action.

Once again, several Ice Ages separated by warmer interglacial periods are recognized (see Table on p. 26). The Elster glaciation advanced the furthest south, but is represented mainly by scattered erratic blocks on the northern slopes of the Central Uplands. Drifts of the succeeding Saale period occupy most of the Northern Lowland west of the Elbe. East of this river, the Saale drifts are covered over all but the southern fringe of the Lowland by drifts of the latest, Vistula, glaciation. Naturally, these latest drifts are fresher and less affected by erosion than the earlier ones, and this provides the main basis for regional division.

Within the Northern Lowland, the dividing line marked approximately by the River Elbe appears again and again. Not only do the glacial drifts differ on either side of this line, but so also do the Secondary and Tertiary rocks on which they are deposited. In historical times, too, the Elbe line has come to be a major division within Germany, separating areas of contrasting development and type of settlement.

The Eastern Lowland. The rather gently flexured Secondary rocks which underlie the eastern part of the Northern Lowland only rarely appear from beneath the drift cover. Over their even surface once spread Tertiary lakes and great swamp-forests, from which widespread brown-coal seams are derived. The characteristic landforms associated with great ice sheets can here be seen at their clearest, for they derive from the most recent (Vistula) glaciation, and have not been worn away by subsequent erosion. The ice sheet originated in Scandinavia, and formed a great lobe over the Lowland east of the Elbe line. It evidently retreated northwards in stages and each time the sheet came to rest a terminal moraine was formed, a tangled mass of rock fragments of all sizes released from the melting ice. There are thus several distinct moraines, named in the Table on page 26, which run in roughly parallel arcs across the Lowland and then converge northwestwards into the Schleswig-Holstein peninsula (Fig. 54). The moraine ridges form the only hills of the Lowland, rising locally to 180 m/600 ft.

As on the Alpine Foreland the terminal moraines divide two contrasting types of terrain. Within each moraine, the rapid decay of the retreating ice normally left behind an irregular sheet of boulder clay, with many hollows filled by lakes or marshes. Outside the moraine, floods of water from the melting ice deposited gravel cones, and wide spreads of outwash sand (*Sander*). The finer silts and clays were often carried away completely, greatly to the detriment of future agricultural development on the Northern Lowland.

One further complication adds to the originality of the scene east of the Elbe. Since the ice sheets came from the north, they blocked the natural escape of drainage to the Baltic. The water of the rivers of the Central Uplands, greatly swollen in summer by meltwater from snowfields, and from the ice sheet itself, could not flow directly to the Baltic, and had to escape laterally round the ice margin into the North Sea. In doing so, it cut a deep ice-margin trench at right angles to the normal direction of drainage. When the ice retreated, a new marginal trench would be established further north. Today a sequence of these trenches, or *Urstromtäler* as they are known in German, can be seen on the Lowland east of the Elbe. The present rivers follow them in part, but have mainly re-established their courses to the north.

The Western Lowland. The Secondary rocks which underlie the glacial drifts west of the Elbe are much more disturbed than those to the east, and the complicated structures of the Lower

Saxon Hills are continued northwards as far as Schleswig-Holstein. Occasionally, as in the island of Heligoland, the 'solid' rock actually breaks through to the surface. The existence of these structures beneath the drift is of great importance in the mining of salt and oil deposits.

The drifts west of the Elbe, and in the extreme southern strip of the Lowland east of the Elbe, are mainly the product of the older Saale glaciation, and so lack fresh, youthful landforms. Terminal moraines have been reduced to fragments by erosion, lakes filled up, and boulder clays leached of their nutriment. Much of the Lowland west of the Elbe accordingly consists of rather featureless sandy heathland, divided by old glacial spillways and by the present river valleys into low plateau blocks, known as *Geest* (Fig. 53). Peat bogs are frequent, especially in the more oceanic northwest.

The Lower Rhinelands. The sandy *Geest* merges without definite break into the vast alluvial cone or delta built up by the swollen Ice Age ancestors of the Rhine and Meuse. The cone begins where the Rhine leaves the Rhenish Uplands, and broadens out to form the whole of the Netherlands and northern Belgium. Since the Ice Age, the Rhine has incised itself into the cone, so that today it flows in a broad flood plain between flights of terraces. As the Netherlands frontier is neared, the flood plains of the Rhine and its tributaries become ever broader, and the rivers themselves have to be embanked to prevent flooding.

The Coasts. Here, too, the contrast between the western and eastern sections of the Northern Lowland may be observed. The North Sea coast continues the type familiar in the Netherlands; an offshore bar, crowned with sand dunes, has been shattered and left as the fringing chain of the sandy Frisian islands. Subsidence, continued to the present day, has allowed the sea to invade the land behind the islands, forming mud banks, exposed at low tide, known as *Watten*. The mud banks build up gradually into salt marsh, which has been embanked and drained by man. The coast is broken by the estuaries of the Elbe, Weser and Ems rivers, and by drowned inlets like the Jade and Dollart bays (Figs 53, 54).

The coast of the calmer Baltic sea is less strikingly developed. The boulder-clay plains of Schleswig-Holstein shelve rather uneventfully beneath the Baltic, although the coast is given interest by long inlets (*Förden*) carved by water moving in tunnel-valleys beneath the ice sheet. The Mecklenburg coast is more varied, with glacial inlets, cliffs like those of the island of Rügen and beach bars. The bars become more continuous eastwards, giving the coast of Pomerania its typically smooth outline, and forming the well-known coastal spits (*Nehrungen*) of the eastern Baltic. In general, the Baltic coast lacks the wide river estuaries which provide such valuable doors onto the world for West Germany (Figs 54, 59).

Periglacial Features. The effects of the Ice Age were not restricted to the area covered by the Scandinavian and Alpine ice sheets. In the Central Uplands, actual glaciers were very small and restricted to the highest massifs, but the whole area was subjected to extremely rapid erosion, since there was no vegetation cover to check the movement of sheets of frost-shattered débris down into the valleys. The material accumulated at far too great a rate to be carried away by the rivers, and choked the valleys, being subsequently dissected into river terraces.

These loose and unprotected surfaces, in particular the outwash deposits surrounding the ice sheets, were most vulnerable to wind erosion. Clouds of dust particles were picked up and deposited as loess along the northern flank of the Central Uplands, and in basins within them. The fine, lime-rich loess provides the basis for extremely fertile and easily worked soils, which were cleared and settled in prehistoric times. Of outstanding importance is the loess belt of the Hercynian Foreland, which stretches from northern France along the northern fringe of the Central Uplands to merge eventually with the loess belt of the Ukraine. Not only is this a region of easy movement, early settlement and rich agriculture, but it coincides with the distribution of Germany's major coal-fields, and also with the main brown coal, potash and iron ore deposits. The human importance of the Hercynian Foreland in Germany will be apparent time and again in the pages that follow.

SUGGESTIONS FOR FURTHER READING

J. F. GELLERT, *Grundzüge der physischen Geographie von Deutschland*, vol. 1, Berlin (Deutscher Verlag der Wissenschaften), 1958.

E. M. YATES, 'The development of the Rhine', *Trans. Inst. Br. Geographers*, 32, 1963, pp. 410–25.

Chapter 3

CLIMATE, SOILS AND VEGETATION

CLIMATIC FORCES

In studying the climate of a country today, we try to deal not with lifeless statistics and averages, but with the movements of restless atmosphere that lie behind them. Seen from this point of view, the climate of Germany is first of all determined by its position between latitudes 47° and 55° North, on the eastern side of the North Atlantic Ocean, which brings the country fully into the belt of disturbed westerly winds. These consist in part of warm air which, flowing northwards from the subtropical high pressure belt, is swung by the earth's rotation into a southwesterly or westerly air stream. More frequently, the air is of polar origin, but is relatively warm in winter because of heating from below during its passage over the waters of the North Atlantic Drift. Since westerly air provides Germany's most important weather type, it is not surprising that coastal Germany has a midwinter temperature 8–10° C/15–18° F above the average for the latitude, and even Bavaria has 3° C/5° F above. When these westerly winds are blowing, there is usually much cloud at all levels, and there is sporadic precipitation, especially on windward slopes.

As this warm maritime air travels northeastwards over the Atlantic, it meets cold dense air moving southwards off the Polar ice cap. At the zone of contact originate the cyclonic storms, with associated low pressure, which are known as depressions. These also move eastwards, sometimes penetrating far into Europe. Since in the depressions air of such differing origin is associated, a very changeable type of weather results from their passing, and they are great bringers of rain or snow.

This procession of warm westerly air, with associated depressions, is naturally modified by the European land mass. All land areas tend to build up their own climates; they are warmer in summer, and colder in winter, than the seas at the same latitude. Germany, centrally placed in the European peninsula, is poised between the Atlantic and Eurasia, the greatest land mass in the world. The mountain barrier of the Alps lies to the south, where it tends to keep out air masses from that direction, leaving Germany to the north as a battleground, with no physical barrier to check the invasion of oceanic influences from the west, or continental influences from the east. The result of the battle is Germany's climate.

THE SEASONS

Winter is the season when continental influences are at their greatest, for then a cold mass of dense air builds up over eastern and central Europe, cut off from the warmth of the Mediterranean by the Alpine ranges. The dense air tends to flow outwards, extending the area of cold and fending off the mild westerly winds. Sometimes the cold air extends to the Atlantic, bringing to Germany Siberian winters with calm, bright weather and many degrees of frost, when the snow cover persists for many weeks. At other times the westerly circulation has the upper hand, bringing milder, stormy conditions with rain on the northern coast and snow showers inland. The further east one goes, the more continuously do continental conditions prevail, the lower are the average winter temperatures and the greater is the annual range between summer and winter figures (see Table on p. 36).

The west to east gradient of winter temperatures is reflected in the January 0° C/32° F sea-level isotherm, which runs from Denmark southwards completely across the country. The more open winters of the west are of great benefit in animal husbandry and the growing of delicate crops. All over Germany the winter (especially February) is the period of minimum precipitation.

Spring is a period of transition, when the Siberian High breaks up and temperature rises rapidly over the land, especially in the hitherto frozen east. Depressions, bringing rain, pass across the country not only from the Atlantic but from the Mediterranean. Total precipitation is everywhere greater than in winter, but distinctly below summer and, usually, autumn levels.

Summer reverses winter conditions, with the land warmer than the sea. A huge low-pressure system covers Siberia and eastern

Europe, towards and within which move shallow depressions, bringing the thundery rains which provide the summer maximum rainfall characteristic of Germany. Prolonged spells of sunny, extremely hot weather, sometimes lasting all August and into September, occur when the Azores High, with its subsiding tropical air, extends across the south of the country.

Summer isotherms run east–west, and nearly all Germany is included between the July 17° C/64° F and 22° C/72° F sea level lines. Actual summer temperatures all over the country are remarkably even, since the greater intensity of insolation in the south is counterbalanced by the greater length of day and lower elevation to the north.

Autumn is again a period of transition. September often differs little from August, but with the breakup of the Azores High a succession of depressions brings unsettled weather and rain again. Over all but the southeast of the country, autumn is distinctly wetter than spring, and the oceanic northwest even comes close to having a typically maritime autumn–winter maximum. Although the rainfall peak comes in late summer, high totals are recorded right into December. From the end of September temperatures fall rapidly, especially in the east, and most places see their first snow in October. Autumn is shorter than in the more oceanic British Isles, the more so the further east one goes.

Annual Rainfall. The total amount of precipitation received diminishes from the coast towards the interior, this being most clearly seen on the Northern Lowland where there is an even decline from over 750 mm/30 in a year in the west to less than 500 mm/20 in beyond the Oder. A similar decline occurs in south Germany, but the effect is masked by relief; the higher hill masses receive over 1,000 mm/40 in, sometimes over 1,500 mm/60 in of rain a year, while the intervening basins have much less, frequently below 500 mm/20 in. All over the country precipitation received in the summer half of the year exceeds that received in winter, and the disparity increases eastwards. Consequently, although the eastern part of Germany has a lower rainfall than the west, at least a higher proportion of it falls in the growing period, when it is most needed.

CLIMATIC REGIONS

Northwest Germany, situated between the Rhenish Uplands and the North Sea, is more affected than the rest of the country by oceanic influences and by the passage of depressions, so that most places have a mean January temperature above 0° C/32° F, and the freezing of rivers is rare. The mild cloudy winters receive a higher proportion of total precipitation than in the rest of Germany, although there is still a summer maximum. Coastal fogs are frequent. Spring is long by German standards and temperatures mount slowly, but eventually reach the respectable July mean of 16·5–17·5° C/62–64° F, thus underlining that the warming effect of the sea is much more pronounced than its cooling effect in summer.

The Eastern Lowland, including the Saxon and Silesian lowlands, has a more continental climate, the contrast lying principally in the greater severity of the winters. In midwinter a brilliant sun shines on a landscape covered with snow for a month or more, where lakes and rivers are frozen for days at a time. At night there is a rapid fall of temperature, often to −18° C/0° F. Spring, when it comes, is short and the rapid rise in temperature leads to a summer just slightly warmer than in the west (July 17°–18·5° C/63°–65° F). There is a marked precipitation maximum in the summer months, but as the rain falls mainly in thundery showers, the sky is rarely overcast for long periods.

The Central Uplands are intermediate in type between northwest Germany and the eastern Lowland, but the climate varies greatly from place to place, according to the relief. The sheltered basins, especially towards the east, have a distinctly continental climate, with summers hot (July 17·5°–19·5° C/64°–67° F), winters rather cold through the accumulation of cool, dense air and rainfall often below 500 mm/20 in a year. As one moves into the uplands spring comes later, the growing period is shorter and snow may last on the peaks from three to five months. Cloud is frequent all the year, and rainfall may exceed 1,000 mm/40 in or even 1,500 mm/60 in a year.

From this general picture the Rhinelands stand out as a region of altogether softer climate, where the breath of the south is felt as far north as Cologne. Winters are at least as

REGION AND STATION	J	F	M	A	M	J	J	A	S	O	N	D	RANGE
Northwest													
Emden	1·0	1·4	4·0	7·9	12·1	15·4	17·0	16·8	14·1	9·8	5·7	2·8	16·0 °C
(6 m/20 ft)	34	35	39	46	54	60	63	62	57	50	42	37	29 °F
Northeast													
Frankfurt-Oder	−1·0	−0·1	3·6	8·2	13·7	16·8	18·7	17·5	14·0	8·7	3·5	0·2	19·7 °C
(48 m/157 ft)	30	32	39	47	57	62	66	64	57	48	38	32	32 °F
Central Uplands													
(Rhineland type)													
Mannheim	1·1	2·2	5·6	10·0	14·4	17·8	19·4	18·3	15·0	10·0	5·0	2·2	18·3 °C
(100 m/328 ft)	34	36	42	50	58	64	67	65	59	50	41	36	33 °F
(Hills type)													
Plauen	−1·9	−1·2	2·0	6·2	11·5	14·4	16·2	15·5	12·4	7·5	2·5	−0·5	18·1 °C
(407 m/1,335 ft)	29	30	36	43	53	58	61	60	54	46	37	31	32 °F
(Basin type)													
Erfurt	−0·9	−0·2	3·1	7·2	12·4	15·2	16·8	16·0	12·9	8·0	3·1	0·3	17·7 °C
(314 m/1,030 ft)	30	32	38	45	54	59	62	61	55	46	38	33	32 °F
Alpine Foreland													
Munich	−2·1	−0·9	3·3	8·0	12·5	15·8	17·5	16·6	13·4	7·9	3·0	−0·7	19·6 °C
(515 m/1,690 ft)	28	30	38	46	55	60	64	62	56	46	37	31	36 °F
Alps													
Zugspitze	−11·1	−11·1	−10·0	−7·2	−2·8	−0·6	1·7	1·7	0·0	−3·9	−7·2	−10·0	12·8 °C
(2,963 m/9,735 ft)	12	12	14	19	27	31	35	35	32	25	19	14	23 °F

Mean monthly temperatures (Centigrade/Fahrenheit) for selected German stations.

REGION AND STATION	J	F	M	A	M	J	J	A	S	O	N	D	TOTAL
Northwest													
Emden	59	44	48	45	49	67	77	89	64	68	59	67	736 mm
(6 m/20 ft)	2·3	1·7	1·9	1·8	1·9	2·6	3·0	3·5	2·5	2·7	2·3	2·6	29·0 in
Northeast													
Frankfurt-Oder	39	31	32	38	46	57	74	63	42	40	40	38	540 mm
(48 m/157 ft)	1·5	1·2	1·3	1·5	1·8	2·2	2·9	2·5	1·7	1·6	1·6	1·5	21·3 in
Central Uplands													
(Rhineland type)													
Mannheim	28	25	31	38	46	61	66	61	56	48	35	33	528 mm
(100 m/328 ft)	1·1	1·0	1·2	1·5	1·8	2·4	2·6	2·4	2·2	1·9	1·4	1·3	20·8 in
(Hills type)													
Plauen	44	36	35	54	70	77	80	79	47	46	42	42	652 mm
(407 m/1,335 ft)	1·7	1·4	1·4	2·1	2·8	3·0	3·2	3·1	1·9	1·8	1·7	1·7	25·7 in
(Basin type)													
Erfurt	28	25	31	41	53	66	71	56	43	43	35	31	523 mm
(314 m/1,030 ft)	1·2	1·0	1·1	1·5	2·2	2·3	2·6	2·2	1·7	1·5	1·3	1·1	19·7 in
Alpine Foreland													
Munich	43	35	48	68	94	117	119	107	81	56	48	48	862 mm
(515 m/1,690 ft)	1·7	1·4	2·0	2·8	3·7	4·7	5·0	4·0	3·3	2·3	1·9	1·9	34·9 in
Alps													
Zugspitze	66	69	74	137	185	201	216	203	135	117	89	86	1,577 mm
(2,963 m/9,735 ft)	2·6	2·7	2·9	5·4	7·3	7·9	8·5	8·0	5·3	4·6	3·5	3·4	62·1 in

Mean monthly rainfall totals (millimetres/inches) for selected German stations.

mild as those of the northwest, but spring comes earlier, so that from mid-April the fruit trees on the warm hillsides are in bloom. Although the maximum rainfall is in summer, the total received is low, so that the showers scarcely interrupt the brilliant sunshine of the Rhine valley. Late autumn is still warm while the Northern Lowland shivers with the oncoming of winter.

The Alps naturally attract a high precipitation, over 1,500 mm/60 in a year on the northern slopes, and both summer and winter temperatures are reduced by height. Within the mountains, the valleys and basins are often quite dry and sheltered. Aspect is particularly important; the north-facing slopes may receive no direct sunlight in winter at all (*Bergschatten*) and be left in forest, while on the opposite south-facing slope (*Sonnenseite*) the forest has been cleared for villages and pasture. Another local influence is the Föhn wind which affects some valleys, especially that of the Alpine Rhine, in spring and autumn. Low pressure north of the Alps causes the cold, dense air that normally fills the valleys to slide out onto the plain. It is replaced by descending, and therefore warmed air from above, which moves down the valleys as a strong warm wind, melting the snow in spring, bringing disastrous avalanches, but also clearing the pastures so that grazing can begin.

The Alpine Foreland has a more uniform but somewhat harsh climate. Winters are cold owing to height, and rainfall is high, especially close to the Alps, where there is a belt receiving 1,000–1,500 mm/40–60 in a year. Locally the climate is ameliorated by lakes, especially around Lake Constance, where the vine appears.

RIVERS AND THEIR RÉGIMES

Rivers are great individuals, each having a distinct character of its own. Very largely this is a matter of landscape; it is difficult to think of the Rhine, for example, without recalling the vine-clad slopes and castles of its gorge through the Rhenish Uplands. But a river has individuality in another way, through the yearly cycle of flood and low water that constitutes its régime.

The rate of flow of a river depends mainly on climate, but the relationship is not a direct and simple one. In all but Alpine Germany the maximum flow of rivers is normally in the winter half year, when evaporation is low, although this is nowhere the season of maximum rainfall. In the Alps on the other hand, winter precipitation is held up in the form of ice and snow, to be released in great spring and summer floods. Finally, river basins may be so large as to include regions of widely differing climate, each of which makes a distinctive contribution to régime; the Rhine is the supreme example.

German rivers may be divided into three main groups those rising in the Northern Lowland, in the Central Uplands, and in the Alps.

Rivers Rising in the Northern Lowland. These placid and slow-moving streams have an even flow throughout the year. In rivers such as the Ems, in the west, this is due to the fact that rainfall is well distributed throughout the year, as well as to the peat bogs which act as sponges, reluctantly giving up their dark water in an even flow. Further east, the irregularities of rivers like the Havel are reduced by the reservoir effect of the numerous lakes left by the last glaciation.

Rivers Rising in the Central Uplands. Here is a livelier pattern of torrents cutting downwards from the Hercynian massifs through steep-sided valleys, to merge in more placid reaches in the intervening basins. Nearly all the streams of the Central Uplands are tributary to the Rhine, but three important rivers, the Weser, the Elbe and the Oder, flow across the Northern Lowland to enter the sea directly.

All Central Uplands streams share a régime with a winter maximum at the time of least evaporation, and a period of summer low water, with consequent difficulties for navigation. The more easterly the stream, the more pronounced the summer low becomes. The severity of icing also increases eastwards; drifting or continuous ice appear on the Weser at Minden for fourteen days a year on the average, on the Elbe at Magdeburg for thirty days and on the Oder at Frankfurt for forty-three days.

Rivers of the Alps. When the winter's accumulation of snow and ice is set free in spring, torrents pour down every hillside and the Alpine rivers rise rapidly, sometimes to six times their normal flow. With late summer they drop again to become in autumn mere trickles among the great banks of boulders and gravel brought down by earlier floods. This régime, entirely unfavourable to navigation, is transmitted to the upper reaches of the two greatest rivers of Central Europe, the Rhine and the Danube. The Danube, unlike the Rhine, flows parallel to the Alpine front, so that the unfavourable régime is accentuated as each new tributary joins; this is one reason why the river has never grown into an international waterway of the highest importance.

The Rhine. This is a river of conflict and contradiction: to the Germans a cradle of their culture and a major artery of their trade, but to the French a long-sought 'natural' frontier. Although referred to proudly as 'the German Rhine' it rises in Switzerland and reaches the sea through the Netherlands. The Rhine is unique in linking the three major physiographic regions of Alps, Central Uplands and Northern Lowland. It is still very much an Alpine stream as far as Strasbourg, with a steep gradient and a maximum flow in spring and summer. Only in the present century has the navigation been improved to permit Rhine barges to reach Basel.

The river crosses the Central Uplands by means of the Rift Valley (Upper Rhine) and then by its spectacular gorge sawn through the great barrier of the Rhenish Uplands massif (Middle Rhine). The tributaries of the Upper and Middle Rhine, which include such major rivers as the Main and Mosel, drain the greater part of the German Central Uplands and part of eastern France as well. Together they contribute slightly more water than the Alpine streams, and have a directly opposite régime, with the maximum flow coming in the winter half year. This combination of two régimes gives the Rhine a remarkably powerful and even flow throughout the year, which is a physical endowment that has enabled it to become the greatest waterway of Western and Central Europe.

SOILS

In the broadest sense, soils are determined by climate, but a country the size of Germany is too small for climatically based soil types to stand out as clearly as they do in the U.S.S.R. or

U.S.A. The nature of the parent material and, in detail, of the vegetation cover often appear more immediately important than climate.

Soils of the Northern Lowland (1).[1] With soils, as with physiography, the broad division into Northern Lowland, Central Uplands and Alps holds good. On the Northern Lowland, especially on the older sandy drifts of the west, soils tend to be badly leached (1a). Owing to the high rainfall, and low evaporation, valuable minerals and humus are washed from the surface layers of the soil and deposited a foot or so lower down as a closely cemented layer known as hard pan or *Ortstein*, thus forming podsol soils. The drifts of the last or Vistula glaciation further east are distinctly less leached (1b), and on the boulder clay soils south of the Baltic even brown-earth soils are developed.

Soils of the Loess Belt (2a) and Central Uplands (2b). In the Central Uplands soils are more variable, because of the greater contrasts in rock type, slope and elevation. Podsols are limited to the Bunter and Keuper Sandstone outcrops and to some of the crystalline areas of the Hercynian blocks. The typical soil is the brown earth, developed under deciduous trees at altitudes up to 820 m/2,700 ft. The even brown colour of the soils, and the lack of sharp divisions between the various horizons, show that they have suffered from leaching to a smaller extent than the podsols. The presence of useful minerals and humus in the upper layers of the soils, and the consequently well-developed crumb structure, render them highly favourable to agriculture.

Naturally there are considerable variations within the brown-earth group; on shales and clays the soils are heavy and require to be artificially drained, while brown earths on limestone and loess are considerably lighter in texture. In the more continental basins, as near Magdeburg, the loess brown earths merge into degraded chernozems (black earths), soils which are typically developed under steppe conditions. On the other hand the higher and steeper limestone areas, such as the Swabian Jura, have the thin black soils with high lime and humus content known as rendzinas. Generally speaking, the predominantly brown-earth soils of the Central Uplands have

[1] The numbers refer to the regions shown on Fig. 3 on p. 42.

facilitated man's early settlement and long-continued agricultural occupation; the soils developed on loess have been particularly important in this way.

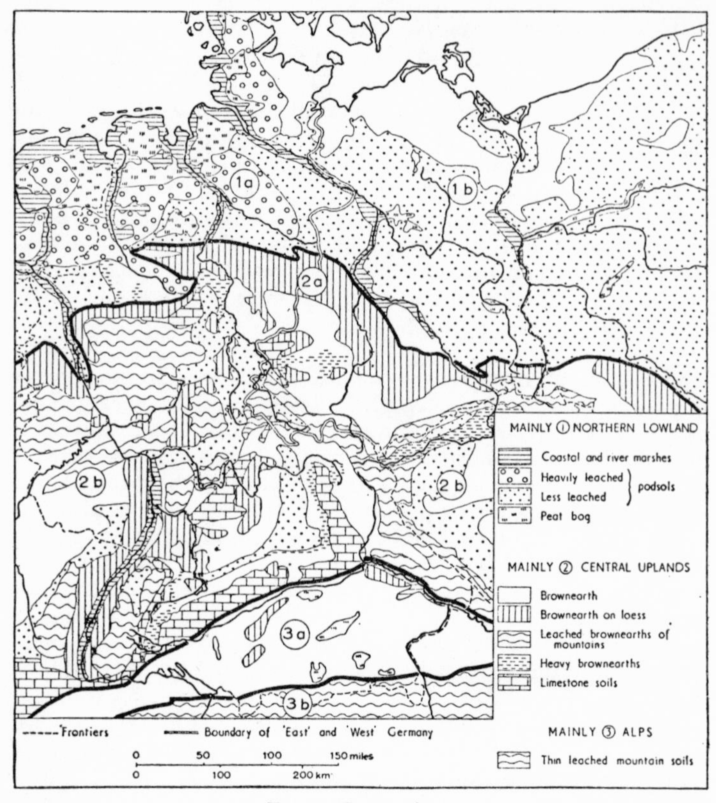

FIG. 3. Soil regions.

Soils of the Alps (3b) and Foreland (3a). The Alpine Foreland can be included within the brown-earth belt. Naturally the soils of the higher and older gravel outwash plateaus are often badly leached, while glacial interruption of drainage has been responsible for large areas of peat bog, like the Dachau Moos. On the other hand there are good medium and heavy soils within the moraines, on terraces and in the Tertiary hill country of the northeast, and there are some loess stretches near the Danube. Soils of the Alps (3b) vary considerably with height and degree of slope, but tend to be shallow, stony and increasingly leached with altitude.

VEGETATION

It is difficult to describe the natural vegetation of a country like Germany, in which very little truly 'natural' vegetation has survived human interference. However, the attempt must be made, because of the fundamental importance of the original vegetational pattern in the occupation and settlement of the country by man, who as a keeper of animals and tiller of the soil, has himself been one of the greatest influences on the distribution of trees and plants.

The Northern Lowland. As seen today the more oceanic northwestern section of the Lowland is primarily a region of heathland, which has been partly replaced by modern conifer plantations. Before man brought fire, the axe and grazing animals, however, the dry sandy plateaus apparently bore a light woodland of oak and birch. The scattered trees allowed light to penetrate, nourishing a shrub layer of heather and other plants, and thus permitted easy passage for man and pasture for his beasts.

This open woodland merged across the Elbe with a rather denser mixed forest that occupied the inner part of the eastern Lowland. Oak, birch and occasional beech trees favoured the better soils, mingled with conifers, especially pine (*Kiefer*) on the poorer. With the increasing continentality of climate eastwards, the pines became more frequent, the forests more sombre, the undergrowth poorer, the soils more leached and the difficulty of clearance and occupation greater. Towards the Baltic, however, on the less leached boulder clays of the last glaciation, beech forest naturally occurred. Everywhere on the Lowland variety was introduced by the willows and poplars of the river flood plains, by the coastal salt marshes and by the acid peat bogs developed where glaciation has interrupted drainage, especially in the oceanic northwest.

The Central Uplands. With their greater variety of lithology, soils and elevation, the Central Uplands have a more varied natural vegetation. Primarily this is the domain of the beech, a tree with a leaf canopy so dense that few plants can survive beneath, so that these forests were very resistant to the incursion of the herds and agriculture of primitive man. They

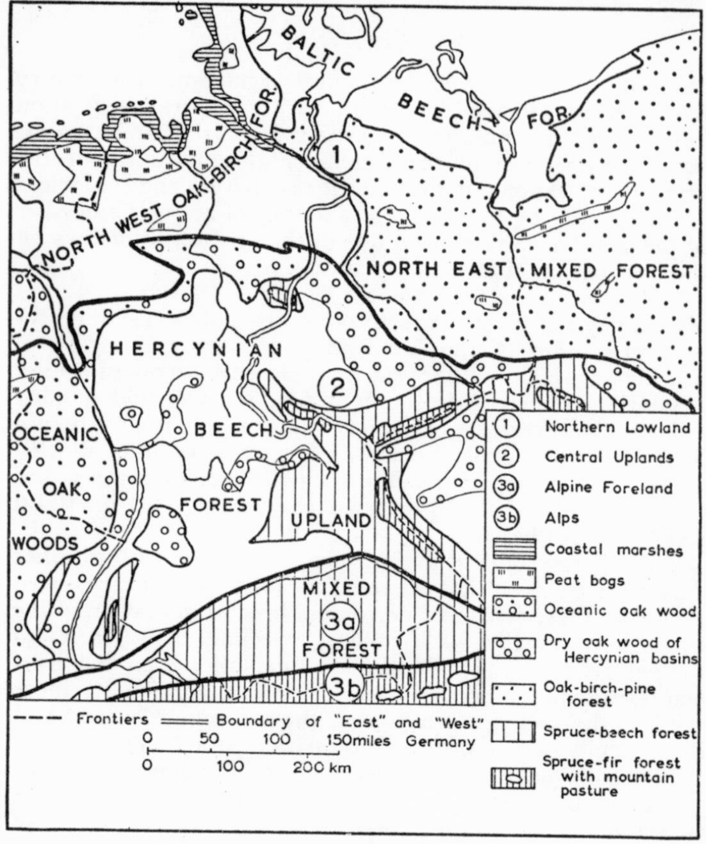

FIG. 4. Natural vegetation

formed a marked barrier from the Rhenish Uplands through the sandstones of Hesse to Bohemia, the 'impenetrable' *Hercynia Silva* of the Romans, only painfully and partially cleared in medieval times.

In some dry, sandy areas the beech gives way to pine, and in the Hercynian massifs spruce (*Fichte*) becomes dominant. The most important interruption to the beech forest came, however, from the extent of oakwood. Mixed oak and hornbeam woods of an oceanic type, with a rich shrub layer of hawthorn and bramble, would naturally cover most of Germany west of the Rhine, and extend along the northern face of the Central Uplands. A somewhat sparser, more open oak woodland is believed also to have occupied the drier sheltered basins of loess or limestone soil within the Uplands, such as the Rhine Rift Valley or Saxon Lowland, providing greater opportunity than the beechwoods for occupation by early man.

The Alps and Alpine Foreland. With its rather raw climate the Foreland was formerly covered by a mixed forest, in which beech, now mainly cleared, predominated on the better soils, spruce on the poorer. Peat bogs had also developed where glaciation had impeded drainage. The Foreland ends southwards with the outer face of the Alps, clothed from its base, owing to rainfall and exposure, with sombre spruce forest. For these same reasons the upper limit of the forest is low; at 900–1,050 m/3,000–3,500 ft the spruces give way to stunted mountain pines and deserts of limestone blocks. The rich mountain pastures of the inner Alps are mainly lacking in this exposed outer zone.

Before the arrival of farming man, Germany from these Alpine forests northwards to the sands of the coast was practically one continuous forest, interrupted only by marshes, rivers and lakes. The forest was not, however, uniform, and it was this diversity that enabled man first to gain a foothold, and which foreshadowed the rich variety of land use characteristic of Germany today.

SUGGESTIONS FOR FURTHER READING

F. K. Hare, *The restless atmosphere* (Hutchinson), 1953, ch. 13, (New York: Hillary; New York: Harper and Row, pap.).

H. J. Mackinder, *The Rhine*, 1908.

Soil map of Europe (with explanatory text), Rome (Food and Agriculture Organization of the United Nations), 1966.

PART TWO
THE PEOPLE

Chapter 4
GERMANY TO THE GREAT MIGRATIONS

GERMANY BEFORE THE GERMANS

Men of the Ice Age. The pattern of 'natural' vegetation described in the last chapter was established only after the final retreat of the ice. During the Ice Age itself there were many changes, for between the various advances of the ice sheets there were interglacial periods, each thousands of years long, in which vegetation, even woodland, had time to re-establish itself.

When the margin of the last retreating ice sheet lay just south of the Baltic, Europe north of the Alps was covered with grassy steppe, which graded northwards into a tundra vegetation of mosses, lichens, heaths and stunted shrubs, such as we find today only on the high mountains or in the extreme north of Russia. In the hills of southern Germany, men found shelter in caves, at least in winter, emerging in packs or clans to go on fishing expeditions, or to hunt reindeer, bison and wild horses.

In summer great herds of reindeer migrated northwards, sometimes hundreds of miles, in search of rich pastures on the margin of the ice. They were followed by groups of Upper Palaeolithic hunters, whose temporary camps, dating from about 11,000 B.C., have been excavated in the neighbourhood of Hamburg. This was in every way a reindeer culture. With stone-tipped arrows the hunters killed the reindeer, which provided not only food but hides for shelter, antlers for harpoons and other tools, and even bones for fuel. A reindeer carcass weighted with a stone was thrown into an adjoining pool as an offering to the Gods, and a reindeer-head totem on a pole guarded the camp.

With the passing of glacial conditions, the forest advanced northwards. First birch trees, then conifers, then oak and beech were established, until something like the pattern of 'natural' vegetation described in the last chapter was evolved. As the forest spread, the reindeer moved away, and with the passing of the reindeer the Upper Palaeolithic culture withered and died. It was once thought that the European forest remained untenanted until the arrival of the Neolithic farmers, but in the last fifty years archaeologists have built up a picture of Mesolithic hunters, so called because they occupied the space in time between the Old Stone Age (Palaeolithic) and the New (Neolithic).

Neolithic Farmers. The most revolutionary event in man's history in what was to become Germany was undoubtedly the arrival of the Danubian peasants, bringing the Neolithic farming techniques by 4500 B.C. or soon after. For the first time, man was not a complete plaything of his environment; to some extent he could adjust it to suit himself. The Danubians practised shifting cultivation, like many African tribes today. They used their stone hoes to cultivate a few irregularly-shaped fields until fertility was exhausted, then moved on to another site. In this way they advanced westwards into Europe as far as the Rhinelands and northern France, following the loess lands of the Lower Danube and the Hercynian Foreland. They preferred the loess because its oak forest had many open glades which allowed easy movement, provided pasture for cattle, and gave a foothold for the beginning of cultivation. The soil was also fertile and easily worked with primitive hoes.

As well as the loess, the Neolithic farmers settled on other areas of light or medium, well-drained soil, such as the river terraces, the limestone plateaus of the Central Uplands and scattered patches of sandy loam in the Northern Lowland. On these early-cleared areas the Neolithic farmers were succeeded by men of a series of Bronze Age cultures, then by the Iron Age Celts, who defied the advance of Rome from their hilltop forts, and finally by the Germans (Fig. 6).

THE GERMANS

Throughout the Bronze and early Iron Ages, northern Germany had remained rather isolated. Here, on the shores of the Baltic and in the Baltic islands, a new people had been slowly developing in individuality and unity. From about 500 B.C., these Germans began to move southwards, occupying first the fairly open heathland of the Northern Lowland and the loess lands of the Hercynian Foreland. They gradually penetrated the forest barrier that stretched from the Rhenish Uplands to Bohemia, and emerged in southwest Germany just in time to clash with the growing power of Rome. Between these advancing forces, the former Celtic kingdoms of southern Germany were crushed and broken.

The Germans were of Nordic racial type, tall men with long, massive heads, fair hair and blue eyes. They seem to have possessed a remarkable degree of energy and restlessness, for their intermittent migrations continued for more than 1,500 years. Their settlements were small: one or two farms, or an irregularly grouped hamlet. Arable fields appear to have been few, possibly cultivated only intermittently, and set in the midst of an outfield of widespread rough grazing. This type of land use would obviously not support a dense population; the Germans were in consequence always moving on in search of new land. In this way, they advanced into southern Germany, seizing, in the main, the areas of light soil that had long been occupied: the loess, the limestone plateaus and the river terraces. The existing Celtic populations were killed, driven out or enslaved.

Caesar's conquest of Gaul made a clash between Germans and Romans inevitable. In 58 B.C., German bands who were filtering into Gaul under Ariovistus were attacked by Caesar, and driven back across the Rhine. There followed a long period of peace, with the frontier of the Roman Empire stabilized on the Rhine and Danube. Augustus, however, was dissatisfied with the frontier, which left a dangerous salient of Germans pointing to within 160 km/100 miles of Italy, and decided to advance Roman power to the river Elbe. This had been largely achieved, when, while Rome's attention was distracted by trouble lower down the Danube, the Germans rose again. In A.D. 9 under Arminius (Hermann), they ambushed three legions commanded by Varus in the forests of the Teutoburger Wald, and utterly destroyed them. Well might Augustus cry out 'Give me back my legions', for while temporary Roman triumphs were still to come, Germany as a whole was never conquered.

The most that could be achieved by the Romans in Germany was an advance to the *Limes*, an earthwork built to shorten the frontier by linking the Rhine and the Danube and so straighten the frontier (Fig. 5). The line of the *Limes* was drawn so as to include within the Empire the varied fertile lowlands of the Rhine–Main and Neckar regions. Behind, on the west bank of the Rhine, lay legionary fortresses like Cologne and Strasbourg, securing the principal crossings of the river.

The defeat of Varus's legions by the Germans was one of the vital battles of history. Arminius well deserves the monstrous metal statue, the *Hermannsdenkmal*, that today crowns the Teutoburger Wald. By ensuring that most Germans would remain outside the Empire, he also ensured that urban civilization, centralized administration and Roman agricultural and industrial techniques would advance no further than the great cultural divide of the Rhine and Danube. When the divide was removed, and the way thus prepared for a unified medieval European culture, it was not by the triumph of Roman civilization, but by a 'levelling down' towards that of the barbarians.

THE GREAT MIGRATIONS

The land hunger of the Germans caused them to keep up their pressure on the Roman frontier, and to endeavour to filter across at every opportunity. Some West German peoples, notably the Frisians of the North Sea coast and the Batavians of the Rhine delta, had been included in the Empire since Caesar's time. Another group of tribes, the Alemans, broke into the Roman territory between the Rhine and the *Limes* about A.D. 260 and proceeded to drive the Romans back to the Rhine. At about the same time, the Franks began to filter over the Rhine from their focus in the Main valley.

The actual hammer blows which broke the Roman Empire in the West came not from these western tribes but from the even wilder East Germans, who had been moving southwards and eastwards beyond the Elbe at the same time as their relations were moving southwest. The East Germans seem to have been set in motion by the Huns and other savage horsemen driving westward from the steppes. In the first half of the 5th century Goths, Vandals, Aluns and others, plundering and destroying, poured into Roman territory, and brought the Empire in the West to its end in 476. The East Germans never formed more than a thin barbarian ruling class in the new kingdoms they set up in southern Gaul, Spain, Italy and North Africa, and were eventually absorbed by the existing more civilized population.

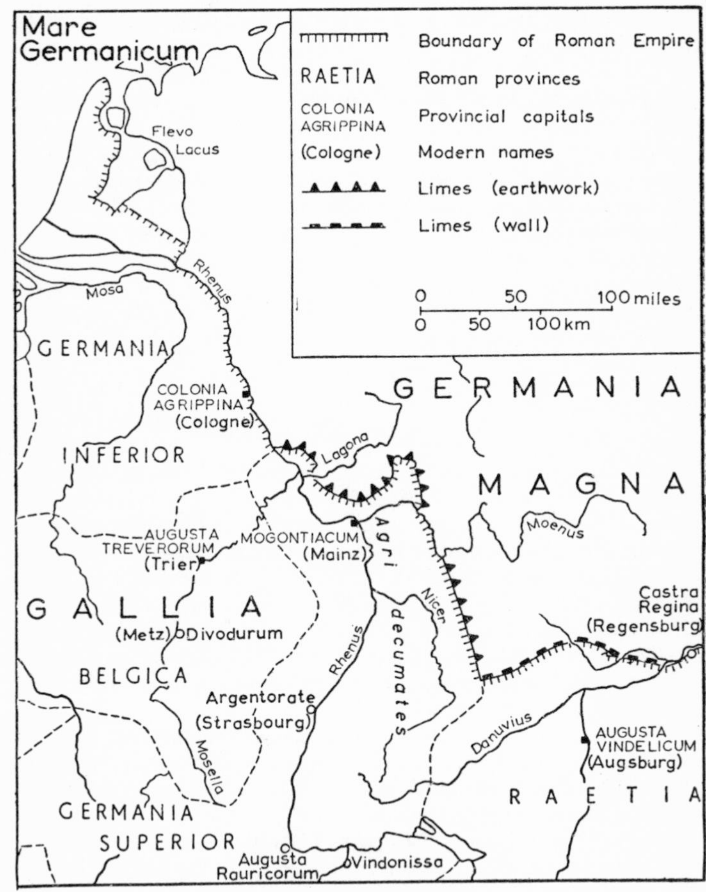

FIG. 5. Roman Germany.

Of much more lasting importance was the movement of the West Germans whom they also set in motion. The Alemans spread from the Neckar and Upper Rhine to Alsace and Switzerland. The Franks settled Belgium and northern France, closely as far as the Seine and Marne, and more thinly from these rivers to the Loire. Some of the Saxons, Angles and Jutes even moved by sea to settle in England. Meanwhile, the lands vacated by the Germans in the east were taken up by the Slavs, who advanced up to about the line of the Elbe and Saale rivers.

The result of these western movements were more permanent, as the land was actually occupied by German farmers, not merely by a few overlords. The German language was firmly established beyond the Rhine, and even today, after centuries of retreat, remains in use in a belt of up to 150 km/100 miles in depth. Finally, with the Roman frontier abolished, the way was clear for a new cultural unity in Europe, from the Mediterranean to the Baltic and from the Channel to the Slav borderlands on the Elbe.

SUGGESTIONS FOR FURTHER READING

CAESAR, *The conquest of Gaul* (London and New York: Penguin Books), 1951.

V. GORDON CHILDE, *Dawn of European Civilization* (6th ed.; New York: Knopf, 1958; New York: Vintage, pap.).

V. GORDON CHILDE, *The prehistory of European society* (Penguin Books), 1958.

J. G. D. CLARK, *Prehistoric Europe: the economic basis* (Methuen), 1952, (Stanford, Calif.: Stanford, 1966).

C. S. COON, *The races of Europe* (Macmillan), New York, 1939.

S. PIGGOTT, *Ancient Europe* (Edinburgh University Press), 1965, (Chicago: Aldine, 1965).

E. A. THOMPSON, *The early Germans*, Oxford: (Clarendon Press), 1965, (New York: Oxford University Press, 1965).

TACITUS, *On Britain and Germany* (London and New York: Penguin Books), 1948.

R. MORTIMER WHEELER, *Rome beyond the Imperial frontiers* (Bell), 1954, (Penguin Books), 1955.

Chapter 5
MEDIEVAL GERMANY

AREAS OF GERMAN SETTLEMENT

During the great migrations, the bewildering pattern of German tribes and constantly changing tribal confederations gave place to a number of major groupings of peoples, which the Germans call *Volkstämme*. Each of these peoples had its centre in one of the stretches of well-drained land that had been occupied by earlier settlers (Fig. 6). The settled areas were surrounded by wide belts of forest or marsh which often still bear the name of the peoples they divided (Thuringian Forest, Bavarian Forest).

In the north, the *Saxons* had spread over the now lightly wooded Northern Lowland west of the Elbe, and had established their centres of power in the loess lands of the Foreland and the hills immediately to the south. They retained longer than the other German peoples the worship of heathen gods. The North Sea coast was occupied by the *Frisians*, a fierce seafaring, fishing and trading people. Southeast of the Saxons, the *Thuringians* occupied the basin which still bears their name. In southern Germany the *Bavarians* had their centre in the Danube valley and Alpine Foreland east of the Lech, while west of them the *Alemans* or Swabians occupied the southern Rift Valley, the Neckar valley and adjoining parts of the Alpine Foreland. Between Saxons in the north and Alemans in the south lay the territory of the greatest people of them all, the Franks. We have already seen how Frankish power was extended over Gaul. They also expanded slowly eastwards, seizing as their German territory the fertile and strategically vital Rhine–Main confluence area, Hesse and the Main basin, which bears the name of Franconia to this day.

THE FRANKS

The Franks eventually established their power over all the other German peoples and created a short-lived period of near unity in western Europe. The focus of Frankish power lay between the Rhine and the Seine; from here they could dominate southern Gaul on the one hand, and advance back into Germany on the other. The Frankish kings first defeated the

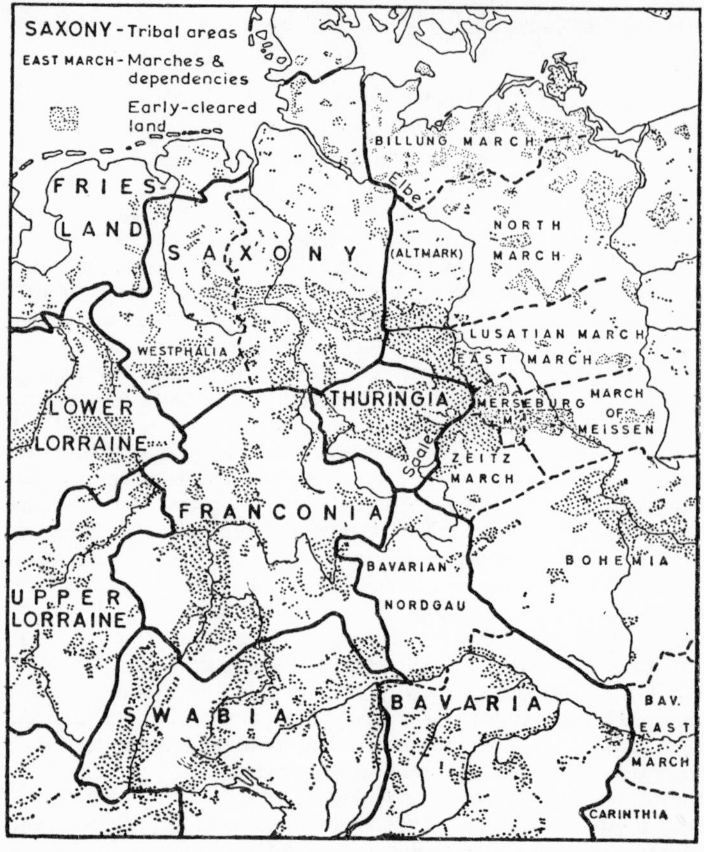

FIG. 6. Principal German tribal groups, as reflected by the great duchies of the 10th century.

heathen German tribes, and established strong points to guard the route centres and fords. After this pacification, it was the turn of the clergy to move in and start the work of conversion and civilization.

Many of the missionary clergy were Irish or English, and the greatest, Saint Boniface (*c.* 680–754), was born in Wessex. He laboured mainly in Hesse and Thuringia, where he baptized, cut down sacred groves, founded churches and monasteries and bound these strategically important areas to the Frankish culture. In 754 he was martyred by the heathen Frisians, and his remains lie buried in the great Benedictine monastery and centre of learning that he founded at Fulda in Hesse.

The Frankish power reached its summit under Charles the Great, king of the Franks for the long period from 771 to 814. He completed the Frankish domination of Germany by the conquest and conversion of the warlike and heathen Saxons, and firmly established the Elbe–Saale line as the frontier between German and Slav. He initiated the system of protecting the frontier by the creation of buffer states known as Marches, each under a 'Marcher Lord' or Margrave.

Charles the Great was more than a brilliant military leader; he made his court into a centre where the old classical learning was revived and religious studies fostered. He drew scholars from all over Europe, the greatest of them an Englishman, Alcuin, born at York. The new learning was carried by the monks into Germany, and helped to give the newly conquered tribes a sense of unity within the Christian tradition. Thus the Elbe–Saale line, separating Germans from Slavs, also separated Christians from heathen, and became the major cultural divide of Europe, just as the Rhine had been under the Romans 600 years before.

Charles's empire was still entirely Frankish, neither German nor French, but the situation of the royal palaces at Ingelheim (near Mainz), Nijmegen and Aachen instead of at Paris or Rheims showed that the East Frankish lands were growing in importance. Westwards the empire stretched to the Pyrenees, southwards to Lombardy. Charles's power in Italy and the traditional Frankish alliance with the Church led, on the last Christmas day of the 8th century, to his crowning by the Pope as Emperor of the Romans.

Magnificent as the Carolingian Empire was, it rested too much on the power and ability of one man, and covered too much geographical diversity to survive. At the Treaty of Verdun (843) it was partitioned; new East and West Frankish kingdoms were created, separated by a 'Middle Kingdom' stretching from the mouth of the Rhine through Lorraine and Burgundy to northern Italy. Further fighting and partitions followed (Fig. 7).

The real weakness of the Carolingian successors of Charles was revealed by their failure to deal with the waves of savage invaders who poured into the Empire at the end of the 9th

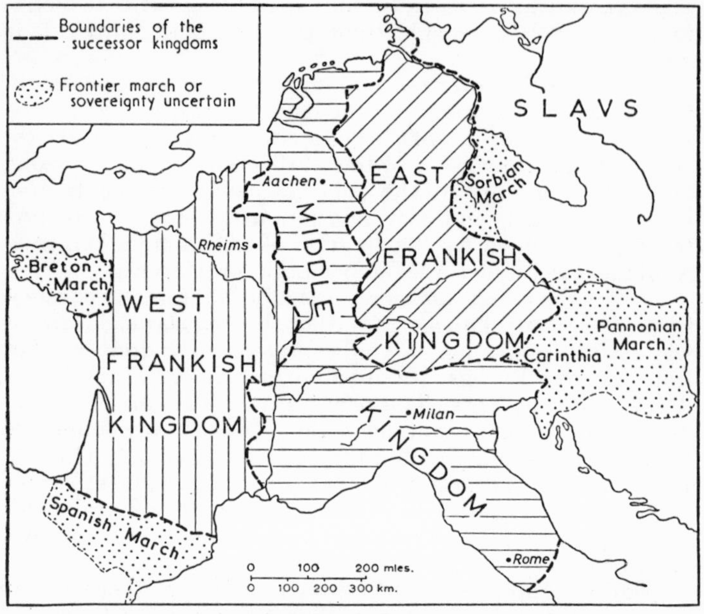

FIG. 7. The Carolingian Empire, as partitioned by the Treaty of Verdun, 843.

century, Saracens in the south, Vikings in the west, Magyars in the east. In despair, men had to look to any local leader who could offer protection. In the west Frankish lands, they became vassals of one of the scores of feudal lords who sprang up there. In Germany, however, the old tribal divisions still retained their vitality for military purposes. Men looked for defence, not to a feudal lord, but to the army of their own people, led by a duke who at first was even elected. In this way Germany emerged into the 10th century not shattered into feudal principalities like France, but divided into five great duchies, Franconia, Saxony, Bavaria, Swabia and Thuringia (Fig. 6).

THE FAILURE OF THE MONARCHY

Instead of the duchies remaining independent, like the feudal principalities of France, they were rapidly brought under the power of a single king. From this first emergence of Germany as a nation there was thus a most hopeful development, in the 10th and 11th centuries, of a centralized monarchy far in advance of France or England at the same period. The traditional alliance of Church and crown was continued, and bishops were made rulers of considerable territories, which became bulwarks of royal and ecclesiastical order against the nobility. The Saxon kings, and their successors of the Salian dynasty, were able to defeat the wild Magyars and Slavs, and strengthen the Elbe–Saale frontier. In the west and in Italy, the provinces of the former 'Middle Kingdom', such as Burgundy and Lombardy, were secured for Germany. Internal peace showed itself in the growth of population, the clearing of the waste (p. 61), the expansion of commerce, the growth of towns (pp. 69–75) and the extension of learning. A wave of churchbuilding in the new Romanesque style spread across the country.

All this progress was brought to an end in the years after 1075 by a combination of internal weaknesses and external interference. The principal internal weakness sprang from the continued existence of the great duchies like Bavaria or Saxony. The dukes were never able to become quite supreme in their own territories, because held in check by the crown. Yet the crown was not strong enough, as it was in England or France, to enforce feudal obedience on the dukes, and through them on the lesser nobility. The chain of feudalism was never completed, and the nobles, remaining independent, were able to gain control of the royal and Church estates, and so cut the economic roots of the monarchy.

All might still have gone well but for external distractions, especially the fatal entanglement with Italy. There is no doubt that most of the German kings felt that the title of 'Holy Roman Emperor' was a recognition of their special place as the Lord's anointed, appointed to guide and control the Church. But there was a strong material interest too, since the title was generally held to justify possession of the lands of the 'Middle Kingdom'. No other power could be permitted to develop in Italy lest it seize the person of the Pope, the Imperial title or the lands of the 'Middle Kingdom'. Accordingly, the resources and energies of the German kings were constantly drained by Italian campaigns.

The crisis was reached in 1075, when Pope Gregory VII decided that, to secure the supremacy of Rome, the special powers of the Emperors over the Church had to be broken. There followed a series of wars in which the Papacy joined with the enemies of the monarchy at home and abroad. Distracted by events in Italy, and harried from within, the monarchy declined in strength, until the collapse of the Hohenstaufen dynasty in 1250 was followed by a period lasting until 1272 when there was no king at all.

By the end of the 14th century, Germany was reduced almost to anarchy. The Emperor was elected by a college of seven princes, consisting of the three Rhenish archbishops (Mainz, Trier, Cologne) and the rulers of Bohemia, the Palatinate, Saxony and Brandenburg. Their main interest was to elect as weak a monarch as possible. Neither the monarchy nor the princes could provide an effective government. The princely territories were divided and divided by inheritance, until Germany became notorious for its *Kleinstaaterei*, its swarms of tiny states, each with its court borne on the backs of the peasantry. Below even this level a new class of knights arose, with practically unchecked power on their own estates. In the chaos, knights, cities or even prelates banded together in leagues to protect and advance their particular interest. The fact that in 1438 the imperial dignity finally passed into the hands of the Habsburgs had little effect on Germany's fundamental disunity. The Habsburgs concerned themselves mainly with their own extensive but scattered territories, and failed to intervene effectively in Germany as a whole.

The years after 1075 saw the decline of Germany from the leading power in Europe to a vacuum, into which the now centralized monarchy of France began the advance that was to lead to the Rhine frontier. Yet, incredibly, the picture is not entirely one of gloom. While all these battles raged, the patient labour of the humbler classes secured the three immense achievements of medieval Germany, the clearing of the waste, the colonization of the East and the growth of the towns.

THE WEST GERMAN VILLAGE

Forms of Earliest Settlements. The oldest German settlements are naturally found in the areas of light soil favoured by the initial tribal settlers, including sandy loam patches in the Northern Lowland, limestone plateaus and gravel terraces in the Central Uplands and, above all, the loess lands. A few settlements in areas like the Rhine valley bear place-names of Celtic origin (*-ach* terminations) or Roman origin (some of the *-weiler* names). The earliest German villages are associated with names ending in *-ingen*, *-heim* or *-ingheim*, usually prefixed by a personal name. In the cadastral maps of the late 18th and 19th centuries these early settled areas, especially in southern Germany, are frequently coincident with the distribution of the very large village (*Haufendorf*) and its associated common open-field system (*Gewannflur*). Usually there were three or more fields (*Zelgen*) divided into irregularly block-shaped furlongs (*Gewanne*) which in turn were divided into the strips of the individual peasants. A man could not grow what he liked on his unfenced strips, but had to follow the common rotation pattern of the fields, usually one year winter corn, one year spring corn and one year fallow. He also shared with his fellows the grazing available on the fallow field, on the stubbles, on the common land and in the forest. It used to be held that this type of farming system, with its related village community, sprang into being with the first German occupation of the land, but it is now believed that these are secondary forms that evolved through the centuries. As already noted above (p. 49), the primary German settlements appear to have been small, up to twelve farms in hamlet form, and appear to have carried on an irregular rotation of small rectangular arable fields (*Blockflur*) set in a large area of rough pasture. A variant form was found in the sea marshes of the mounds (*Terpen*) for protection against floods.

As early as the 6th to 7th centuries new foundations began to thicken the pattern in the old-settled areas, without greatly expanding their margins. Characteristic place-name endings of this *Ausbauzeit* are *-hausen*, *-dorf*, *-statt*, *-beuren* and *-weiler*. The Franks added their quota of new rural settlements in the same area as part of the process of consolidating their hold on Germany, and a minority of their foundations had a consciously planned form with broad-strip holdings running right across the communal territory. With this exception, the old-settled lands of western Germany, both north and south of the Rhenish Uplands, had by about the middle of the 11th century acquired a homogeneous cover of hamlets with associated *Blockflur*, a pattern very different from the great villages with fragmented common arable fields found over much of the area today.

Intensification and the Clearing of the Waste. The change from the rural settlement pattern of the 11th century to the one that we know today took place in stages at various periods. Perhaps the most significant of these was the great period of high medieval prosperity between the 11th and 13th centuries, when a rise in population coincided with the growth of towns, the development of mining and manufacture and the expansion of trade. Some of the new urban prosperity spilled outwards to the peasants through an increased demand for agricultural products, especially grain. In areas near to expanding towns, like the Gau plateaus of Swabia, the Upper Rhine Plain, the Mosel valley and the Wetterau this led to the intensification and expansion of production. Intensification initiated the process that the German scholars called *Vergewannung*, the subdivision of holdings and the change from individual fields and irregular rotations to common arable fields and fixed rotations. The expansion of the open fields, growing grain two years out of three, cut down the amount of grazing available, but a minimum of common pasture (*Almende*) had to be left which, together with the scanty herbage of the fallow field, would nourish the beasts which were essential to keep up the fertility of the arable land with their manure. A stretch of meadow land was also essential in order to provide hay for wintering the nucleus of the herd. As the process of creating the common arable fields went on, and holdings were progressively subdivided, so too the number of families in the associated settlement increased: hamlets grew into small villages, which began their rise to the swollen and overcrowded *Haufendorf* settlements that we know today.

On the lowlands of northwest Germany, where much of the land is coarse sand or peat bog, development took a different course. Superimposed on what is believed to have been an initial *Blockflur* there evolved a system of single large *Esch* fields, typically found on slightly raised sandy areas, just above the surrounding marshy hollows (Fig. 8). The *Esch* was cropped every year, its fertility maintained by the application of manure and turf derived from the surrounding waste. The relationship of *Esch* to waste was about 1 : 21, so obviously the proportion of any parish that could be devoted to arable cultivation was strictly limited. The *Esch* was divided into long arable strips running across it from side to side (*Langstreifenflur*). The strips were shared among a small group of substantial farmers who lived beside the *Esch*, commonly in an irregular hamlet known as a *Drubbel* (Fig. 8). The northwest German tradition of undivided inheritance by a single heir (*Anerbenrecht*) has preserved these farms from subdivision, in contrast to developments further south. Before the age of artificial fertilizers the *Esch* cultivation represented the highest degree of arable intensification possible in an area of poor soils and high rainfall, physically best suited to a livestock economy.

The Clearing of the Waste. The medieval rise in population and the strong demand for agricultural produce led not only to an intensification of existing agriculture but also to a dramatic expansion of the frontiers of settlement. All over Germany the peasants advanced into the primeval forest, felling trees and carving out farms from the poorer land of the hills and of the sandy plateaus. The movement gathered speed after 1050 in southern Germany and 1100 in the north, reaching its peak in the 12th and 13th centuries. The settlements thus created are distinguished today by place-name endings indicating clearance, such as *-roth*, *-rode*, *-holz* and *-feld*.

The forests that bordered the old-settled lands of western Germany were in the hands of the territorial aristocracy or of the Church, lords who welcomed the chance of increasing their subjects and their tax income through encouraging clearances. Many lords used the woodlands to carve themselves new bases of power, clear of the thoroughly confused landownership patterns of the older settled areas. Perhaps the best-known example is provided by the Dukes of Zähringen, who were the main organizers of settlement in the central and southern Black Forest. They secured their new territory by peripheral castles and newly founded towns, like Freiburg-im-Breisgau, Offenburg and Villingen (Fig. 13).

The characteristic settlement form of the clearing of the waste in western Germany is the isolated farm, with its lands in a unified block around it. Perhaps the best-known example of the type is the Black Forest house, with its single wood-

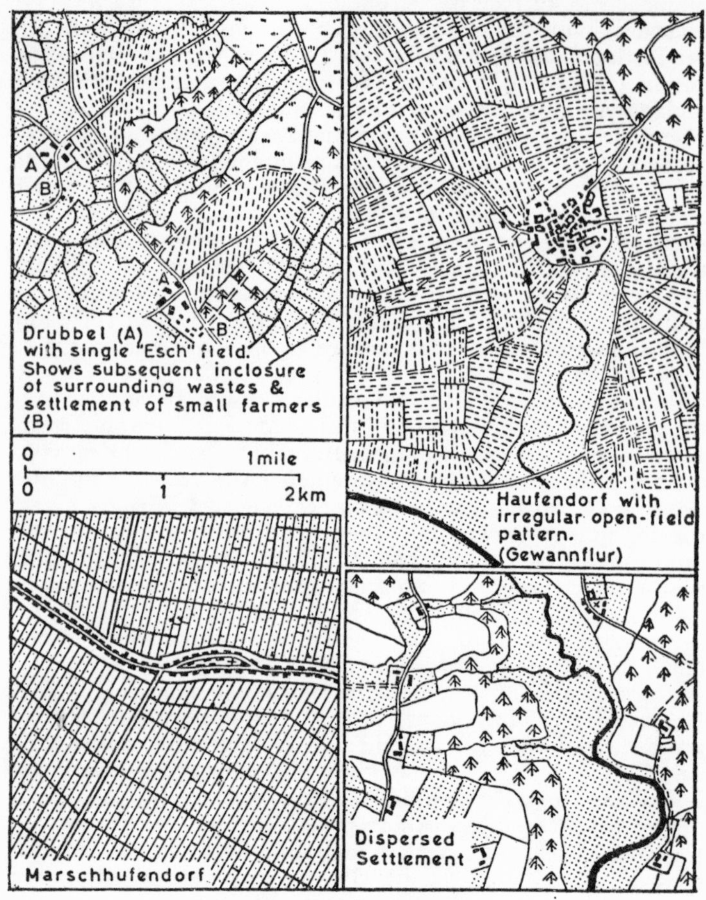

FIG. 8. Rural settlement forms of western Germany. For key to symbols see Fig. 9.

shingled roof sweeping down to shelter man and beast. In the more rugged areas, single farms or small hamlets have remained to this day, but where extensive plateau surfaces are available, as in the southern part of the Rhenish Uplands, open-field systems and village settlements sometimes developed. Occasionally when a lord ordained a particularly orderly form of settlement we find the linear forest village (*Waldhufendorf*), as where the Lords of Calw settled the Bunter Sandstone plateaus of the northeast Black Forest. This particular form of settlement is much more commonly associated with the German eastern colonization, in connection with which it is described in more detail (p. 67). Just as the settlers advanced into the woods so too they advanced into the coastal marshes and began to protect them with dykes. The corresponding settlement form here is the *Marschhufendorf*, the long double row of farms clinging to the security of the dyke, with strips of land perhaps 50 m/160 ft wide and occasionally 7 or 8 km/4 or 5 miles long stretching out at right angles into the marsh on either side.

Although the medieval clearing of the waste was an enormous achievement, it appears that much land was occupied that was too marginal in quality for sustained arable cultivation. Yields eventually declined, and even the better lands were affected by the shortage of manure due to the reduction of the area of waste available for grazing. Fragmentation of holdings was also a problem, especially on the long-settled lands. Given the agricultural techniques of the time, there was a degree of overpopulation, and the consequent malnutrition reduced resistance to the epidemics of the 14th and 15th centuries.

THE GERMAN EASTERN COLONIZATION

The hunger for land that drove western Germany's expanding peasant population to clear the woods was also the main force behind the advance into the Slav lands to the east. The movement was something of a crusade; the peasant who undertook the long and dangerous journey to the east was offered not merely the best of soils, rich in fruits and abounding in fish and flesh, but also the chance of salvation through the conversion and civilization of the Slavs. Reliance on German sources has probably given us an exaggerated idea of the backwardness of the tribes who occupied the 'shatter-belt' between the Elbe–Saale line and the Christian Polish state in the Vistula basin. Certainly these peoples were sufficiently advanced and solidly established for their settlements to have passed on their names to thousands of German towns and villages, notably including Berlin itself.

The first decisive eastward movement came in the south where, between 800 and 1100, the Bavarians completed the settlement of the Ostmark, which was roughly equivalent in extent to the present Austria. Further north, the victories of the German kings over the Slavs in the 10th century did not lead to any decisive advance beyond the general Elbe–Saale line that had been established in the time of Charles the Great. Only in the 12th century was the advance renewed, this time not under the weakened crown, but under the lords of the Marches, such as Henry the Lion, Duke of Saxony and Albert the Bear, Margrave of the North Mark, later Brandenburg. The movement began with conquest, in particular with Henry the Lion's Wendish crusade of 1147, but did not, as in the past, end in retreat. The gains were consolidated by the settlement of German peasants on conquered land beyond the Elbe.

Once this first attack was over, the German colonization was relatively peaceful, except in East Prussia. Here, the Teutonic Knights, one of the militant orders originally formed for the conquest of the Holy Land, were called in. It took them thirty years to subdue and baptize the heathen Prussians and even after German peasants had been brought in, a strong Masurian Slav element persisted in the population.

The greatest German advances were made in the first half of the 13th century. In the centre, the moderately peaceful extension of Brandenburg reached the Oder in 1240. To the north, the Slav princes welcomed German peasants and monks into eastern Mecklenburg and Pomerania, which were thus linked with the Germans in East Prussia. The Slav prince of Silesia also invited German settlers, who spread southeastwards as far as Moravia and also advanced into the mountain border of Bohemia.

At this stage, reached in the mid-14th century, German settlement was checked by the decline in the supply of peasants from the west, and opposition from the modernized and revived Slav kingdoms of Hungary, Bohemia and Poland. Even the mighty Teutonic Order was humbled at the Battle of Tannenberg in 1410. The Germans came to rest with their advanced settlements forming three prongs, pointing down the Danube through Austria, along the Hercynian Foreland through

Silesia and along the Baltic shore. Between the prongs were the partially isolated Slav areas of Bohemia and Poland, a pattern of potential conflict which lasted until the 20th century.

Beyond even these prongs of continuous settlement there were islands of Germans, where Slav lords had invited peasants, miners and merchants to settle. These scattered peoples clung for centuries to their German language and culture, which they regarded as superior to that of their Slav neighbours. Their descendants were to form the *Volksdeutsche*, the German minorities of eastern Europe, in the nationalist struggles of our own time (Fig. 20).

There were also considerable Slav survivals within the main area of German settlement. Even to this day some 100,000 Sorbs or Wends, remnants of a formerly more widespread Lusatian people, have preserved their slavonic language and particular customs in the shelter of the Spreewald marshes, only 100 km/60 miles from Berlin. Further east there was great intermixture of Germans and Poles, especially in Silesia. Most fatefully for the history of Europe a corridor of predominantly Polish population was maintained following the Vistula to the sea, cutting across the northern arm of German settlement following the Baltic coast. The struggle for control of this corridor was to be the immediate occasion of the outbreak of the Second World War.

Eastern Village Forms. The great characteristic of the German eastern settlement is its remarkable uniformity over wide areas. The lord who controlled the land employed a professional organizer, a 'Locator', who laid out the villages and attracted the peasants from the west by promises of land and freedom from feudal restrictions. Because so many settlements had to be established in so short a time, a few well-tried forms were used time and again.

The classical planned forms of the German colonization of the lowlands were the long-green and long-street villages. In the long-green village (*Angerdorf*) the farmsteads are in two rows facing the spindle-shaped green (*Anger*), which bears the duck-pond, the church and other public buildings (Fig. 9). In the long-street village (*Strassendorf*) the green has disappeared, and the farmhouses face each other across a road. In spite of their planned form *Angerdorf* and *Strassendorf* were just as much open-field villages as the *Haufendorf* of western Germany, but

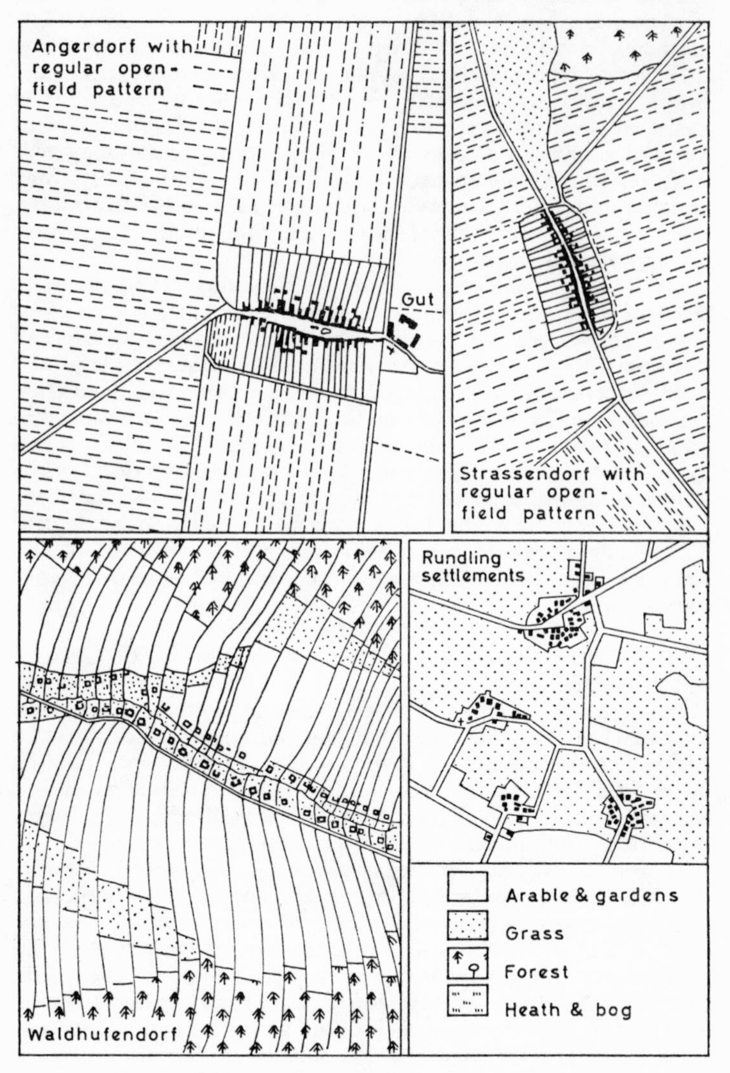

FIG. 9. Rural settlement forms of eastern Germany.

instead of their arable land consisting of a mosaic of furlongs each divided into strips there were characteristically three great open fields filling almost the whole of the village lands, divided by regular narrow strips that ran right across them from side to side (*Plangewannflur*).

Unlike the Slavs, the Germans were willing to attack the forested uplands, and the planned form used was the linear forest village (*Waldhufendorf*). This form combines the social and administrative advantages of the village community with the placing of each farm on its own land. The farmhouses are normally spaced out along a stream, with each farmer's land stretching in a narrow ribbon up the hillside. In this way each farmer had a balanced holding, meadow by the stream, arable on the lower slopes, then rough pasture below the forest that crowned the valley side. Forest villages are often continuous for miles along a valley; they are particularly characteristic of the Ore and Sudetan Mountains.

It would be a mistake to imagine that these striking planned forms are everywhere present in the area of German settlement; a number of smaller forms, regular and irregular, are also found. Along and east of the Elbe–Saale line, land of good quality, on which one might expect to find planned villages with the three-field system, is found to have a variety of small settlements associated with small rectangular fields (*Blockflur*) and intermixed irregular strips. The most striking of these settlement forms is the small round village (*Rundling*). They are frequently sited on the break of slope where well-drained, cultivated land rises above swampy depressions. A circle of farmsteads turn their backs to the depression to look onto a central green, from which there was originally only one, easily barricaded, exit to the higher, cultivated land where movement was easier. Not unreasonably the *Rundling* was long regarded as a defensive form, but equally the green may have been a cattle corral. It is possible that the *Rundling* villages, together with hamlets and other small forms with which they are intermingled, were established at a time when German control was being extended over the Slav populations, but without the establishment of the open-field systems characteristic of the settlement areas further east. Small settlements are also typical of the irregular, damp terrain of the Brandenburg river valleys, where the land was not fit for the development of open-field cultivation, and also of the Mecklenburg coastal lowland and islands. In general the initial form of the eastern settlements can most easily be related to the economy prevalent at the time of their foundation. The economy in turn however was affected by the date of establishment, and whether the settlers were predominantly German or Slav.

Results of the Eastern Colonization. The occupation of the eastern lands changed the whole political and economic balance of

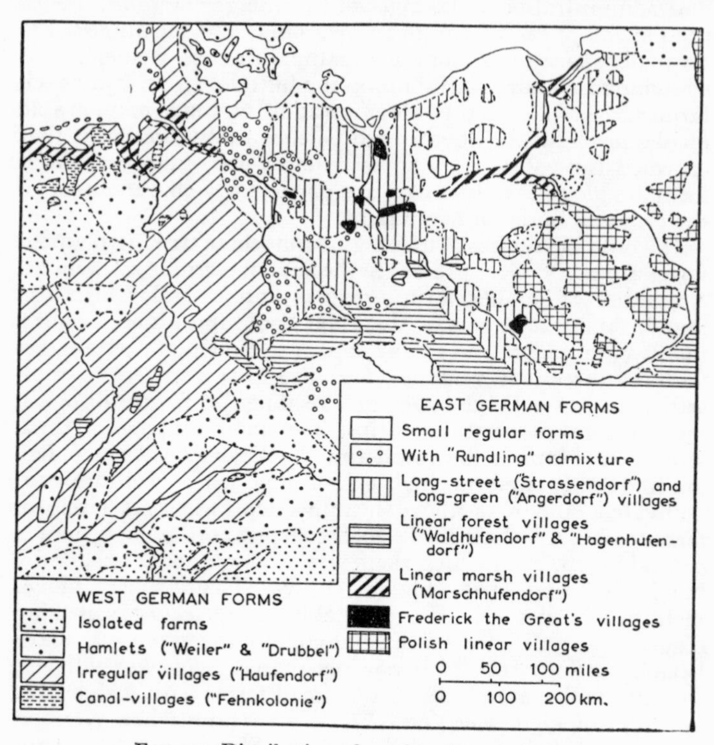

FIG. 10. Distribution of rural settlement forms.

Germany. The new principalities carved by the Marcher Lords out of the eastern Lowland had a fresh start, unhampered by the feudal ties, the ancient jealousies and the political fragmentation of the west. The Elbe now ran through the heart of the German lands, instead of being a frontier. On the other hand, the axis of the older Germany, the Rhine, was itself in danger of being reduced to a frontier through the advance of French power into the petty principalities that now lined its banks. The centre of gravity in Germany had moved decisively to the east.

The 'Wüstungen'. The good times came to an end after the beginning of the 14th century. It would seem that the population growth of the period 1150–1300 had exceeded the capacity of the environment, and the 14th and 15th centuries saw a period of agricultural decline. An economic depression lasting into the 15th century coincided with repeated visitations of pestilence, notably the Black Death that spread over Europe in the period 1347–51. The area under cultivation was larger than was needed for the reduced population, cereal prices fell and all over Germany there was a retreat from the margin of cultivation as poorer lands were given up. In what the Germans call *Wüstungen* thousands of farms and villages were abandoned; in Württemberg alone over 500 'lost villages' date from the 14th and 15th centuries. In eastern Germany the abandoned farms were often taken up by the lords, and merged with their own land. International trade through the Hanse ports encouraged the development of large-scale grain production, but because labour was short the lords could only work their enlarged farms by the forced labour of the formerly privileged eastern peasants, whose legal position steadily deteriorated.

THE MEDIEVAL TOWN

The Form of Towns. The German tribesmen scorned the town, and during the Dark Ages urban life all but disappeared. It is true that many of the former Roman towns of the Rhine continued to have a Bishop's seat or a Frankish palace huddled in one corner of the ruins, but of urban life in the sense of communities of merchants and artisans enforcing their own town laws within their own walls there was none. Only with the improvement of administration and the rise of trade from the Carolingian period onwards, and especially after 1000, did towns once more emerge.

The early west German town evolved from a settlement of

merchants clinging to the protection of a previously existing fortified nucleus. On the Rhine and Danube these were mainly provided by the Bishop's seats, often on former Roman sites,

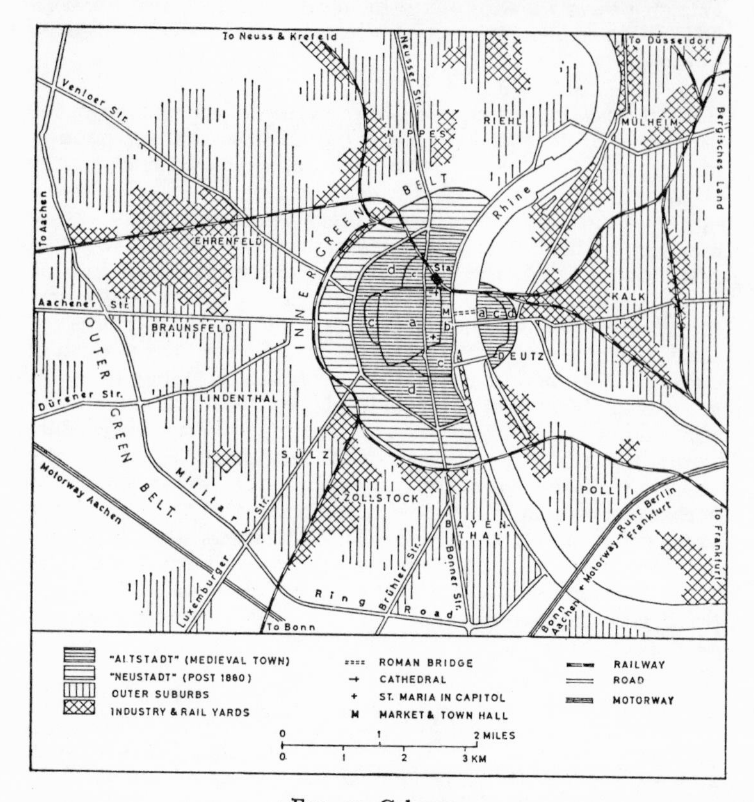

Fig. 11. Cologne.
(a) Roman town; (b) 10th-century extension; (c) extensions of 1106; (d) final medieval extensions 1180.

such as Cologne, Mainz and Strasbourg, or by imperial residences such as Aachen or Frankfurt. East of the Rhine, the nuclei were generally Frankish fortresses established to hold down the German tribes or to consolidate the Elbe–Saale frontier, which were again often Bishop's seats, as at Münster or Hamburg. At this earlier period, southern Germany had far fewer towns than the north.

The later Middle Ages saw a spate of deliberate foundations of towns, due in part to the increase in trade and the development of new trade routes, but reflecting above all the political

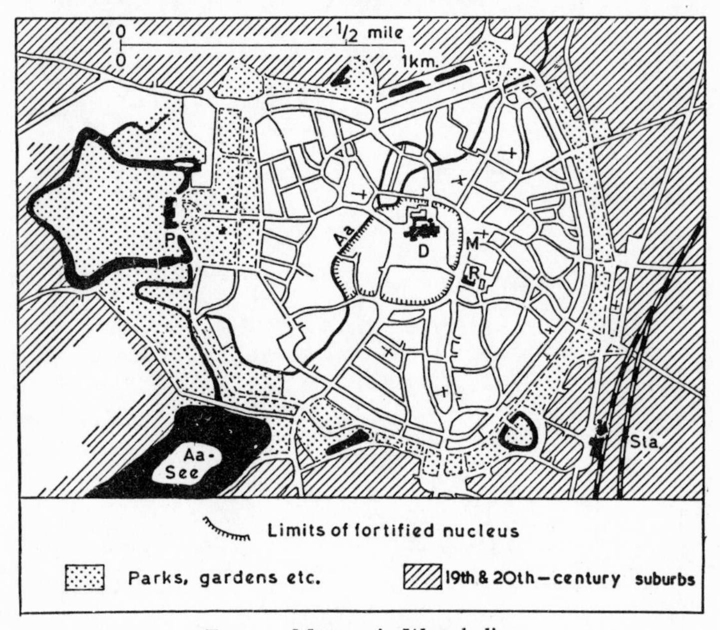

FIG. 12. Münster in Westphalia.
(D) Dom (cathedral) square; (M) market place; (R) town hall (*Rathaus*); (P) bishop's palace, now university.

fragmentation of the period. Towns were founded as administrative centres or petty capitals, to guard frontiers, to provide the lord with an income from market dues, or even because a village had grown so wealthy from its vines that it could afford to buy a charter. Reference has already been made to the town foundations of the counts of Zähringen in southwest Germany (p. 61). Other notable founders of towns were Henry the Lion (München), and the Hohenstaufen emperors. Because territorial fragmentation was at its greatest in southern Germany this area in particular is studded with towns, some of which have never grown at all, and remain as mere collections of farmhouses within their crumbling medieval walls.

The development of the west German town can be traced in its street plan to this day. The outline of the pre-urban

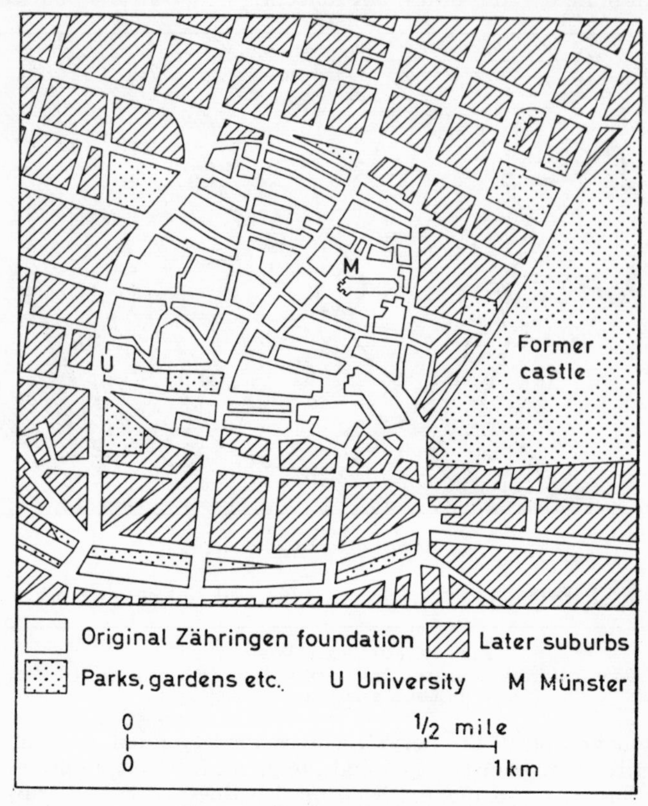

FIG. 13. Freiburg-im-Breisgau.

nucleus is usually clear, whether it was a partially occupied Roman city as at Cologne (Fig. 11) or a fortified cathedral precinct, as at Münster (Fig. 12). The market settlement will normally be found just outside the nucleus; at Cologne, for example, it is situated between the Roman town and the river.

In the market place will be the Town Hall (*Rathaus*), the tall, gabled houses of the merchants, and an elaborate fountain. Near by may be found the church of the townsfolk, challenging the Bishop's or Lord's church in the nucleus. This merchants' town was itself walled, and often there are signs of one or more extensions before the town reached its full growth, which at both Münster and Cologne was as early as the end of the 12th century. The towns founded later in the Middle Ages are often much more regular in form. The Zähringen foundations like Freiburg-im-Breisgau or Bern in what is now Switzerland form a remarkable group, with a broad market street running across the walled town from gate to gate, and lesser streets going off at right angles (Fig. 13).

In the east German lands, fortified towns were carefully created in the process of colonization to act as centres of administration and refuge for the inhabitants of the new villages of the surrounding countryside. They rarely show signs of growth from a nucleus; like the villages, they were planned as a whole, and so have very regular plans. At their most typical, they have a rectangular grid of streets, with one complete block left out for the market place, and sometimes another for the church (Neubrandenburg, Fig. 14).

Townsfolk and their Leagues. The development of the town and its culture was perhaps the greatest achievement of medieval Germany. A new class developed, the burghers, independent of the lords, but distinct from the peasants, gaining a living from trade and manufacturers. The various crafts were controlled by guilds which, with their feasts, religious processions and mystery plays provided their members with a rich social and spiritual life. In the towns a recognizably modern administration first came to Germany, with laws governing building and sanitation, and taxes to pay for defence and the care of the poor and needy. Such towns, too, left us a splendid legacy of Gothic churches, public buildings and rich merchants' houses, all too much of which was destroyed between 1939 and 1945.

In the troubled times of conflict after 1250, towns were largely independent of control either by the crown or by a local territorial lord. They frequently banded together for trade or defence in leagues, the greatest of which was the association of northern towns, including Lübeck, Hamburg,

Bremen and Cologne, that made up the Hanseatic League. The Hanse grew out of the achievements of German merchants in developing the trade which exchanged the grain, fish, amber and tar of the Baltic for the cloth and wine from England, the Low Countries and further south.

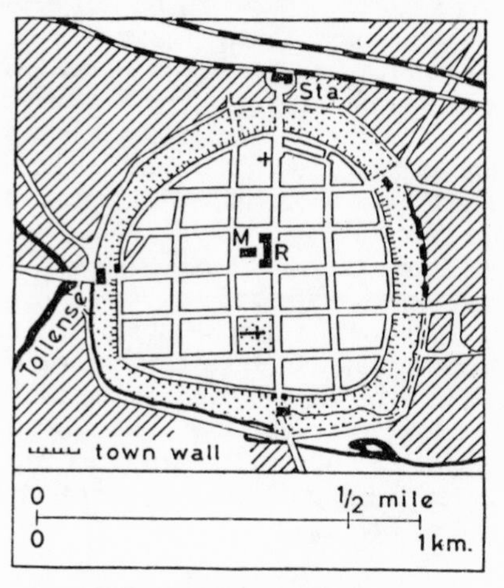

FIG. 14. Neubrandenburg.
For keys to letters and symbols see Fig. 12.

The Hanse towns were on or near the great maritime trade route which carried this trade along the southern shore of the Baltic, overland across the base of the Schleswig-Holstein peninsula, and then by water again from Hamburg to London or Bruges. It was not surprising that Lübeck, the transhipment point on the Baltic, dominated the League. It was one of the two largest towns of the Empire, with over 30,000 inhabitants; the other was also a great route centre, Cologne, at the intersection of the Rhine and the Hercynian Foreland.

The age of forest clearance, of eastern colonization and of the foundation of towns was over by 1350, when the period of population expansion ended. Trade declined, but many merchants, like the Fuggers of Augsburg, continued to prosper by moneylending. The golden afternoon of the medieval town, lasting into the 16th century, has left us many splendid merchants' houses in the early Renaissance style.

SUGGESTIONS FOR FURTHER READING

G. Barraclough, *The origins of Modern Germany*, 2nd ed. (Blackwell), 1947, (New York: Macmillan, 1964; New York; Pitman, 1963, pap.).

The Cambridge Economic History of Europe. Vol. 1, The agrarian life of the middle ages, 2nd ed., 1966.
Vol. 2, Trade and industry in the middle ages, 1952.
Vol. 3, Economic organization and policies in the middle ages, 1963 (esp. ch. 1, 'The rise of towns').

B. H. Slicher van Bath, *The agrarian history of western Europe A.D. 500–1850* (Arnold), 1963, (New York: St. Martin's, 1963).

R. E. Dickinson, *The west European city* (Routledge and Kegan Paul), 1951, esp. ch. 17, (Rev., 2nd ed.; New York: Humanities, 1961).

G. Pfeiffer, 'The quality of peasant living in central Europe', in W. L. Thomas (ed.), *Man's role in changing the face of the earth* (Chicago), 1956, pp. 240–77.

K. F. Reinhardt, *Germany: 2000 years*, rev. ed., vol. 1 (Constable), 1961, (New York: Ungar).

C. T. Smith, *An historical geography of western Europe before 1800* (Longmans), 1967.

Chapter 6

THE AGE OF THE PRINCES

THE RISE OF THE PRINCELY STATES

In the anarchy of late medieval times, it had seemed possible that the power of the princes would go the same way as the power of the monarchy that they had done so much to destroy, and that the leagues of lesser nobles, knights and townsmen would inherit the land. From this fate Germany was saved by the transformation of the prince into the sovereign lord of a secular state, with a centralized administration of the kind that had long been developed in England and France.

Many forces helped to consolidate the power of the prince. The people were tired of anarchy and war, and welcomed any force that promised to restore peace and order. Gunpowder was also a most powerful force for unity, breaching the walls of robber baron's castle and free city alike, while the growing use of mercenary troops reduced the prince's dependence on the support of nobles and knights in times of war.

In the age of princes, Germany remained a mosaic, but at least a mosaic of states that were moderately efficiently ruled, according to the standards of the time. Of the most important states, four had their roots in the colonial east: Austria and Bohemia, ruled over by the Habsburg Emperors, Saxony and Brandenburg. In old Germany the greatest units were Bavaria, Hesse, Brunswick-Lüneburg and the Palatinate, a state which straddled across the northern end of the Rhine Rift Valley. But the territorial unity of the principalities was interrupted by the ecclesiastical states, by fifty to sixty Imperial free cities and by the lands of minor rulers, ranging downwards in importance to the Imperial Knights of southwest Germany, many of them lords of 'states' of 300 souls.

REFORMATION AND REACTION

Luther. At noon on All Saints' Eve of 1517, Martin Luther, a monk and Professor at the University of Wittenberg, nailed his ninety-five Theses against Indulgences to the door of the castle church. The speed of reaction all over Germany to this fairly orthodox incident of theological disputation indicates that Luther merely provided the spark; the explosion that was to change the face of Germany had been prepared long before. Resentment against the Papacy had been building up for some time; princes who had been prepared to join with the Pope in attacking the monarchy, now resented Papal influence in their own domains, and were covetous of ecclesiastical revenues. Among the people as a whole, criticism of abuses in the lives of Pope and clergy led naturally to criticism of the doctrines that apparently permitted such abuses. Scholars, meanwhile, had begun to examine assumptions about the Bible and early Church in the light of the new classical learning.

The German Bible. From the metropolis of Protestant learning at Wittenberg, Gutenberg's invention of printing with movable metal types took the words of Luther to the whole of Germany. The most potent force was the German vernacular Bible, of which Luther's own version was not the first but by far the most influential. With astounding energy Luther completed the translation of the New Testament from the Greek during the year that he spent sheltered from his enemies in the Wartburg castle in Thuringia. His translation of the Old Testament followed later, and the complete Bible was published in 1534. Luther's Bible stamped itself into the minds and speech of the people, and in so doing established the German language as we know it today. The vigorous and direct language which had evolved in the courts of colonial Saxony and Bohemia triumphed over all other dialects and became as *Neuhochdeutsch* the standard speech of educated people all over Germany.

Princes and Peasants. Luther's doctrines spread rapidly among all classes, among princes like the Elector of Saxony, townsmen like the Nuremberg poet Hans Sachs or the artist Dürer, among even the peasants. But the princes who protected Luther in the Wartburg took good care that his ideas of spiritual equality were not applied in the earthly sphere. The peasants, especially in southwest Germany, were suffering from over-population and the excessive fragmentation of farm holdings. The old outlets were blocked; the eastern colonization was at an end, the towns no longer expanding. In 1525, driven to despair by fresh exactions of the nobility, they rose against their lords, the words of Luther on their lips, only to be denounced by the reformer himself. The rising was suppressed with appalling brutality, and the peasantry remained crushed until the end of the 18th century, cut off from the chance of political action or economic advancement.

The Peace of Augsburg (1555). The Reformation ended with a prostrate peasantry, and with the princes, Protestant and Catholic, more firmly established than ever, through their control over the Church in their territories. At the Peace of Augsburg, both Catholics and Protestants recognized that, since neither religion had succeeded in driving out the other, room must be found for both. The principle was established, not of toleration, but that each prince might enforce his own religion in his own territory (*cuius regio eius religio*).

The Thirty Years War (1618–48). The war that was set off by the rebellion of the Bohemian Protestants against their Catholic Habsburg ruler was only in part a continuation of the religious conflict. For once there was an emperor, Ferdinand, who had sufficient determination, and a strong enough backing of Spanish troops, to hope to unite Germany by force. The German princes who opposed him were fighting for their independence from Habsburg control as much as for religion. Germany could not even be left to fight her own battles; the enemies of the House of Habsburg in Europe, especially France, were only too pleased to see the Emperor embroiled in Germany, provided that he was not too successful, and only too willing to prolong the struggle whenever peace seemed like breaking out.

In the end, thirty years of bitter struggle resulted in relatively unchanged religious divisions, but caused the most appalling hardships and miseries to the peoples of Germany. Armies of unpaid mercenaries roamed the countryside, ever moving on to find an unravaged district or another town to sack, leaving the peasants to live until the next harvest on a diet of acorns and roots, and without a roof over their heads.

The Peace of Westphalia which ended hostilities in 1648 finally decided that the German Imperial crown was henceforth to be only a picturesque and meaningless ornament of the House of Austria. It also confirmed the establishment of foreigners on German soil; Denmark controlled the mouth of the Elbe, Sweden the mouth of the Oder. The final recognition of the independence of Switzerland and the Netherlands meant that both the source and the outlet of the 'German Rhine' lay outside German control. Even more menacing to the future of German power on the Rhine was the recognition of the French possession of Metz, Toul, Verdun and Habsburg Alsace. In what remained of Germany, the sovereign powers of the princes were confirmed over a mosaic of 170–200 secular states, 63 ecclesiastical states and the independent lands of 1,000 or more Imperial knights.

RELIGIOUS DIVISIONS IN GERMANY

The Peace of Westphalia confirmed, in the main, the position reached at Augsburg nearly 100 years before. Germany was not to be united under either Protestant or Catholic religion. The dividing lines, hardened by the hate and mistrust born of years of struggle, were to endure, substantially unaltered, until the great migrations of our own time (Fig. 15).

The heart of Protestant Germany lay in the north and east, including East Prussia. From this broad base a narrowing belt of Protestant territory stretched southwards through Hesse towards Württemberg, with an important outpost in the Rhenish Palatinate. Catholicism had its base in the south, in Bavaria and Austria. The Rhinelands were more mixed, reflecting the multiplicity of states there, but had great Catholic bastions in the territories of the Bishops of Trier, Mainz, Cologne and, further north, Münster. On the Northern Lowland, the principal islands of Catholic population were in Habsburg Silesia, among the Polish population of the far east and on the Netherlands border.

The religious division of Germany had important consequences in economic and social geography. Each religion has made its own distinctive artistic contribution to Germany, whether the baroque churches and statues of Catholic Bavaria, or the church music of the Protestant north. In economic life, also, differences appeared; the Protestants who fled from the Catholic lands were often skilled town artisans, who enriched the Protestant lands that received them. Catholic Cologne, for example, lost skilled weavers and other tradesmen to Mülheim and Elberfeld in Protestant Berg, across the Rhine. In the main, also, Catholicism tended to discourage usury and capitalism; this was certainly one of the factors underlying the slow industrial development of south Germany prior to the 20th century.

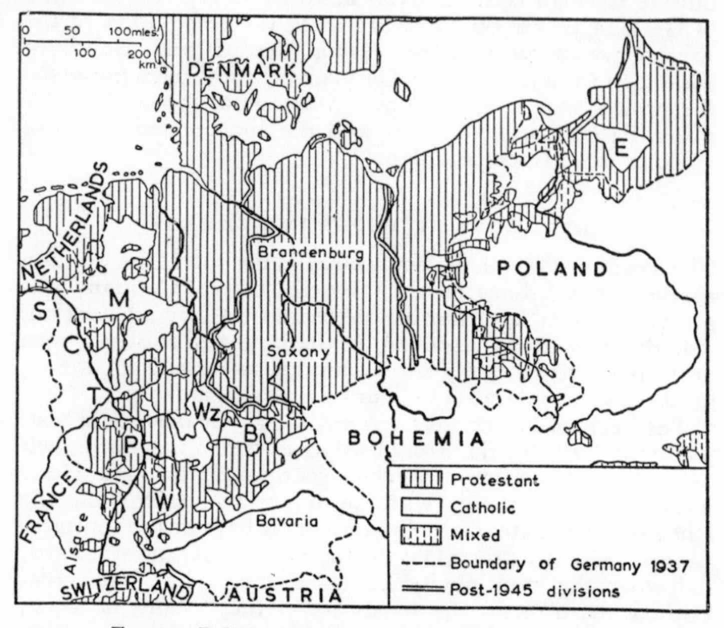

FIG. 15. Religious divisions in Germany before 1945.
The initials indicate the former ecclesiastical territories of (E) Ermeland; (B) Bamberg; (C) Cologne; (M) Münster; (T) Trier; (Wz) Würzburg, and also the states of (W) Württemberg; (P) Palatinate; (S) Southern Netherlands.

THE AGE OF ABSOLUTISM

The Palace. The exhaustion of the peasants and townsfolk in the Thirty Years War left Germany's hundreds of princes in more complete control than ever. The physical sign of the might and power of the prince was the palace, built in the theatrical Baroque style to make the maximum impression on the beholder. Ruler vied with ruler in magnificence; even the Bishops were not behindhand in earthly splendour, as shown by the palace that was built at Würzburg by Germany's greatest 18th-century architect, Balthasar Neumann.

The furnishing of the palace and the supplying of the needs of the court called into being an army of cabinet-makers, tailors, jewellers and craftsmen of all kinds. Actors, artists and

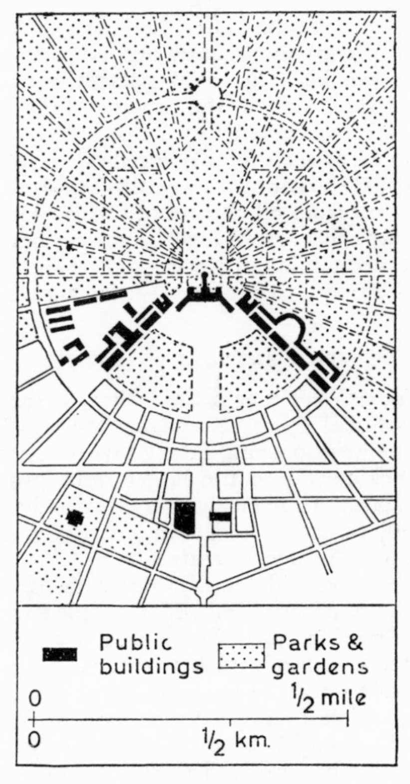

Fig. 16. Karlsruhe in Baden.

musicians added to the amenities of the court, and writers found that princely patronage was the only way to advancement. Although this period culminated in the age of Schiller and Goethe, the highest point of German literature, the dependence of writers on the court did not encourage political speculation. Both philosophy and religion tended to be inward-looking, rather than concerned with the practical conduct of affairs. Even when, in the 18th century, the ideas of the 'Age of Enlightenment' (*Aufklärung*) began to filter through from France, paper criticism of absolutism rarely led to political action.

In the century and a half after the Peace of Westphalia, the princes gave Germany an urgently needed period of order, but the price paid was high. So many palaces, courts and armies could be maintained only at the expense of the townsfolk and peasants, already weakened by war. Administration became the preserve of an excessively privileged official class, but those who really earned the country's wealth, the farmers and townsmen, were cut off from all control of affairs. The main object of the prince was to keep himself in power; beside this need, political and economic advance, and even the continued existence of Germany, were of lesser importance.

THE PRINCELY TOWN

The Thirty Years War was a final blow to the independent town as a political force. Even the towns which escaped seizure by some neighbouring prince saw their trade and political power trickle away to the larger units provided by the surrounding states. Conversely, some initially small towns, like Düsseldorf, Stuttgart or Berlin, increased in importance because they were princely capitals.

The characteristics of the new princely towns were a Renaissance desire for symmetry and order coupled with a princely desire for self-glorification. There was a regularly planned pattern of streets, one of which would be made particularly wide and imposing in order to form a processional way leading to the palace, which dominated the town. At first towns were surrounded by a broad belt of the elaborate fortifications that military engineers had evolved to counter the use of cannon, with wide moats, earthen scarps and counter-scarps, and elaborate star-shaped bastions. In more peaceful times, after the middle of the 17th century, each German prince tried to adopt the more open plan of Versailles, in which palace, town and formal park were united in a grandiose transformation of the entire landscape.

Generally the princely quarter was added to an existing

town, as at Münster (Fig. 12), but some completely new towns were founded. Karlsruhe, founded in 1715, is the most perfect example of the later, Versailles-influenced princely town (Fig. 16). Towards the palace of the Margrave a full circle of vistas converge, like spokes to the hub of a wheel. In the north they form the avenues of the park, in the south the main streets of the town. All eyes are drawn to the prince, who is the state in person.

THE VILLAGE

After the depression of late-medieval times renewed population growth once more increased the pressure on land in 16th-century Germany. Opportunities for clearing new land were far fewer than they had been in the Middle Ages, and there could be no second eastern colonization. Population pressure was reflected rather in a further intensification of production from existing lands, so producing a second decisive stage in the process of *Vergewannung*, the move towards a Germany of open-field agriculture and large villages of the *Haufendorf* type. Much of the financial benefit of the higher grain prices of this period was tapped off into the coffers of the lords and princelings, so numerous in Germany, whose demands were made the more insistent by rising prices. Peasant resentment expressed itself in the abortive revolt of 1525 (p. 77).

The 17th century was another period of agricultural depression, but not as severe as that which closed medieval times. The Thirty Years War caused a marked decline in population, and thus in the demand for corn. Many parts of the country were devastated by war, and the effects were particularly serious in the former colonial lands of eastern Germany. By the close of the war the descendants of the original free settlers had been reduced to a servile condition, obliged to plough and labour on the estates of their Junker lord, and to send their womenfolk to work in his kitchens and stables.

New Settlement Forms. In this absolutist age, it is scarcely surprising that new village settlements were mainly the work of princes, and especially of Frederick the Great of Prussia. He realized that a prosperous peasantry was a necessity for the state, as a source of tax income and of soldiers. Accordingly, he created a 'new Province' for Prussia by draining marshland, especially in the Oder, Warthe and Netze valleys. Frederick's settlements are easily recognized, with their farms widely spaced along a straight road or dyke, each with its own land stretching away at right angles (Fig. 17).

Another planned settlement form, used in the great peat bogs of northwest Germany, was the canal-village or *Fehnkolonie* (Fig. 17), introduced from the Netherlands. Here the

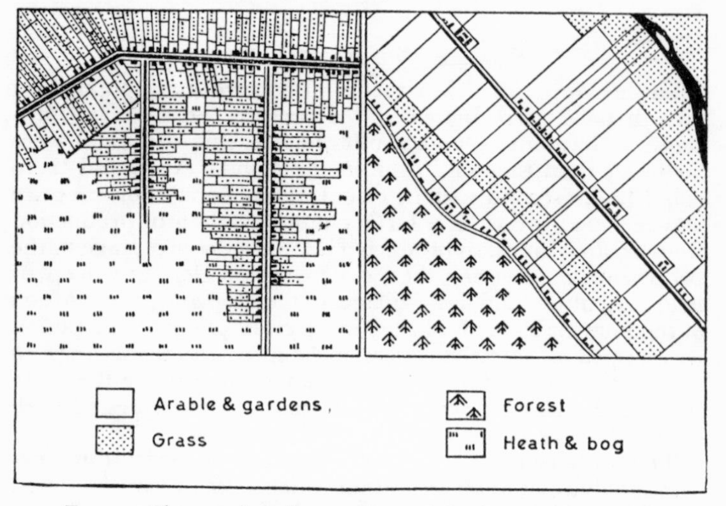

FIG. 17. Two rural settlement forms of the Age of the Princes. (*Left*) canal-village or *Fehnkolonie*; (*right*) planned village form of Frederick the Great.

farms were built on a canal, which provided both drainage and transport in the quaking ground. Each farmer was allowed to clear a strip of land running from his house into the bog. He sold the peat, and by years or generations of ill-rewarded toil, reclaimed the sands that lay beneath.

Agricultural Revolution. The period 1750–1870, taken as a whole, was a 'golden age' for European agriculture, when population increased steeply, corn prices rose and cheap imported grain was yet to affect farm incomes. A major innovation, the introduction of fodder crops into the rotation, permitted a marked intensification of agriculture through the elimination of the fallow year in the traditional open-field system. With adequate fodder for the stall-feeding of livestock available throughout the year the commons ceased to be necessary for grazing, and in areas of good soil could be added to the common arable fields. This intensification of production and extension of the cultivated area permitted a further subdivision of open-field holdings and a consequent further enlargement of the villages. The irregular *Haufendorf*, with its scores of clustered farmhouses and its surrounding fragmented open fields is therefore not, as was once thought, a settlement form that can be traced back to the medieval German village community but something that emerged in stages, reaching its final form only in the late 18th and early 19th centuries.

Even within the open-field areas of western Germany the settlement pattern is not a uniform one, but reflects the mosaic of former princely territories. In many parts of southern Germany the peasants had secured almost complete freedom even before the arrival of the French revolutionary armies. Any remaining seigneurial rights were promptly abolished in the areas that fell directly or indirectly under French rule in the Napoleonic period. One of the most prized peasant freedoms was the right to bequeath land as the owner wished, and over most of the open-field area the custom was *Realteilung*, division among all the children. Clearly such a system encouraged the division of holdings and the fragmentation of the common open fields into ever more numerous strips. Some principalities resisted this process, mainly because more tax could be extracted from larger farms, and insisted that holdings descend entire to one heir only (*Anerbenrecht*). Although the principalities concerned may have disappeared entirely from the political map they still stand out in the cultural landscape as areas with smaller villages of larger farmhouses and less extreme fragmentation of holdings than in the open-field area in general. *Anerbenrecht* was also traditional in Bavaria and north-west Germany, which also stand out to this day as areas having farms of larger size than the average (Fig. 26).

INDUSTRY AND TRADE

The aims of each prince were to increase his income from taxes in order to pay for larger palaces and more armies, to be economically independent of his neighbours, and to strive for the favourable balance of trade that would give his state a reserve of treasure in case of war. These considerations led to a system of state fostering and control of industry and trade, generally known as mercantilism. Silesian iron and linen, Dresden lace and Meissen porcelain in Saxony, glass in the hills of Hanover, iron in Nassau-Siegen, are but a few examples of industries that were carefully stimulated or protected in this way.

Mercantilism encouraged the dispersal of manufacturing in small units all over Germany, since each of the many states tried to be self-sufficient. Particularly in mountain regions, peasants tried to supplement the yield of their poor land by developing domestic industry. In the Black Forest, they used the local wood to make clocks and toys, while in the Ore mountains of Saxony the miners developed textile industries as their mineral reserves became exhausted. Industries using large quantities of fuel, like iron smelting or glass making, or those using water power, like iron forging, were also necessarily situated outside the towns. In particular, the northern fringe of the Rhenish Uplands had a well-developed metal industry in which charcoal iron from the hills to the south was processed at water-driven hammer works, in part with the aid of coals from the near-by Ruhr valley. It was from these origins that the heavy iron and steel industry of the Ruhr coalfield was to develop.

AUSTRIA AND PRUSSIA

The period after the Thirty Years War saw a slow withdrawal of Austria from Germany. No effective opposition was offered to the French advance to the Rhine through the former Austrian lands in Alsace, while Silesia was lost to the Prussians. In spite of the reforming efforts of Maria Theresa (1740–80) and of her son Joseph II (1765–90), Austria remained a ramshackle conglomeration of largely non-German peoples, sunk in conservatism and memories of ancient glories.

The one centralized and rapidly expanding state was Prussia, which evolved out of the frontier march of Brandenburg. The change in title came in 1701, when the Hohenzollerns, who ranked merely as Electors within the Empire, acquired the title of king in respect of their East Prussian territory, which was a fief of Poland. It was this rather crude state, under a series of remarkable rulers, which reacted to the challenge of a frontier situation, a poor soil and the ravages of the Thirty Years War with such vigour that it was eventually

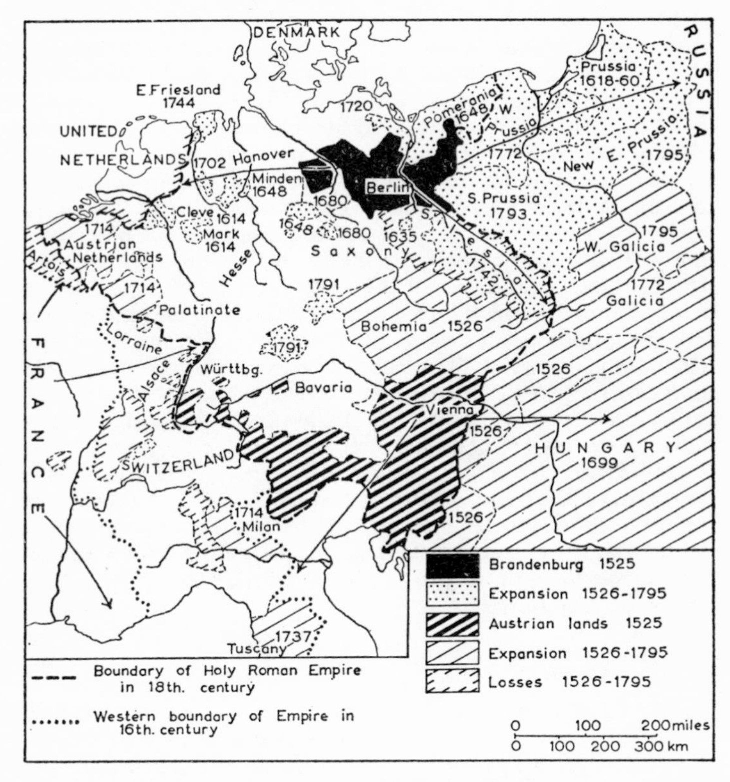

FIG. 18. Germany in the Age of the Princes.
The arrows show the principal directions taken by the expansion of France, Prussia and Austria. The dates when Austria and Prussia acquired their principal territories are also given.

able to dominate not only eastern Germany but also the more cultured states of old Germany to the west.

The extraordinary genius of the rulers of Brandenburg-

Prussia for snapping up strategically vital territory was manifested as early as the 17th century. By 1648 they had acquired eastern Pomerania, East Prussia, the vital Elbe crossing town of Magdeburg, the Weser gap town of Minden, the industrialized district of Mark in the Rhine Uplands and Cleve which controlled the exit of the Rhine into the Netherlands. By the death of Frederick the Great in 1786, Prussia also held the Baltic shore from Stettin to Memel, and had seized Silesia (1742) with its rich loess lands and minerals. When revolutionary France began its advance to the Rhine, Prussia was already deeply involved in partitioning Poland (Fig. 18).

Not less remarkable than the growth of territory was the nature of the Prussian state. The whole life of this extraordinary country was built round the maintenance of a standing national army, itself a novelty in this age of mercenary troops. Out of the needs of the army grew a new and efficient civil administration, which controlled taxation and the recruiting and housing of troops, and was the forerunner of the Prussian civil service. The need for arms led to the encouragement of industry, the need for money led to the fostering of trade, the need for strong recruits led to the founding of new villages. In an ominously modern fashion, it began to be felt that the interests of the state were supreme over all its inhabitants; even the king, however powerful, was but the highest servant of the state. In spite of Frederick the Great's flirtations with Voltaire, cultural and all other achievements were secondary; it was the maintenance of the army and the state machine that really mattered.

GERMANY AND THE FRENCH REVOLUTION

The complete disregard of wider German interests by the princely states, not least Prussia, was finally revealed under the impact of a France revitalized by the revolution of 1789. Prussia soon abandoned the apparently profitless struggle against the revolutionaries, and turned to her interests in dismembered Poland. Austria resisted with more determination, but by 1801 was obliged to recognize the transfer of the whole left bank of the Rhine to France, and give up the meaningless imperial title itself in 1806.

The division of the people from the government which was typical of the Age of Absolutism prevented any popular national resistance to France; indeed the revolutionaries were often welcomed as liberators. Even the warrior state of Prussia, returning belatedly to the attack, went under at Jena in 1806, crushed like any petty principality of the Rhine. Napoleon was able to do what he liked with Germany. The Rhinelands he absorbed into France, and out of the mosaic of minor territories and ecclesiastical states that lay beyond he created a line of puppet states stretching from Bavaria and Württemberg in the south to Westphalia in the north. These he grouped in a loose 'Confederation of the Rhine'.

The effect of the French invasion was threefold. Napoleon was able to override the interests of minor rulers and greatly simplify the political map of Germany. Secondly, his forces carried with them the political and social ideas of the Revolution, which swept through the stuffy atmosphere of the princely states. The reformed French law was established in the Rhinelands, and spread its influence far beyond. The old guild regulations and other restrictions on free enterprise were swept away, leaving the way clear for future commercial development. Finally, humiliation at the French occupation and at German princes who were willing tools of a foreigner led to a revival of national feeling. The popular uprisings that led to the defeat of the French at Leipzig in 1813 were not regarded with great enthusiasm by the Prussian and other rulers, but could scarcely be repressed, although wartime promises of reform were frequently forgotten. Fortunately, although the French were expelled, the best efforts of the German princes could not prevent them leaving behind the dangerous seed of their revolutionary political and social ideas.

SUGGESTIONS FOR FURTHER READING

E. H. Slicher van Baath, *The agrarian history of western Europe A.D. 500–1850* (Arnold), 1963, (New York: St Martin's, 1963).

W. H. Bruford, *Germany in the eighteenth century* (Cambridge Univ. Press), 1935.

R. E. Dickinson, *The west European city* (Routledge and Kegan Paul), 1951, esp. ch. 18 (Rev., 2nd ed.; New York: Humanities, 1961).

H. Holborn, *A history of modern Germany: the Reformation* (Eyre and Spottiswoode), 1965, (New York: Knopf, 1959).

H. Holborn, *A history of modern Germany 1648–1840* (Eyre and Spottiswoode), 1965, (New York: Knopf, 1963).

C. V. Wedgwood, *The Thirty Years' War* (Cape), 1938, (Penguin Books), 1957 (New York: Doubleday, pap.; Gloucester, Mass.: Peter Smith).

Chapter 7
MODERN GERMANY

THE GERMANIC CONFEDERATION

The victorious allies who met at Paris in 1814 and Vienna in 1815 to settle the fate of Europe paid little attention to German strivings for unity. In the south, states like Bavaria, Baden and Württemberg were preserved at the behest of Austria as a barrier against France and Prussia. In the north, Prussia received the former Napoleonic territories on the Rhine and in Westphalia, as well as parts of Saxony and Pomerania. The lands gained by Prussia in the west were already among the most industrialized of Germany, and contained the Ruhr coalfield, awaiting development. There was no doubt where the real power in Germany lay.

The Empire was not revived at the Congress of Vienna; instead the thirty-five independent states and four free cities of Bremen, Hamburg, Lübeck and Frankfurt were joined in a 'Germanic Confederation'. This was purely a Princes' club, concerned with the defence of the states against external attack; it was certainly not intended to limit their independence in any way. Until the abortive revolution of 1848, it seemed possible that the forces of nationalism and liberalism that had risen under the stimulus of the Napoleonic invasion would eventually sweep away the states and give Germany unity. When the liberal movement failed, the absorption of Germany into the most powerful of the states, Prussia, was the next best thing.

THE RISE OF PRUSSIA

Prussia's way to power was cleared by the German customs union, or *Zollverein.* The Prussian customs had been rationalized in 1818, and between that date and 1829 a number of smaller states which were embedded in Prussian territory adopted the Prussian tariff. A more important step was taken in 1834, when the southern and central German states joined, leaving only Austria and the northern seaboard states outside. The removal of internal customs barriers by the *Zollverein*, together with the building of railways and the growth of industry, forged Germany into an economic unity, and made some form of political unity appear inevitable.

The rise of Prussia under the leadership of Bismarck was forwarded by a series of wars. In 1864 Austria and Prussia forced Denmark to cede the two duchies of Schleswig and Holstein. Picking a quarrel over the disposition of the spoils, Prussia fell on Austria, who was supported by most of the other German states. As a result of Prussia's victory, Austria was finally excluded from Germany, while by absorbing Schleswig-Holstein and Hanover, Prussia obtained complete control of the Northern Lowland. The states of southern Germany were treated with deliberate moderation, and rapidly fell into the arms of Prussia as their only possible protector against the France of Napoleon III.

The unity of Germany under Prussia was finally sealed by the Franco-Prussian war of 1870, which also announced the emergence of Germany as a major world power after centuries of impotence. As a result of the war, France was obliged to pay a large indemnity and to cede Alsace and most of Lorraine, including the city of Metz. In the Hall of Mirrors in the Palace of Versailles itself, built by the French monarch who had done most to humiliate Germany, the Hohenzollern William I of Prussia was proclaimed Emperor of a united and triumphant Germany.

THE HOHENZOLLERN EMPIRE

On the eve of the outbreak of the First World War in 1914, the Hohenzollern Empire stretched from Alsace and Lorraine in the west as far as Upper Silesia, East Prussia and Memel in the east. The only substantial German-speaking areas left outside the Empire were in Switzerland and Austria (which included Bohemia). On the other hand, considerable minorities speaking languages other than German were included in Germany: Danes in Schleswig, French in Lorraine and, above all, over 3 million Poles in the eastern districts of Prussia.

Economic Progress. The years between 1871 and 1914 saw the transformation of Germany from a country that was still predominantly rural into one of the world's greatest industrial powers. The cumulative effect of the adoption of the new techniques of the industrial revolution, of the new railways, the *Zollverein* and political unity resulted in a vast upsurge of industrial production and a parallel rise in population. Coal output, which had been 29 million tons in 1871, was 190 million tons in 1913, and iron production rose in the same period from less than 2 million tons to nearly 17 million tons, so outstripping Britain. German steel, chemicals and machines were sold all over the world. The first colonies had been obtained in Africa and the Pacific; never, in fact, had Germany been more prosperous and more powerful.

During this same period the population of the country rose from 41 million to 67 million. All over Germany men were on the move to the new industrial towns; in 1871 two-thirds of the population lived in the country and only one-third in the towns, but by 1914 the position was almost exactly reversed. Since most industry and towns lay in the centre and west of the country, a marked east-to-west migration resulted.

Only in agriculture was progress less impressive. The abolition of the fallows in the open-field area (pp. 84–5) was not followed by further significant progress; the inefficient small-farm structure survived. On the sandy lands of northwest Germany fodder crops and artificial fertilizers broke the dependence of cultivation on the preservation of large areas of waste, permitting the creation of new farms and a general dispersal of settlement, which was also encouraged by the growing importance of livestock farming. In eastern Germany the Junkers preserved their estates, and until the agricultural crisis of the 1880s continued to produce large quantities of cereals for export. The desirability of breaking up the estates to provide holdings for small independent farmers was recognized on social grounds, and also so as to prevent the depopulation of the eastern frontier areas, but little effective action was taken up to 1945. It was primarily to benefit the influential estate owners that Germany in 1879 initiated a policy of agricultural protectionism that was to last, with variations, to the present day. The result in the long term was to permit the survival of an inefficient and high-cost agriculture, which was to cause particular difficulty when West Germany came to enter the EEC.

The First World War and its Consequences. The victories of Germany over Austria and France, and her rapidly-growing economic and military power, aroused the anxiety of the other nations of Europe. It is generally agreed now that none of the major powers contemplated a career of conquest on the Napoleonic model, but all were willing to face the use of war

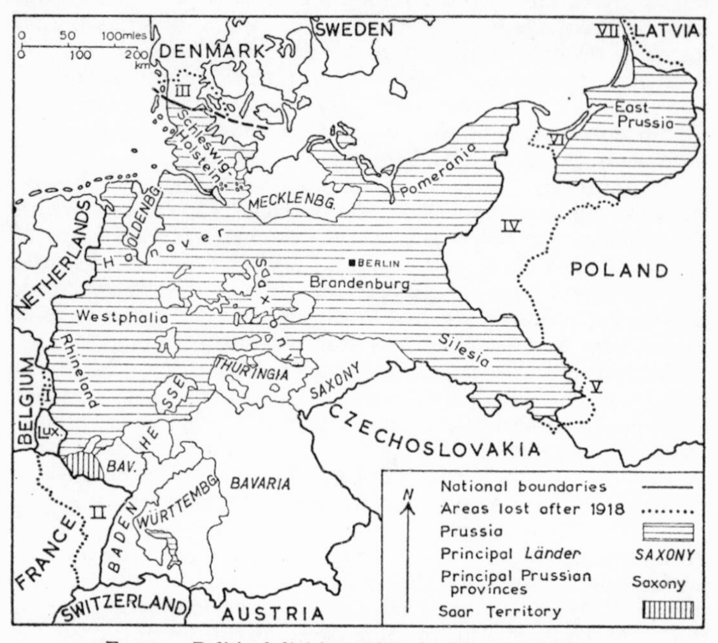

FIG. 19. Political divisions after the First World War.
(I) Eupen and Malmédy; (II) Alsace-Lorraine; (III) North Schleswig; (IV) Poznan and Polish Corridor; (V) Upper Silesia; (VI) Danzig; (VII) Memel.

as a last resort, rather than compromise. When a comparatively minor dispute arose between Austria and Serbia, Europe drifted into war.

The result for Germany was disaster, with 2 million dead and red revolution sweeping the country. The armistice of 1918, however, left the German army in being, so that the officer and Junker class was ultimately able to obtain the co-operation of the Social-Democratic leaders of the new 'Weimar Republic' and prevent revolutionary change.

The Versailles Treaty after the war, by restoring Poland as an independent state, resulted in the loss to Germany of part of Upper Silesia, the Posnan district and the 'Polish Corridor', which by giving the new state an outlet to the Baltic cut off East Prussia from the rest of Germany. The areas transferred had a population of 3·8 million people, most of them Polish-speaking. Danzig was made a 'Free City' and the Memel district transferred from East Prussia to another newly-created state, Lithuania (Fig 19).

In the west, North Schleswig was returned to Denmark after a plebiscite, the districts of Eupen and Malmédy transferred to Belgium and Alsace and Lorraine returned to France. In all, Germany lost an eighth of her former area and a tenth of her population, as well as all overseas colonies. The Versailles Treaty also involved the payment of reparations to the victors, and contained conditions designed to prevent the restoration of German military power. The restrictions imposed by the treaty were severe enough to handicap the young German democracy and to stimulate German nationalism, yet were quite inadequate in themselves to prevent rearmament under a determined leader like Hitler.

HITLER'S EMPIRE

The Rise to Power. The leader of the revived German nationalism was not even born a German. Adolf Hitler was the son of a minor Austrian official, but he came to despise what he considered to be the ramshackle Austrian Empire, and saw his future only in a united Germany. The failure of his early attempts to become an architect or a painter gave him a maniacal hatred of capitalists and Jews, whom he regarded as responsible for his misfortunes. Hitler's 'National Socialist German Labour Party' (NSDAP) never obtained more than one-third of the votes in a free election, but his opposition to Socialism and Communism led to his being put into power in 1933 by the aristocratic and industrialist classes, who soon found that they had not a puppet but a master.

Racial Theories. A keystone of National Socialism was a belief in the purity and superiority of the 'Aryan' or 'Nordic' race, as exemplified by the Germans. These beliefs were completely without scientific foundation. The Germans are no more 'Aryan' than their neighbours; the belief that a people called 'Aryans' developed in what is now Germany at the close of Neolithic times and gave the Indo-European language to the rest of Europe is now generally abandoned. Secondly, the Germans are far from being pure Nordics. It is true that the original Germans who migrated southwards from the Baltic

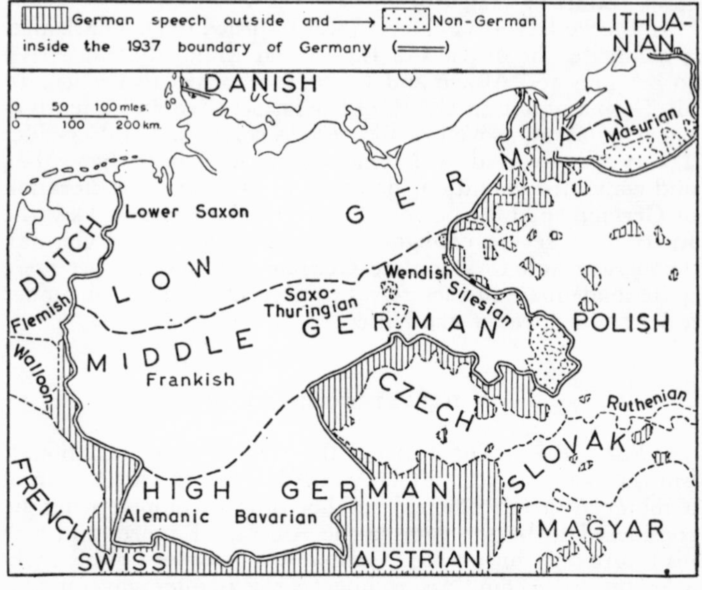

FIG. 20. The Germans in Europe, about 1930.

were Nordic, with tall stature, light colouring and long, massive heads, so that this type predominates in northwest Germany today. Elsewhere, however, the Germans are predominantly Alpine, with broad heads, thick-set frames and dark hair. The eastern colonization also brought in a considerable admixture of Slav types. Few of the National Socialist leaders were of Nordic type, least of all the slight, dark Hitler. Finally, even if the Germans had in fact been racially 'pure', it is still completely false and unscientific to claim mental or moral superiority for this, or any other, race; no connection between race and intellectual or moral qualities has ever been proved. Unfortunately these racial theories were not merely academic; they were used to justify the murder of millions of members of the 'inferior' non-German peoples, especially Jews and Slavs.

Territorial Expansion. Having absorbed Austria in 1938, Hitler proceeded to utilize the alleged wrongs of the German minority groups scattered across Europe from Alsace to the Volga as a pretext for interfering in the affairs of other countries (Fig. 20). He first turned his attention to the 3·5 million Germans whose forefathers had inhabited the upland border of Bohemia, the so-called Sudetenland, since the medieval colonization period, and who had been included in the new Versailles state of Czechoslovakia. The Sudetenland was transferred to Germany under the terms of the Munich Agreement of September 1938, and Hitler guaranteed the independence of the remainder of Czechoslovakia, but his troops marched into Prague in the following year. Then it was Poland's turn; in September 1939 German troops crossed the frontier, and the Second World War began.

At its greatest extent, prior to the decisive battles of Stalingrad and Alamein, Hitler's empire stretched from the Channel to the gates of Moscow and the Caucasus, and from the North Cape nearly to the Nile. Within it he initiated the heartless process of uprooting millions of innocent people from their homes in vast population transfers, which were to go on for ten years or more, and rebound in the end against the Germans themselves. Millions of slave workers were sent to labour in Germany, and more millions, especially Jews, were murdered. All these sufferings were to bring a terrible retribution upon the German people in their hour of defeat.

TERRITORIAL CHANGES AFTER THE SECOND WORLD WAR

Severe as the losses after the First World War had been, they were nothing compared with the consequences of the Second. This time the war swept over German soil itself, leaving nearly every German city destroyed, and the country occupied by foreign troops. On 30th April 1945, Hitler killed himself in his underground shelter as Russian troops fought their way through the ruined streets of his capital. The empire that was to last for a thousand years was at an end.

In the west, the frontier of 1937 was restored with minor changes, but an enlarged Saar Territory was placed under a

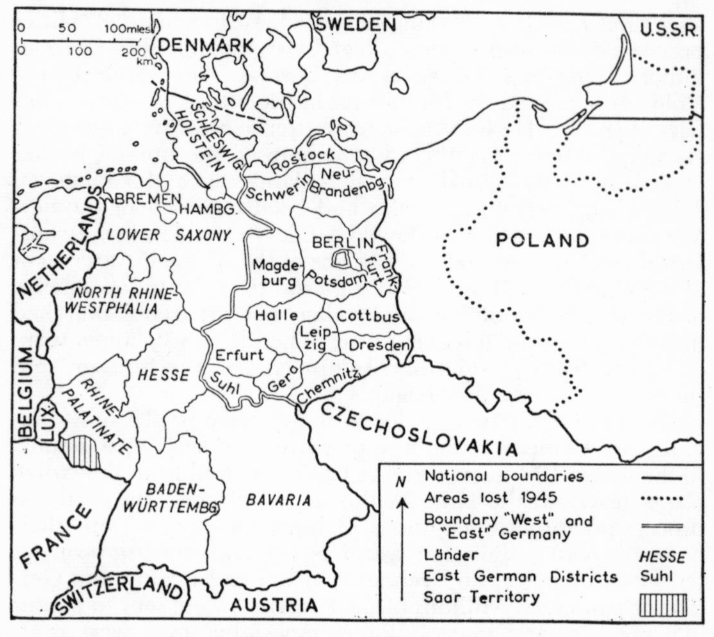

FIG. 21. Political divisions after the Second World War (1952).

French-dominated government and economically tied to France. Germany was able to resume control of the Saar by 1959. In the east, not only was all the territory seized by Hitler lost once more, but 100,000 sq. km/40,000 sq. miles of land that had been German since the Middle Ages as well. Russia seized Königsberg (renamed Kaliningrad) and northern East Prussia, and Poland was allowed to occupy the remainder of eastern Germany as far as the line of the Oder and Western Neisse, with a bridgehead west of the Oder to include the

Baltic port of Stettin. The final disposal of these territories was nominally left to the decision of a later peace conference with Germany, but in fact they were completely absorbed into Poland and the U.S.S.R. (Fig. 21).

Even more devastating than the loss of territory were the related forced movements of the German population, both from the former German minority areas in neighbouring countries, and from the lands seized by Poland and the U.S.S.R. Many of the Germans had already left in front of the advancing Soviet army, but those that remained were packed into rail wagons and sent to Germany. By 1950 at least 12 million refugees had reached the home country.

These unhappy people had to leave behind them practically all they possessed. Suffering and loss of life in the movements were heavy, both in the early stage of evacuation in front of the Soviet army, which the German authorities often organized very badly, and in the later period of expulsions. All these refugees poured back into a Germany that was ill-prepared to receive them, reduced in size by a quarter, with cities in ruins, factories idle and administrative machine destroyed.

POLITICAL RE-ORGANIZATION AFTER 1945

Before the Second World War, Germany was politically divided into sixteen states or *Länder*, which retained some degree of independence on internal matters until the onset of National Socialist centralization (Fig. 19). The size of the various states was extremely unequal, as Prussia alone contained 42 million people, or 60% of Germany's inhabitants. The remaining 40% was shared by the other fifteen states, which ranged downwards in size from Bavaria with 8 millions to Schaumburg-Lippe with 54,000.

The victors of the Second World War, believing that Germany had in the past been excessively centralized, and unduly dominated by Prussia, proceeded to redraw the political map in a manner reminiscent of Napoleon 150 years before. The Prussian ogre, weakened by territorial losses in the east, was dismembered by the division of Germany into seventeen initially autonomous *Länder*. Germany was also divided into zones of occupation for the forces of Britain, the United States, France and the Soviet Union. Berlin, although contained within the Russian zone of occupation, was divided into sectors of occupation for the four powers.

It was assumed that the occupying powers would eventually give way to a new German government, but in fact the conflicting political and economic views of the western and Soviet occupiers led to the setting up of two separate states in postwar Germany. The *Länder* of the three western zones were united in 1949 into the 'German Federal Republic' (*Bundesrepublik Deutschland*), commonly known as West Germany, with its capital at Bonn. West Germany adopted parliamentary democracy as a political system, although both the Communist Party and extreme right-wing parties are banned. The President is a representative figure with functions resembling those of the English Crown. Much greater powers are vested in the office of Chancellor, and these were certainly enlarged by the first holder of the office, Conrad Adenauer, the dominant political figure of postwar Germany. The lower house (*Bundestag*) of the West German parliament is directly elected, but the federal structure of the state is expressed by the *Bundesrat*, a second chamber consisting of representatives of the governments of the *Länder*. The *Länder* have their own parliaments with considerable powers in internal matters, for example in education. West Berlin was not made into a constituent *Land* of the Federal Republic, but is closely linked to it. Economically West Germany retains the version of the capitalist system common in most western countries, in which the state is expected to attempt some degree of overall economic planning, and endeavours to protect the weak and temper the adverse effects of competition by various welfare measures.

The five *Länder* of the Soviet Zone were similarly united into the 'German Democratic Republic' (*Deutsche Demokratische Republik*), officially abbreviated as DDR and commonly referred to as East Germany. The capital is East Berlin, which is officially regarded as an integral part of the DDR state territory, although sovereignty is qualified by various residual rights of the western occupying powers both here and over the access routes to West Berlin. Although three shadowy 'bourgeois' parties and a farmers' party are allowed to survive, effective power is wielded by the leadership of the 'Socialist Unity Party' (*Socialistische Einheitspartei Deutschlands* or SED), formed in 1946 by a forced amalgamation of the Social Democrats with the Communist Party. As First Secretary of the

Central Committee of the SED, Walter Ulbricht exercised a political predominance in postwar East Germany longer even than that of Adenauer in West Germany. All parties and various other communal organizations are united in a 'National Front', which puts up a single list of candidates for election to Parliament (*Volkskammer*), a body which meets somewhat infrequently. The Council of Ministers (*Ministerrat*) is the chief executive organ. Since economically the DDR is characterized by virtually complete nationalization of the means of production, distribution and exchange, the *Ministerrat* consists of many representatives of the various branches of industry, as well as of the more usual political appointments.

At a more local level, the DDR rejected the degree of decentralization implied by the postwar creation of the *Länder* by abolishing them and substituting fourteen smaller administrative districts (*Bezirke*) under much more direct control of the central authorities. The *Bezirke* are named after the chief town on which each one centres. At all administrative levels from the *Ministerrat* down to the smallest group of dwellings (*Haus- und Hofgemeinschaften*) there exists a parallel SED organization, which from the *Politbüro* downwards initiates policies and controls their implementation by the administrative machine.

With the assistance of the armed forces of the U.S.S.R. this government machine survived an attempted rebellion in 1953, and following the final sealing of its frontiers by the building of the Berlin wall in 1961, appeared to have achieved stability. The claim of the DDR to be given diplomatic recognition as a sovereign and independent state was however long resisted by the 'western' powers.

A Divided Country. It has already been noted (pp. 16–17) that the belated political reunification of Germany in the 19th century enabled a larger degree of regional individuality to survive than in countries of long-continued centralization like England. One of the areas of distinctive regional character was undoubtedly 'colonial' Germany, east of the Elbe–Saale line. Some writers have assumed from this that the present division into 'West' and 'East' in Germany is in some way an inherent one, reflecting fundamental and continuing contrasts in social geography, but the argument is a difficult one to sustain. The present DDR boundary only occasionally corresponds with the historic frontier between 'old Germany' and the 'colonial' east, running for the most part well to the west

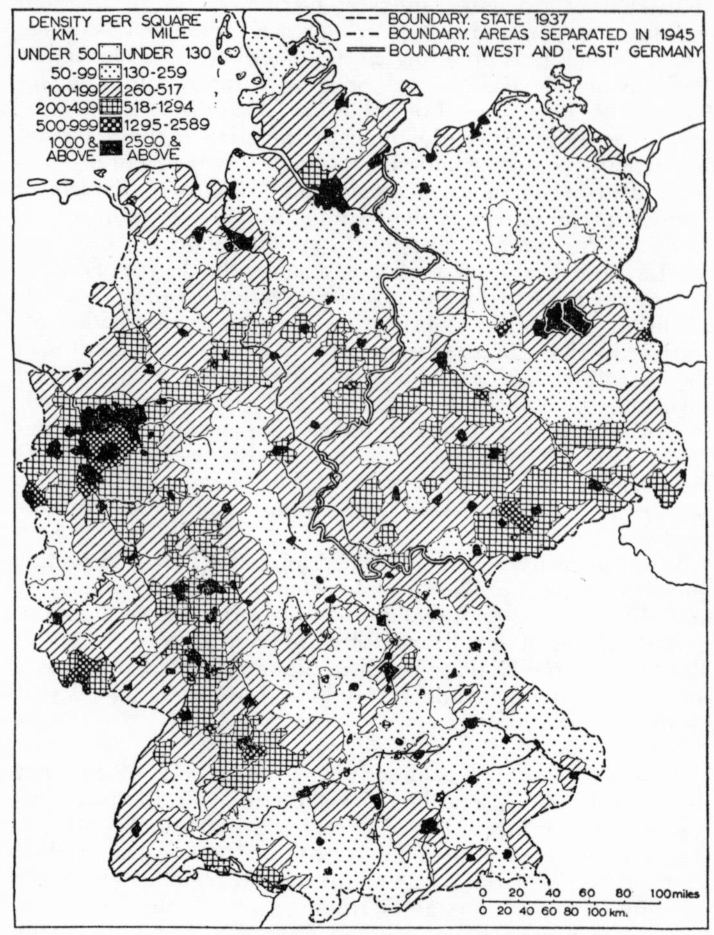

FIG. 22. The distribution of population (1953).

of it. In terms of historical origins the territory of the present DDR is wholly composite, including an area between the Harz and the Thuringian Forest which in terms of settlement forms and past political fragmentation is wholly of west German type, an area in lowland Saxony that was long disputed between German and Slav, as well as the more purely 'colonial' areas of Brandenburg and Mecklenburg. Since the unification of Germany the western and eastern parts of the country had become economically closely integrated. The means of communication and the flows of goods all had a strong east–west component (pp. 162–4). Clearly it is not possible to find any historical justification for the present division of the country. What is equally clear, however, is that owing to the great contrasts in their economic systems, the longer the two parts of Germany remain separate the greater become the contrasts in their present economic and social geography.

THE GERMAN POPULATION

The Distribution of Population. The spread of population in Germany is extremely uneven; the regions of greater density reflect the distribution of good-quality farmland or of industrialization, which in fact often coincide. In the population map (Fig. 22) two major axes stand out in which densities generally exceed 200 per sq. km/500 per sq. mile. The first axis follows the Hercynian Foreland in a roughly east–west direction, and reflects the rich loess soils, the early industrialization of the northern flank of the Central Uplands, and the modern industrial development based on the coal, iron and potash which are found beneath the loess. There are two major concentrations of population within the belt, one based on the Ruhr coalfield, the second based on the industrialized uplands of Saxony and the Central German brown-coal field at their foot.

The other axis of population runs from southern Germany down the Rhine valley to the Netherlands and the North Sea coast. In Germany it has four main nuclei, the Stuttgart industrial region in the south, the Rhine–Neckar region around Mannheim, the Rhine–Main region centred on Frankfurt and finally the Rhine–Ruhr region, at which point it intersects the Hercynian Foreland axis.

Away from these main axes, there are only islands of denser population. The poor, sandy land of the Northern Lowland usually has less than 100 people to the sq. km/250 per sq. mile; the only 'island' of importance is Berlin, the divided capital, with a total population of 3·2 million people. On the coast the ports stand out, the greatest of which, Hamburg, has nearly 2 million people (and a total of well over 2 million in the agglomeration); it is Germany's second largest city, and West Germany's largest. Southern Germany away from the main axis has a number of widely spaced centres of population, notably Nürnberg and Munich. West of the Rhine, the Saar coalfield provides a conspicuous nucleus.

Germany must be counted among the highly urbanized and industrialized countries; in 1871 two-thirds of the population had lived in rural areas and only one-third in towns, but by the 1930s these proportions had been reversed, and by 1960 less than a quarter of West German population was rural. A characteristic of German urban structure is the relatively large number of substantial towns. The long period of political fragmentation endowed the country with a number of important regional capitals, so that urban structure is much less dominated by a single city than in countries of earlier centralization such as France and England. In view of the postwar fate of Berlin it is perhaps fortunate that West Germany has two cities of over a million (Hamburg and Munich), as well as eight towns of between half a million and a million, six of which are in the Rhinelands. To underline the importance of social history in urban development it may be noted that France, a country of comparable population to West Germany, has apart from its capital no other city of over a million, and only two in the half to one million category, the same number incidentally as the much smaller East Germany, with Leipzig and Dresden. All these figures take no account of conurbations; the towns of the Ruhr, for example, which appear separately in the population statistics, in fact contain about 5 million people.

The Results of the War. Owing to the toll taken by war, the total German population in 1946 was 4 millions fewer than in 1939, in spite of the arrival of expelled minority groups from Czechoslovakia and other foreign countries. The density of population was about 10% higher than before the war, owing to the loss in the east of nearly a quarter of Germany's former territory.

The war temporarily reversed the long-term trend to urbanization. The refugees did not spread evenly over the country; they settled in the rural areas, where they could find some shelter, avoiding the bombed and evacuated towns, and avoiding the eastern and western frontier districts, which had been devastated by fighting in the closing phases of the war. The greatest proportionate increases of population were recorded in Schleswig-Holstein and adjoining Mecklenburg, where many rural districts had twice as many people as in 1939. Since 1946 the total German population has risen again, to exceed the 1939 figure in the early 1950s, and to reach 75 million by the mid-1960s. In detail there have been great contrasts in development between rural and urban areas, and between West and East Germany.

Population Developments in West Germany. The population of West Germany and West Berlin expanded rapidly from 46 millions in 1946 to reach 60 millions in the mid-1960s. Less than half the rise was due to natural increase, the rest to the excess of immigration over emigration. Three main groups have contributed to the increase by immigration. Those who were expelled from their homes in foreign countries such as Czechoslovakia, or from German territory occupied by Poland and the U.S.S.R. arrived mostly in the period 1944–6: today with their children born since their arrival they total 9 million or 16% of the population. Refugees from East Germany arrived in a more even stream, with a peak in 1953–7, but the flow was cut off abruptly by the building of the Berlin wall in 1961. Today these people and their children total 3 millions or 5% of the West German population. From 1959 the demands of West German industry for labour caused a new type of immigration, this time of foreign workers from southern Europe. By 1965 there were well over a million of them, the largest groups coming from Italy (30%), Greece (15%), Spain (15%) and Turkey (11%). Foreign workers at this time constituted about 5% of the German labour force, undertaking many of the heavier and more unpleasant tasks in industries such as building.

As in most industrialized countries, West German population structure has been affected by a long continuing decline of the birth rate, from 40 per thousand in 1875 to a minimum of 15·3 in 1953. In spite of some moderate recent recovery in the birth rate, this has given a structure 'top heavy' with the elderly, whose expectation of life has been greatly increased by medical progress. The economically active age groups have further been weakened by low birth rates associated with two world wars and the depression years of the early 1930s. In addition the number of males above the age of forty has been drastically affected by the losses of the Second World War,

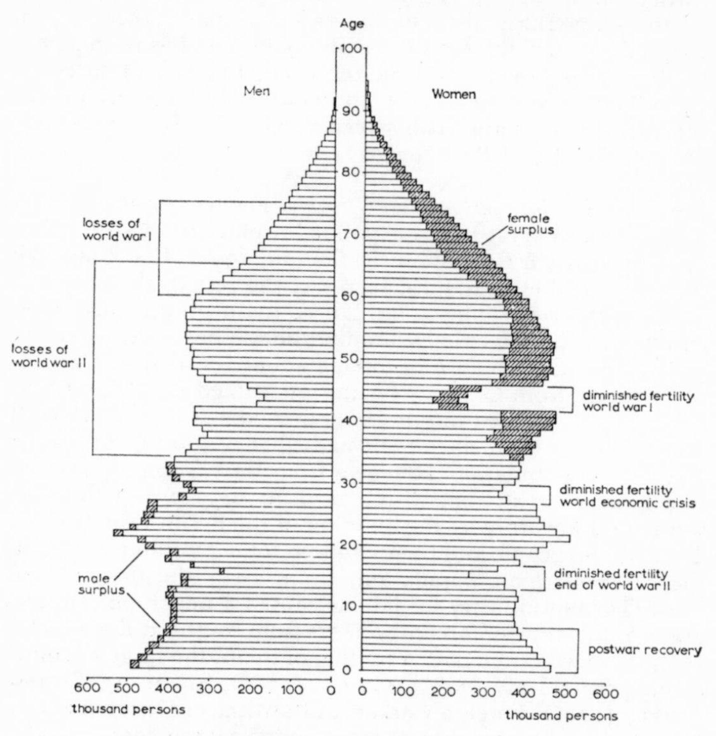

FIG. 23. West German population structure 1961.
Each bar of the graph represents one annual age group, divided between men (*left*) and women (*right*). Direct war losses are mainly reflected on the male side. Variations in fertility, although for convenience shown on the female side, affect both men and women.

accentuating the female surplus which is a normal feature of the older age groups in any population (Fig 23).

This quantitative weakness of the active population, the element most significant for economic progress, would have

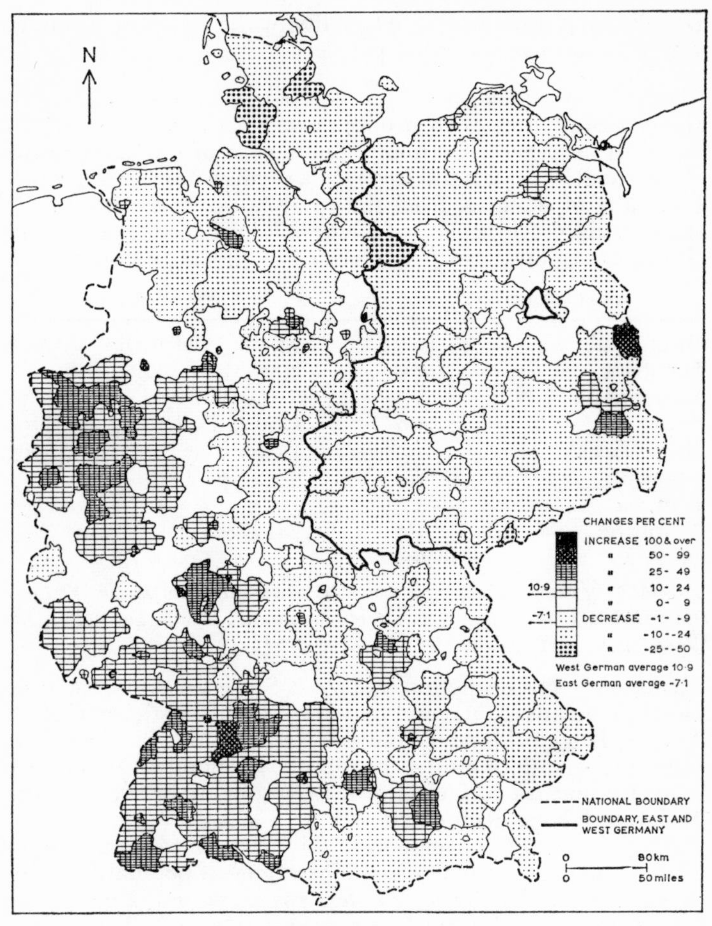

FIG. 24. Population change 1951–61.

been much more marked but for the effect of immigration, especially from East Germany. It was the young people, and especially the young men, who were prepared to tear up their roots and face a difficult journey to West Germany. The result was not only to increase the quantity of the West German population but to improve its quality by the injection of young, vigorous and hard-working people

Population Redistribution in West Germany. With the recovery of the economy after 1948 people moved back from country to town all over West Germany. Since most of the large towns are in the Rhinelands this involved a massive transfer of people, especially of refugees, from the rural east and north into the industrialized Rhine–Ruhr, Rhine–Main, Rhine–Neckar and Stuttgart regions, which experienced a rise in population of

WEST GERMANY		EAST GERMANY	
Rhine–Ruhr	10·4	East & West Berlin	4·16
Hamburg	2·3	Karl-Marx Stadt (Chemnitz)	1·78
Rhine–Main	2·5	Leipzig-Halle	1·96
Stuttgart	1·8	Dresden	0·85
Rhine–Neckar	1·4		
Munich	1·4		
Hanover	1·0		
Nürnberg	1·0		
Bremen	0·8		

Population of the major agglomerations (Verdichtungsgebiete) *in West and East Germany* (*in millions*). After H. Lehmann, *Informationen Inst. für Raumforschung* 18/64, pp. 652–64.

about 40% in the period 1947–62. Since at the same time rapid population increase was also characteristic of eastern France, Belgian Flanders and the Netherlands, it seemed that with the creation of the European Economic Community most European population growth was being drawn into the Rhine or Rhône–Rhine axis.

The population movements of this period threw into prominence a number of major agglomerations of population (*Ballungsgebiete* or *Verdichtungsgebiete*), spreading far beyond the bounds of a single administrative unit (Fig. 25). They range in size from the 10 millions of the great Rhine–Ruhr agglomeration down to isolated centres like Hanover, Nürnberg or Bremen, each uniting a million people or slightly less (see table). The development of these agglomerations is associated with major changes in the socio-economic structure of the West German population. There has first of all been a striking movement out of agriculture. About 1860 half the German

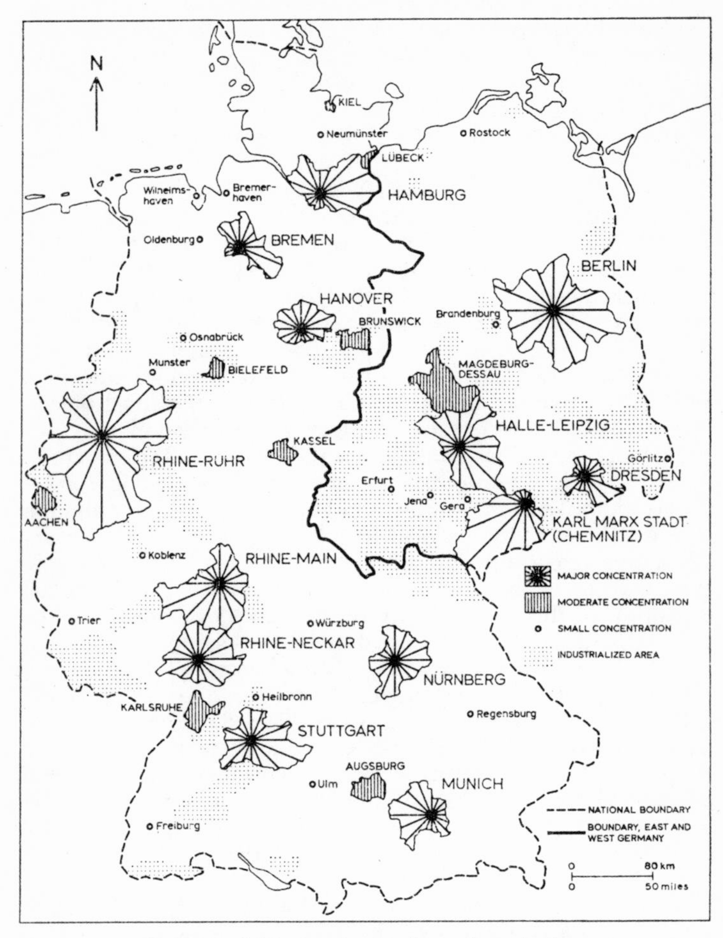

FIG. 25. Major agglomerations of population.

occupied population was in agriculture, and in the 1939 *Reich* this had only been reduced to a quarter. Even in 1950 West Germany had 23% of the employed population in agriculture, but from that date decline was rapid: in the late 1950s agriculture was losing workers at the rate of 173,000 a year and, by the mid-1960s the agricultural sector accounted for less than 10% of total employment. In German conditions movement out of the agricultural sector does not necessarily imply geographical mobility, since in overcrowded rural areas like southwest Germany or Hesse it is very common for workers to remain in their villages after changing to some non-agricultural employment. Nevertheless many of those who left agriculture undoubtedly joined the movement to the towns.

Agriculture's loss has not altogether been industry's gain: over the last 100 years the share of industry in the total labour force has increased only slightly, from 40% in 1960 to just under 50% today. The dramatic increase has been in the service sector, from a mere 6% in 1860 to about 40% today. Because activities like administration, social services, transport and distribution are inevitably concentrated in central places, their remarkable recent growth, a sign of great changes in our whole way of life, has contributed powerfully to the growth of the great agglomerations of population. A related feature is the striking rise in the employment of women, which although it in part reflects the marked female surplus in the economically active age groups is also a sign of significent social changes. It is no accident that the great agglomerations, with the partial exception of the Rhine–Ruhr region, are not centred on the old coalfield industrial regions but on the regional capitals; it is in the latter that the expanding service sector of the economy is particularly concentrated. As will be seen later (p. 156) the agglomerations also attract a great deal of modern industry, particularly on their fringes. Characteristically the actual centres of the agglomerations are growing below the national average or even losing population. In the age of the motor car it is particularly on the fringes of the agglomerations that we find the most explosive population growth.

Population Developments in East Germany. In total, the development of the East German population has followed an almost directly opposite course to that of the West. From 18·4 millions in 1950 there was a decline through emigration until in 1961 the minimum point of 17 millions was marked by the building of the Berlin wall. From this time population began slowly to rise again through natural increase.

The East German population structure has the same adverse features as that of West Germany, but accentuated by the selective effect of refugee movements up to 1961. The advantages gained by West Germany from a net gain of 2 million young and active people have already been referred to: the impact of their departure on the very much smaller population of East Germany may well be imagined. One result of East Germany's acute shortage of labour and massive female surplus is that the proportion of women in employment is extraordinarily high; women do work like driving cranes on construction sites that elsewhere would be done by men. The stopping of the drain of scarce male labour to the west was one of the reasons for the building of the Berlin wall in 1961.

Until 1961 regional population changes within East Germany were very much masked by the overall decline due to the outflow of refugees, but certainly the greatest proportionate losses were in rural areas, where the programme of agricultural collectivization encouraged many to leave (p. 122). There is no parallel to the West German concentration into the *Ballungsgebiete*; in East Germany the growth of the largest towns has been slow, perhaps reflecting the slow rate of rebuilding after wartime destruction, and few of them have regained their prewar populations. Planned industrial development has tended to concentrate population growth into small and medium towns of the Baltic coast, the Oder valley and the Lower Lusatian brown-coal field (Fig. 24).

RURAL SETTLEMENT

Since the close of the 18th century, the main changes in the pattern of rural settlement have been in eastern Germany. The first half of the 19th century saw a further extension of the large estate, with its associated estate farm (*Gut*). This consisted typically of a group of very substantial farm buildings, including a manor house, extensive barns, byres and stables, houses for the labourers and often a distillery or similar enterprise for processing crops. Curiously enough, the growth of the *Gut* at this stage was largely the result of the emancipation of the Prussian peasants, who had to compensate their lords for the loss of their services with up to one-third of their land.

After 1945, the great landlords of East Germany were dispossessed as a result of communist land reform measures. Their large, regular fields were divided once more into numerous peasant strips, but this was only a stage in the movement towards collectivization (p. 122). Since 1960 individual plots other than a half hectare per farmer have given way to vast fields, not only on the former estates but also in former small-farm areas such as Thuringia. The visitor who walks through an East German village today finds the scene curiously derelict, the yards of the small farmsteads weed-grown. Only at the end of the street may perhaps be found a group of new buildings, often of wood, marking the centre of a state or collective farm.

Change in West Germany has been less dramatic. Postwar land reform was not very significant, as there were few large estates to break up. The effect was greatest in Schleswig-Holstein, into which the East German area of estate farming extended. In contrast to East Germany, land reform here resulted in the creation of small and medium farms, and the addition of many new farmhouses to the settlement pattern. The most significant change in West Germany is, however, that the progress of consolidation of holdings (*Flurbereinigung*) in the open-field area is at last beginning to produce numbers of new farmhouses standing isolated or in pairs in open country, well outside the crowded *Haufendorf* nuclei.

THE MODERN TOWN

The typical German town entered the 19th century almost unchanged from the end of medieval times, except, perhaps, for a small formal extension dating from the Age of Princes. Gabled houses still huddled on narrow streets, surrounded by medieval walls, beyond which lay a girdle of gardens and orchards, and then the open countryside. Yet a hundred years of industrialization, followed by the destruction wrought in the Second World War, has almost entirely altered this picture.

The walls were commonly removed in the early 19th century and replaced by pleasant green promenades (as at Münster, Fig. 12), or by ring roads. At this stage, in the middle of the 19th century, the railway arrived, so that the station is commonly found on the ring road, just outside the crowded medieval nucleus. Stimulated by the railways and by the growth of industry, the town exploded in all directions, in a burst of building. Essen, for example, had 9,000 inhabitants in 1850 and 119,000 at the end of the century, and all these people had to be housed.

The appearance of the large German town, at least as it existed until 1939, was very different from that of towns in England. In the centre, the crowded medieval *Altstadt* was still clearly marked off by its ring road or promenade, although many of its old houses had given way to modern offices and shops. Another part of the town might show the dignified avenues and squares of the Age of Princes. The same regularity, without the dignity, was carried forward into the 19th-century town. In rich and poor districts alike, the streets were continuously built up with apartment houses, 3 or 4 stories high. Only in the 20th century, under the influence of the English Garden City movement, was this extremely rigid form of town planning abandoned for smaller houses and less formal street patterns.

Most German towns owe their present appearance to reconstruction following wartime bombing, to which the crowded medieval houses within the walls were particularly vulnerable. Some towns attempted to maintain continuity with the past by faithfully reconstructing their more picturesque quarters. Elsewhere the ruins gave place to gleaming buildings of concrete, steel and glass, far more convenient and imposing than what had gone before, but leaving the central areas of West German towns indistinguishable from each other. The opportunity was generally taken to drive wider roads through the old crowded centres, but the rapid rise in car ownership in a prosperous postwar Germany was not foreseen. The regional capitals in the *Ballungsgebiete* have in particular been submerged under the motor vehicles flooding in from the rapidly expanding suburbs on their fringes. A characteristic reaction, as at Munich, Frankfurt and Cologne, has been the initiation of highly expensive underground railway or tramway systems.

The slower rebuilding of the East German towns was at first in the overdecorated 'Stalin' style, which repeated the formality and rigidity of the town plans of the Age of Princes. Changing political directives after 1953, and the widespread use of prefabrication to save scarce labour, led to the adoption of simpler if sometimes monotonous building styles, and greater informality of layout. The latest rebuilding of the centre of East Berlin is very much in the contemporary international style.

	1939			1946
	000s	PER SQ KM	PER SQ MILE	000s
Eastern Territories	9,621	84	218	—
East Germany	15,157	140	363	17,180
East Berlin	1,588	3,941	10,207	1,175
West Berlin	2,751	5,743	14,874	2,013
West Germany	43,008	173	448	44,547
Total	69,314	147	381	64,915

	1950	1965		
	000s	000s	PER SQ KM	PER SQ MILE
Eastern Territories	—	—	—	—
East Germany	17,199	15,970	148	383
East Berlin	1,189	1,078	2,675	6,928
West Berlin	2,147	2,202	4,594	11,898
West Germany	48,639	56,839	229	593
Total	69,174	76,089	213	552

The German Population

SUGGESTIONS FOR FURTHER READING

A. Bullock, *Hitler, a study in tyranny* (Odhams), rev. ed. 1964 (Penguin Books), 1962, (rev. ed.; New York: Harper, 1964).

Cambridge Economic History of Europe, vol. VI: *The industrial revolution and after*. 2 vols (Cambridge and New York: Cambridge University Press), 1965.

J. H. Clapham, *The economic development of France and Germany, 1815–1914*, 4th ed. (Cambridge and New York: Cambridge Univ. Press), 1963.

E. Eyck, *Bismarck and the German Empire* (Allen and Unwin), 1950, (New York: Macmillan; New York: Norton, pap., 1964).

A. Grosser, *Western Germany: from defeat to rearmament* (Allen and Unwin), 1955.

A. Grosser, *Federal Republic of Germany* (New York: Praeger, 1964).

R. Hiscocks, *Democracy in western Germany* (Oxford and New York: Oxford Univ. Press), 1957.

WEST GERMAN *Länder*	1965 TOTAL 000S	1961 REFUGEES 000S	%	EAST GERMAN DISTRICTS	1965 TOTAL 000S
Schleswig-Holstein	2,423	744	32	Rostock	843
				Schwerin	595
Hamburg	1,857	336	18	Neubrandenburg	633
Lower Saxony	6,893	1,967	30	Potsdam	1,127
Bremen	738	146	21	Frankfurt	661
North Rhine–Westphalia	16,664	3,207	20	Cottbus	839
				Magdeburg	1,324
Hesse	5,139	1,120	23	Halle	1,933
Rhineland–Palatinate	3,568	404	12	Erfurt	1,250
				Gera	735
Baden–Württemberg	8,375	1,620	21	Suhl	549
				Dresden	1,888
Bavaria	10,059	1,940	20	Leipzig	1,511
Saar	1,124	41	4	Karl-Marx-Stadt (Chemnitz)	2,083
West Berlin	2,202	532	24	East Berlin	1,078
W. Germany and W. Berlin	59,041	12,055	21	**East Germany (DDR)**	17,048

Population of West German Länder *and East German Districts*

R. Hiscocks, *Germany revived: an appraisal of the Adenauer Era* (Gollancz), 1966.

E. J. Passant, *A short history of Germany, 1815–1945* (Cambridge and New York: Cambridge Univ. Press), 1959.

W. M. Simon, *Germany: a brief history* (Batsford), 1967.

Walter Simon, *Germany: a brief history* (New York: Random House, 1966).

H. R. Trevor-Roper, *The last days of Hitler* (Macmillan), 1950, (Pan Books), 1952, (New York: Collier, pap.).

E. Wiskemann, *Germany's eastern neighbours* (Oxford Univ. Press), 1956.

E. Wiskemann, *Europe of the dictators, 1919–1945* (Collins), 1966.

PART THREE

THE ECONOMY

Chapter 8

AGRICULTURE, FORESTRY, FISHING

THE BACKGROUND TO AGRICULTURE

The Physical Basis. Germany in general has a moderate climate and a lack of really high mountains. This allows nearly two-thirds of the land to be used for some form of agriculture, and most of the rest to be forested. A contrast to Britain is the unimportance of grassland in the agricultural area. Extensive areas of permanent pasture are limited to districts of western Germany which have a high rainfall and cool summer conditions, such as the oceanic northwest, the Alps with the adjoining Foreland, and the higher Hercynian massifs. There is an undoubted tendency for the grassland areas to expand, especially in hill country where arable cultivation is marginal. Otherwise, cattle in Germany are typically not grazed in the fields but are fed in the stall with arable crops and with hay from the restricted areas of meadow along the streams. Grassland is particularly restricted by the severe winters and scorching summers of the more continental eastern Germany, where, however, the ordinary arable crops can be grown without difficulty. This partly explains why in East Germany 74% of the agricultural land is arable, as compared with 55% in West Germany. The milder winters and earlier springs of western Germany, especially the Rhinelands, also favour the growth of fruit, vines and other delicate crops.

In more detail, the pattern of cropping depends also on soils, the brown earths and degraded chernozems of the loess providing the richest wheatlands, the leached sands being used for rye and potatoes, and so on. Even within the main soil belts, minor variations of slope or drainage are reflected in the changing patterns of crop, pasture, heath and wood which in detail make up each of the agricultural regions of Germany.

West Germany—the Social and Economic Background. West Germany is overwhelmingly a country of small family farms; over 80% of those engaged in agriculture are either farmers or their dependents. Of farm holdings larger than 0·5 hectare/1 acre, 70% have less than the 10 ha/25 acres traditionally regarded as the minimum to support a family, and such farms account for about a third of the total agricultural area. It is today doubtful whether even double this figure (20 ha/50 acres) is really sufficient to give a standard of living comparable to that obtainable in non-agricultural activities. About 90% of West German holdings fall below this figure, and they occupy 60% of the land.

Small farms are particularly associated with areas where the death of the farmer was traditionally followed by the division of his land between all the heirs (*Realteilung*). Subdivision was carried furthest in the most fruitful areas, so that although very small farms predominate numerically in most regions, they are particularly concentrated in the climatically favoured Upper Rhine Plain, the foreland of the Swabian Jura and the Swabian-Franconian Gaulands. More surprisingly, small farms are also characteristic of some of the poorest areas of the Central Uplands, such as the Eifel or Hesse. A medium-size farm structure is found on the Northern Lowland and the Bavarian Alpine Foreland, areas where inheritance by one son only (*Anerbenrecht*) is customary. Really large farms (over 50 ha/120 acres) are particularly concentrated in the western part of Schleswig-Holstein and on the Börde lowland of the Harz Foreland in Lower Saxony (Fig. 26).

Linked to the problem of farms that are too small is the problem of fragmentation of holdings, caused by the process of repeated subdivision. The typical West German village today is still surrounded by unenclosed fields, divided into hundreds of parcels, providing each summer a mosaic of varied crops. In a Württemberg village visited by the writer, the largest holding (and the only one with a full-time farmer) was 20 ha/50 acres; it was divided into 104 separate parcels. Inevitably the farmer wastes much time in moving from one plot to another, and rational cultivation is scarcely possible. Although the old system by which everybody with plots in the open field grows the same crop at the same time survives only in a few remote areas, it is nevertheless difficult to make major changes of land use, such as the substitution of grazing for arable land.

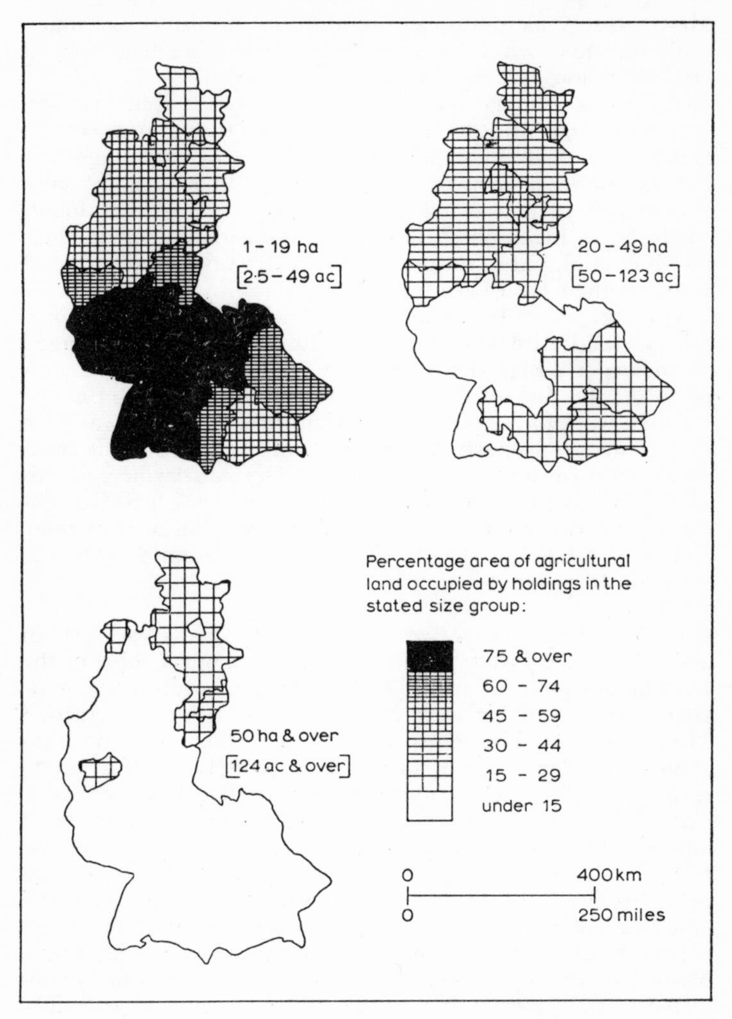

FIG. 26. Size of agricultural holdings in West Germany.

Although special small-scale agricultural machines are made to fit the small-scale German parcels, the full advantages of mechanization can obviously not be obtained.

The extraordinary situation has thus arisen that even on some of the most fertile land in Germany, the farmers cannot make an adequate living and are forced to seek employment in industry or services, which often involves them in long daily journeys to neighbouring towns. Partly through sentiment, partly as an insurance against bad times, they cling to their shreds of land, but naturally cannot both work in industry and cultivate their land with full efficiency.

The survival of the small farmer with his mixed farm producing standard field crops has traditionally been encouraged by means of a high degree of protection against cheaper imports. At the time of the Second World War a quarter of the German work force was still in agriculture, and there was little change in this proportion until the mid-1950s, when the comparable British figure was about 3%. German farmers at this time were meeting three-quarters of the country's food requirements, but earning only 8–10% of the total national income. The need for major structural adaptation in agriculture was clear for all to see.

Agricultural Crisis and the Common Market. By 1960 West German agriculture had lost 1·7 million workers, about a third of the 1939 labour force. The really rapid decline began in the mid-1950s, when workers were leaving agriculture at the rate of 170,000 a year. The figure was still over 60,000 in the mid-1960s. The departure of so many workers by itself acted to raise the land per head and the incomes of those that remained. Furthermore the West German government in a series of annual 'Green Plans' from 1956 progressively abandoned its traditional intervention to protect the level of agricultural prices in favour of intervention to improve the structure and efficiency of agriculture. Such measures became the more urgent from 1963 when with the inception of the Common Market in agriculture German farmers were increasingly subjected to competition from more efficient producers in neighbouring countries.

Visually the most obvious of the measures of structural improvement is the consolidation of holdings (*Flurbereinigung*). The farmers of a village are persuaded to redivide their lands so as to produce units that, if not as a rule fully consolidated, are at least less fragmentary than before. It is usual today for the land most distant from the village to be formed into completely unified holdings around farmhouses, which provide a striking new element in the German rural scene. The newly created units benefit from generous government assistance towards the cost of new buildings and improved livestock. *Flurbereinigung* is not a new feature of the German scene, but in the past has tended to be of only temporary benefit, owing to renewed subdivision on inheritance. Today, with such a large flight from the land there is some hope that the benefit will be permanent. To produce holdings that are of viable size the state also buys land from industrial workers, where necessary providing them with houses elsewhere. For the same reason measures are taken to enable elderly farmers to retire in reasonable comfort, leaving their land to younger men.

Agriculture also benefits from efforts to improve the general economic structure of regions which suffer from physical difficulty or remoteness (pp. 159–60). Government money helps to pay for new roads, drainage, water supply and rural electrification schemes, all of which benefit agriculture. Investment in education is particularly important, both to produce a better-educated farmer and to prepare the younger generation for entry into non-agricultural employment. With all these measures the scale of agriculture is creeping up; in the period 1949–64 there was a diminution of 460,000 holdings or 23%, with the decline concentrated in the units of less than 10 ha/25 acres. By 1966 the 10–20 ha/25–50 acres category had also begun to decline, indicating a welcome tendency to develop units of 20 ha/50 acres and above. Nevertheless the average size of holding was still desperately small, 9 ha/22 acres in 1966, or 12 ha/30 acres if small specialized market garden and vineyard enterprises are deleted. Progress in West German agriculture has been impressive, but there is still far to go, and many more farmers must leave the land if the industry is to be fully competitive in the Common Market.

East Germany—the Social and Economic Background. In Thuringia and most of lowland Saxony the size of farm was in 1945 much as in West Germany. Beyond the Elbe, however, the plains of Mecklenburg and Brandenburg are the traditional home of the large agricultural estate (*Gut*), the origin of which has already been described (p. 111). In the postwar land reform all estates of more than 100 ha/250 acres were expropriated and most of them split into small 5–8 ha/12–20 acres farms for the benefit of small farmers, landless labourers and refugees. In a period of economic collapse such units were perhaps appropriate, but they appeared increasingly wasteful of scarce labour as East Germany developed as a major industrial country.

As in West Germany a period of concentration of holdings then followed, but for political reasons it took the form of the creation of collective farms (officially Agricultural Producer-Cooperatives). Most were formed under heavy government pressure in the winters of 1958–9 and 1959–60. At the beginning of 1965 some 16,000 collective farms, averaging 400 ha/1,000 acres each controlled 86% of East German agricultural land and about a third of the forest. A further 6·4% of agricultural land belonged to state farms, averaging 618 ha/1,530 acres each. There are even producer-cooperatives of market gardeners.

There are various stages on the road to collectivization, but in the fully developed form all land, machinery and animals are held in common. The members receive most of their annual income in the form of payments for work done, but are also paid something for the land they contributed on joining. In addition, the member is allowed to hold privately up to half a hectare of garden, meadow or field land, two cows with their calves, two sows, five ewes, as many chickens, rabbits and goats as he likes and ten beehives.

Collectivization has certainly achieved its object in reducing the rural labour force, which was 1·1 million in 1964 as against 1·7 million in 1952. The benefit to the East German economy is less certain, since until 1961 many of those who left made their way to West Germany. As one would expect from its lower population density East Germany has a higher proportion of its employed population on the land than has West Germany (16% as against 10%), but in proportion to available agricultural land the labour employed is actually somewhat less.

Much has been written about the chaos brought by collectivization, but it must be remembered that even before the war the output of arable crops in what is now East Germany was somewhat below that of West Germany, and livestock husbandry in particular was less well developed. It must be remembered also that it was only belatedly, from the 1960s, that the collectives began to receive satisfactory quantities of machinery to enable them to develop the large-scale methods for which they were designed. The amount of fertilizer made available has only recently begun to be satisfactory. In view of the dislocation inevitably involved in the creation of a completely new system it is not perhaps surprising that East German yields per unit area in the early 1960s were still about a third below even the rather unimpressive West German levels. Nevertheless progress in all branches was being claimed. The country was self-sufficient in sugar, potatoes, milk and eggs, while steady improvements were being made in the supply of butter and meat.

Crops. The principal grain crop is rye, which will tolerate the poorer soils of the Northern Lowland and of the Hercynian massifs. Rye in most areas of Germany is 'corn', the traditional bread grain, as wheat is 'corn' in England, and many Germans still prefer the dark rye bread over the wheaten variety. Wheat exceeds rye in West Germany; like barley it prefers the more favourable loess and loam soils, which also serve for sugar-beet growing. West Germany is able to grow about 90% of its sugar requirements, even more in good years.

After the grains, the next largest crop area is devoted to potatoes, which like rye will tolerate the poorer, and especially the sandy soils. Much of the crop is used for feeding animals, especially pigs, the chief source of meat. The quality of cattle is very variable, and in the south cows are still expected to draw carts and ploughs as well as to give milk. Very few sheep are kept.

In the general pattern of mixed farming there are naturally some islands of specialization, which will be described in more detail in the treatment of agricultural regions. Some of the largest farms in western Germany specialize in sugar beet or potato growing, and some of the smallest in growing fruit, vegetables, tobacco and the vine.

AGRICULTURAL REGIONS

1. The Grassland Regions[1]

1a. Marshland Grass Belt.[1] Permanent pasture in Germany

[1]The numbers in the section headings refer to the regions shown on Fig. 27.

occurs in regions that are too poorly drained, too cool or have too high a rainfall for successful arable cultivation. One such predominantly grass region is found in the coastal and river marshes of northwest Germany, where a high water-table

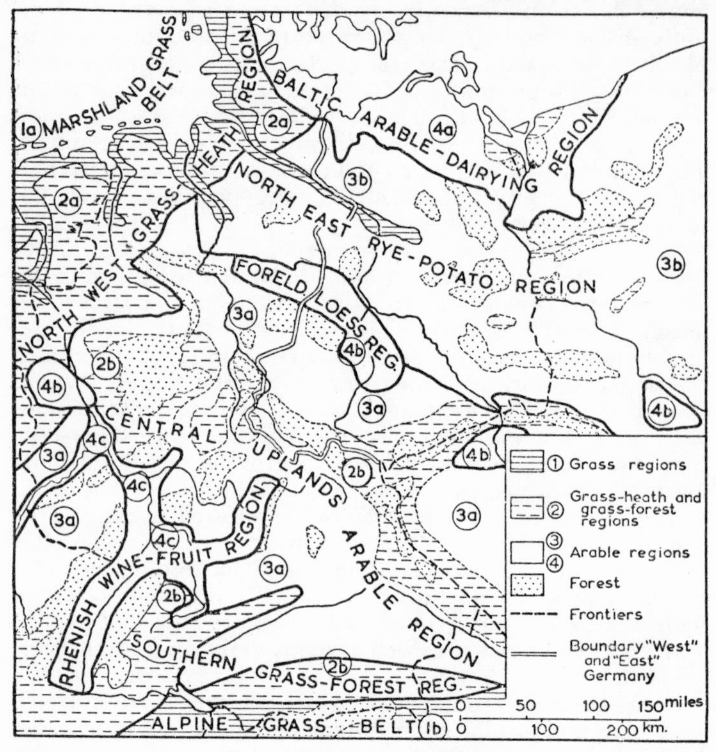

FIG. 27. Agricultural regions.

combines with the mild climate and well distributed rainfall to favour the growth of grass. The damp, cool summers are not particularly good for haymaking, so that there is a tendency to adopt livestock specializations that can be fitted to the seasonal growth of grass, such as the rearing of young stock for sale to other regions of Germany, and the grass-fattening of beef cattle, although milk production is also important. Certain favoured areas of marshland are also used for wheat growing, and near Hamburg specialized fruit and vegetable farms serve the urban market.

1b. The Alpine Grass Belt. In the Alps and the adjoining higher parts of the Alpine Foreland, the high rainfall, rugged conditions and winter low temperatures force most of the land to be left as forest or rough grazing. Although the economy is based on livestock, the farming system is very different from that of the northwest. The period during which beasts can graze out of doors is limited by the climate, so that the farmers' efforts must in the first place be directed to obtaining sufficient hay to feed their stock through the long winter. Formerly the limited valley land was conserved for hay production by a form of transhumance, known as *Almauftrieb*. The cattle were sent in summer to graze the Alpine pastures (*Almen*) that lie above the tree line. The herdsmen moved with them, living in crude chalets, where they turned the milk into cheese. The system was most fully developed in the Allgäu Alps, but today it is falling into disuse, as few men are now prepared to live the isolated life of a herdsman. Farmers have turned to a better management of the valley grasslands to provide feed for both winter and summer. Milk is still the main product; because of the distance from urban markets it is mostly turned into cheese, butter or other milk products.

2. Grass-Arable Regions

2a. Northwestern Grass and Heath Region. In a number of intermediate regions of generally poor soil the amount of arable land is higher than in regions of type 1, but grass, forest and heath still occupy more than half of the land. The largest continuous region of this type occupies the sandy *Geest* land of the west of the Schleswig-Holstein peninsula and of the western part of the Northern Lowland. Arable, conifer plantations and heathland occupy the sandy interfluves; grassland is found on the heavier soils, on the river marshes and on the reclaimed peat bogs. As in the marshes, cattle are able to remain out of doors for much of the year. A mixture of rearing and dairying is common, but the dairying element increases southwards because of the proximity of the industrial Rhine and Ruhr. The arable land grows rye, oats and potatoes, which are used to feed animals, especially the great numbers of pigs which provide meat and bacon for the industrial towns.

2b. Upland Grass and Forest Regions. The Central Uplands are as a whole poor in grassland, but some of the higher massifs receive enough rain and are cool enough to support a grass cover of 20–50% in addition to forest and limited arable. The grass area is particularly high in the Eifel and Berg Hills, on the northern fringe of the Rhenish Uplands, partly because of the high rainfall, partly because of the demand for dairy produce in the near-by industrial towns. Other grass and forest regions are the volcanic Westerwald, Vogelsberg and Rhön, and the Vogtland and Bohemian Forest. A mixture of grass, arable and forest is also typical of most of the Alpine Foreland and of the adjoining higher parts of southwest Germany. In recent years there has been a marked tendency for the grass area to expand at the expense of marginal arable land, and for livestock enterprises to replace the growing of field crops. There has also been some expansion of forest in the poorest and most remote areas.

3. General Arable-Farming Regions

3a. Central Uplands Mixed-Farming Regions. The basins and low plateaus of the Central Uplands are the home of western Germany's characteristic mixed farming. Many parts of the Central Uplands, especially the loess and limestone lands, have been farmed by man since Neolithic times, and are characterized today by vast open arable fields divided into strips. Grass is normally limited to narrow ribbons of meadow along streams, and some rough pasture on the higher massifs, so that the whole farming economy is based on arable crops.

Naturally there are variations from place to place in the crops grown and yields obtained; the Central Uplands contain both the rich wheatlands of the loess-covered Muschelkalk plateaus of Neckar and Main and also poor, sandy outcrops capable only of crops of rye and potatoes. Almost everywhere, however, the farms are too small, and too fragmented, to allow the introduction of the progressive farming methods which alone would give a reasonable income to their proprietors.

3b. Northeastern Rye and Potato Region. East of the Weser, the Northern Lowland between the loess of the Hercynian Foreland in the south and the youthful (Vistula) moraine belt in the north forms another region of general mixed farming. The soils are predominantly derived from sands or sandy clays, and since total rainfall diminishes and winters become more severe with distance from the sea, the maintenance of good permanent pasture is difficult. The better soils, mainly developed on boulder clay, are consequently almost entirely arable, growing rye and potatoes, which are used to fatten the large pig population. Between 30 and 50% of the area consists of forests, planted on the former sandy heathlands. A rather more varied element is brought into the agricultural scene by the drained marshes of the river valleys and *Urstromtäler*. Here the water table is often high enough to maintain reasonable pasture, and there is some dairying and vegetable growing for Berlin and other towns.

A subdivision of this region can be made west of the Elbe, where the farmers, undisturbed by the land reform and collectivization that took place further east, were able to increase their output considerably in order to make up for the loss of produce which used to come from eastern Germany. They raised their yields of potatoes, took up the growing of seed potatoes, and even managed to grow sugar beet on their sandy land. There was also a striking development of dairying to supply the 'island' of West Berlin, 160 km/100 miles away across East German territory.

4. Specialized Arable Regions

4a. The Baltic Arable-Dairying Region. The ice sheet of the last stage of the Vistula glaciation of the Northern Lowland left behind a sheet of boulder clay on the shores of the Baltic, in eastern Schleswig-Holstein and coastal Mecklenburg. On these fertile heavy soils, arable predominates. Rye is the main cereal, although wheat is grown in favoured locations, but the great feature of the region is the growing of rotation grass, potatoes and fodder crops. These are not sold but are fed to pigs, beef cattle and above all dairy cows. This Danish system of dairy farming, based on arable crops, is suited to a region where the maintenance of good permanent grass and the keeping of cattle out of doors are alike limited by climate.

4b. The Foreland Loess Region. The belt of fertile loess soils that follows the Hercynian Foreland from Saxony to the Lower Rhinelands is the home of farms specializing in the growing of sugar beet, with the addition of wheat and malting barley for sale off the farm. The even loess plains, with soils approaching black-earth type in the more continental east, are almost entirely arable. Only rarely are the open, unhedged fields broken by a strip of meadow along a stream. The farms are normally concentrated into large villages, where beef cattle are fattened on sugar-beet residues and on fodder crops such as lucerne. The West German part of the region has some quite large farms, which make considerable use of machinery to save labour costs, and are among the most efficient in the country.

4c. Specialized Wine, Fruit and Vegetable Regions. Germany has some of the world's most famous vineyards, but it stands on the physical margin of the area where vine growing is possible. Vineyards are found only in the southern half of the country, and even here only on slopes with a favourable orientation. The slopes have to be elaborately terraced; the harvested grapes, and the very soil in which the vines are grown, must be carried in baskets on men's backs. It is small wonder that Germany is a high-cost producer of wine, and that many abandoned terraces point to a steady decline in the area devoted to the vine since medieval times. The principal remaining vineyards are found on the valley sides of the Upper and Middle Rhine and its tributaries, especially the Mosel. In East Germany vine growing is restricted to small areas on the Saale and near Dresden.

Other climatically favoured valley slopes are used for fruit growing. Germany's foremost fruit areas are in Baden-Württemberg, especially in the Rhine and Neckar valleys and on the shores of the Bodensee. Other important regions are the famous *Bergstrasse* north of Heidelberg, the Main valley, the Rhine near Bonn and Cologne and the Elbe marshes near Hamburg. Tobacco is mainly grown in the warmth of the Upper Rhine Plain, and meets about a quarter of West German requirements. Most of the fruit-growing districts also grow vegetables. Particularly important market-gardening areas are the Neckar valley near Stuttgart, the Main and Rednitz valleys from Würzburg to Nürnberg, the Rhine valley generally, the Hercynian Foreland near Brunswick, the Thuringian Basin near Erfurt and the Elbe marshes near Hamburg. Specialized vegetable growing and dairying are also found near all the large cities.

FORESTRY

History of the German Forest. The country which the migrant German tribes took for their own, although not so completely covered by bristling woods and festering swamps as Tacitus once led us to believe, was nevertheless at least three-quarters forested (Fig. 4). Today the position is reversed; the trees have been driven back until they cover only about a quarter of the land. This clearance was almost entirely the work of the medieval farmer, in the years 700–1300 (pp. 61–3).

The composition of the forest has changed also. When men first knew it, the German forest was predominantly deciduous in the west, mixed deciduous and coniferous in the east; pure conifer stands were rare (pp. 44–5). By the end of the 19th century, the forest consisted primarily of coniferous softwoods, which were preferred because they grew more quickly, produced straighter timber and were more tolerant with regard to soil conditions. Although the softwood trend has been reversed in the last fifty years, coniferous trees still account for 65% of the West German and 80% of the East German forests.

Distribution and Composition. The proportion of forest increases from north to south. On the Northern Lowland forest is mainly limited to the poorer sand spreads from the Lüneberg Heath eastwards, while the Central Uplands and Alps are more heavily forested; half of the West German forest area is in the two southern Länder of Bavaria and Baden-Württemberg alone.

The most important tree of eastern Germany is the pine (*Kiefer*), which alone will tolerate the poor, sandy land east of the Elbe. In West Germany it makes up only about a quarter of the forest, being common on the extensive Bunter Sandstone outcrops of the Central Uplands. The most prominent West German tree is the spruce (*Fichte*), which occupies 40% of the forest area, and flourishes in the cool, damp conditions of the Hercynian massifs from the Harz southwards. The fir (*Tanne*) demands even more moisture than the spruce, and so is found on the highest mountains of southern Germany, such as the Black Forest, the Bohemian and Bavarian Forests, and the Alps below the snow line.

Deciduous woodlands are mainly characteristic of the lower hills of western Germany, from the Weser Hills southwards to the Bodensee. The main tree is the beech, accounting for about a quarter of the West German forest. The oak, with its preference for the lower and milder regions, bore the brunt of the prehistoric and medieval forest clearances, and so is of limited importance today. The greatest remaining oakwoods grow in the relatively oceanic conditions of the Rhenish Uplands.

Utilization. In East Germany 63% of the forest is managed by State Forestry establishments, and another 30% belongs to the collective farms or their members. Even in West Germany over half of the forest belongs to the state or other public bodies. The trees are carefully tended by a skilled forestry service, and even the private woods are strictly controlled. The practice of planting pure stands of conifers has recently fallen out of favour as it had been found to result in soil deterioration and, diminishes yields. Now the ideal is *Dauerwald*, a naturally regenerating mixed forest of all ages, in which the mature trees alone are felled each year, leaving their younger neighbours to grow on undisturbed. A varied forest of this type is infinitely more pleasant to the eye than the grim rectangles of pure spruce stands.

The German forest suffered severely from overcutting in the years of war economy and shortage; in Berlin, even the trees in the parks disappeared during the bitter winters of 1946 and 1947. Nevertheless, West Germany remains Europe's fourth producer of timber, as well as being the second largest timber-importing country. In East Germany, damage by overcutting was even greater. The country had the good fortune to inherit a high proportion of the prewar German pulp, paper and rayon plants, located in areas like the Thuringian Forest.

FISHING

Germany takes third place among the fishing countries of Europe, following Norway and Britain. Half of the West German trawler landings are at Bremerhaven, which rivals Hull and Grimsby for the position of Europe's greatest fishing port. Fast trains take the fresh fish to all parts of western Germany. Other trawler ports are Cuxhaven, Hamburg-Altona and Kiel.

The herring-drifter fleet is also predominately based on the

Weser ports, although not so much Bremerhaven as smaller harbours like Nordenham, Brake and Vegesack (Fig. 56). The second drifter base is Emden. The East German deep-sea fishing fleet is divided between the two fishing 'combines' of Sassnitz and Rostock (Fig. 59). Coastal and inland fishermen are also grouped into seventy fishery-workers' producer-cooperatives.

SUGGESTIONS FOR FURTHER READING

E. Otremba, *Die deutshe Agrarlandschaft*, 2nd ed., Wiesbaden (Steiner-Verlag), 1961.

E. Otremba, *Atlas der deutschen Agrarlandschaft*, Wiesbaden (Steiner-Verlag), 1962.

M. Tracy, *Agriculture in Western Europe* (Cape), 1964.

Chapter 9

INDUSTRY

The Industrial Revolution came late to Germany, but with the development of railways after 1840 and the smelting of iron by means of Ruhr coke after 1849 there began the creation of a new heavy industry. In the distribution of iron, steel and heavy engineering works the Hercynian Foreland belt, on the northern flanks of the Central Uplands, stood out especially clearly. Here were the major coalfields of Aachen, the Ruhr and Silesia, as well as the brown-coal fields that were developed from the 1890s, and the great potash and salt deposits. The Ruhr coalfield developed especially rapidly, by reason both of its resources and of its splendid situation where the great European overland route of the Hercynian Foreland crosses the great European water route of the Rhine.

The lighter forms of industry did not follow the movement of basic and heavy industry to the coalfields to anything like the same extent as in Great Britain. In Germany the railways brought the Industrial Revolution rather than followed it. Consequently, the Saxon potters and weavers, the smiths and cutlers of the Rhenish Uplands and the metal workers of Nürnberg were able to obtain their raw materials and the coal for their new steam engines by rail, and so were not forced to move to the coalfields. Subsequent developments such as the growth of widespread electricity and gas grids and the use of motor transport have increased the viability of industrial centres away from the coalfields.

Today Germany is one of the small band of major industrial powers in the world. In 1965 West Germany was the world's fourth producer of coal and steel, was contesting with Japan for the position of second world producer of motor cars, and was one of the leading exporters of machinery, electrical equipment and chemicals. East Germany was the world's largest brown-coal producer and the major exporter of machinery to the Communist countries.

THE POWER BASIS

Coal. The most important indigenous source of power in Germany is the bituminous coal of Carboniferous (Westphalian) age. It is geographically significant that coal is not uniform but varies in its physical and chemical characteristics. In particular, the proportion of carbon normally diminishes and the volatile content, such as oxygen and hydrogen, normally increases with the passage from the older and deeper to the younger seams of the coalfields. The high-carbon coals, more or less anthracitic, provide the best domestic fuels. About the middle of the range are the coking coals, so important for heavy industry, while the higher-volatile gas and long-flame coals are today mostly consumed in industrial and power-station boilers. Because of variations both in the conditions of deposition and in subsequent erosion the proportions in which the different types of coal are present vary from field to field with significant consequences for the geography of industry.

In the coalfields of the Hercynian Foreland the coal seams dip northward off the older rocks of the Central Uplands (Fig. 28). This great belt of coalfields traverses France and Belgium to enter Germany at the small Aachen field, where the lower and older seams of the Coal Measures predominate. Accordingly output is mostly of low-volatile domestic and steam coals, with very limited coking coal. East of this is the most productive single coalfield of western and central Europe, the Ruhr, which contains an estimated 48,000 million tons of coal (to 1,200 m/4,000 ft), 85% of West Germany's estimated reserves. The industrial impulse of the Ruhr derived from its wide range of available coal types, and especially from its high-grade coking coal. East Germany's negligible reserves of about 40 million tons of workable coal are now virtually confined to the small Zwickau-Lügau-Oelsnitz field at the foot of the Ore Mountains. The production of about 3 million tons a year is inadequate to meet East German requirements, and has to be supplemented by imports from the U.S.S.R., Poland and, to a lesser extent, West Germany.

The only field of importance within the Central Uplands is the Saar, in which the low-volatile coals and fine coking coals are absent, and output consists predominantly of the gas and long-flame varieties. The field is continuous with the concealed coalfield of Lorraine, beyond the French frontier; reserves are estimated at 8,000–10,000 million tons.

Traditionally the Ruhr coalfield was the power-house of Germany, and Germany in turn a net exporter of energy to her neighbours. In particular the steel industries of Belgium, Luxemburg, Lorraine and Italy were heavily dependent on German coke or coking coal. This key position of Germany as a supplier of coal to continental Europe was reflected in various attempts by neighbouring countries to obtain control over deliveries, notably the demands for reparations deliveries after the First World War, and two French attempts to detach the Saar coalfield. With the development of the European movement, the Coal and Steel Community was introduced as a measure of control with German co-operation, and this led in turn to the formation of the wider European Economic Community.

In the immediate postwar years of energy shortage, coal was produced at almost any cost, and would find eager buyers throughout Europe. Now all is changed; although the overall demand for energy continues to rise, the share of coal declines, owing to competition from alternative fuels, notably oil. Not even heavy industry remains faithful; coastal steel plants in neighbouring EEC countries prefer to make their coke from cheaper overseas coal, and German coal has even to be subsidized to make it acceptable to reluctant German steelmasters. From a peak output of 145 million tons in 1958 the coal industry went into steady retreat, as millions of tons of unsold coal accumulated at the pit heads. A programme of pit closures and labour reduction was not at first reflected in a substantially lower total output, since increased efficiency tended to make up for the lost capacity. The crisis sharpened in 1966 (total output 131 million tons), by which stage even the largest and most efficient mines were being closed for lack of markets. The social and economic effects on the coalmining communities of a decline in employment running (in 1966) at 23,000 a year can easily be imagined.

Brown Coal. Having been deposited comparatively recently, in Tertiary times, brown coal is nearly always found within 180 m/600 ft of the surface beneath a loose overburden, and so can be mined economically in vast open pits. The deposits are thick, often 10 m/30 ft and exceptionally 100 m/300 ft for a single seam. The heating value of the coal is small; it takes 4 or more tons to equal a ton of bituminous coal, but the low

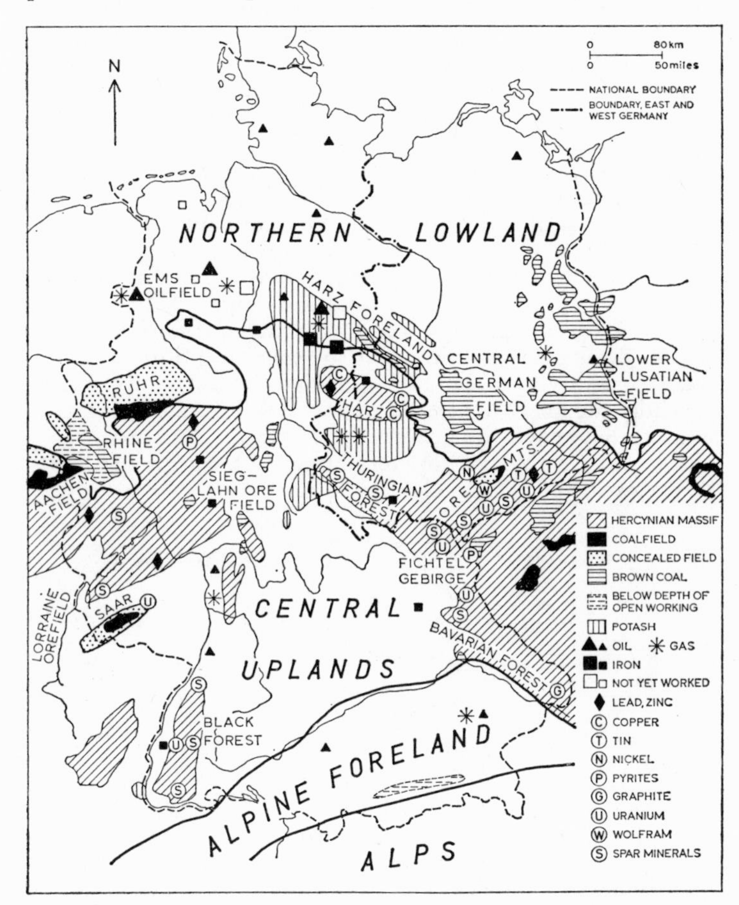

FIG. 28. Mineral resources.

cost due to highly mechanized working compensates for this. To avoid the expense of transporting such a low-grade and waterlogged fuel by rail or road, it must be transformed at the pit head into compressed briquettes, electricity or, in East Germany, oil and chemicals.

Once more, the main fields are found in the Hercynian Foreland belt, spreading out from there beneath the Northern Lowland (Fig. 28). This time the dominant partner is East Germany, with an estimated 25,000 million tons of workable reserves, 61% in the expanding Cottbus or Lower Lusatian field, and most of the remainder in the earlier developed Central German field near Halle and Leipzig. As with coal of Carboniferous age, areal differences of quality are reflected in differences of utilization. The predominantly Eocene and Oligocene coal of the Central German field, with its relatively high bituminous content, is best suited as a basis for chemical processing, while the low-ash and low-sulphur Miocene coal of Lower Lusatia provides the better material for coking processes. Both fields provide coal suitable for briquette manufacture, as well as the high-ash coal suitable only for the specially-designed boilers of power stations. East Germany, which relies heavily on brown coal as its main source of energy, accounts for 70% of total German output, and is the largest producer in the world (Fig. 29).

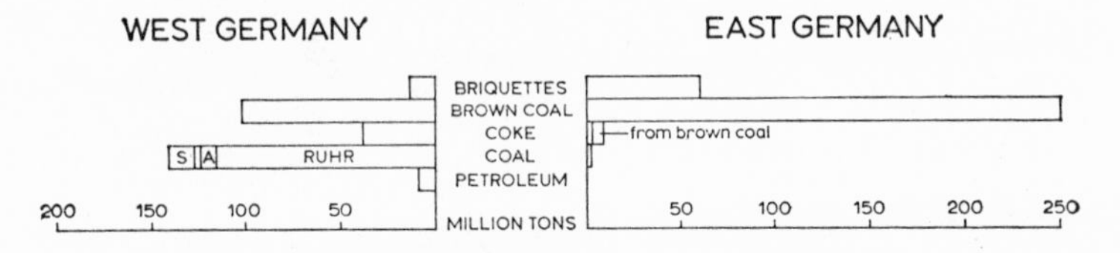

FIG. 29. Output of fuel minerals (1965).

West German brown coal comes from the Rhenish field west of Cologne, which provides Miocene coal used decreasingly for briquette manufacture and increasingly for the pit-head generation of electricity. The efficiency of this operation has meant that brown coal has suffered less than Ruhr coal from failing markets. Smaller supplies of brown coal come from Hesse and from the northwestern extremity of the Central German field in Lower Saxony. Underground mining of the hard brown coal (*Pechkohle*) of the Alpine Foreland, more demanding of labour, has sharply declined.

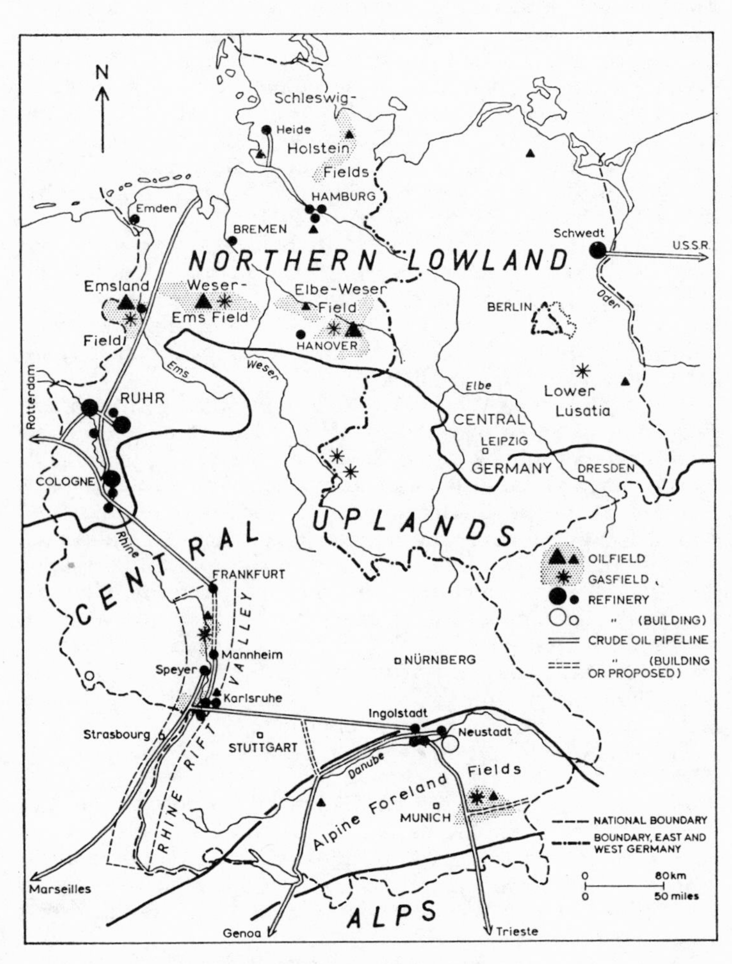

FIG. 30. Oil and gas in Germany.

Petroleum. West Germany is the largest oil producer in western Europe, but although output rose from a few hundred thousand tons a year before the war to over 7 million tons in the 1960s, massive imports are still necessary to meet the soaring home demand. Most of German oil and gas production comes from Lower Saxony, where the principal fields stretch in a belt lying north of the Central Uplands from the Aller valley near Brunswick to the Ems valley on the Netherlands border. Smaller fields are worked in Schleswig-Holstein, the Rhine Rift Valley and the Alpine Foreland (Fig. 30).

Oil has dramatically increased its hold on the rapidly expanding West German energy market, its share rising from about 10% in 1958, when coal was at its peak, to over a third by the mid-1960s. Both for domestic heating and for many industrial purposes oil is now cheaper than coal, especially in areas distant from the coalfields.

Before the Second World War, Germany obtained its refined petroleum in three ways: through the import of petroleum products, especially by way of the Rhine; from home oil refined on the North German fields; and by the refining of imported crude oil at the North German ports, especially Hamburg. A coastal location for refining has the advantage that bulk supplies of crude oil can be unloaded directly from tankers, and then the refined products distributed by various forms of transport to the widespread inland market. Hamburg at that time was well situated for supplying Central Germany and Berlin by rail or barge routes. Wartime plants for the production of motor fuel and chemicals from coal were also erected in the Ruhr, in Central Germany and elsewhere.

The resumption of refining after the war broadly re-established the former pattern, and as late as 1955 well over half West German capacity was still either at the ports or on the oilfields of northwest Germany. With the cutting off of East Germany, however, the ports now offered only an inconvenient location for supplying a market that was now predominantly in the Rhine–Ruhr region and South Germany.

Meanwhile in the difficult postwar years when all industrial equipment was scarce, the wartime motor fuel plants of the Rhine–Ruhr area were re-opened, although this time to operate not on coal but on crude oil brought in by Rhine barge. Refinery location in the midst of such a large market proved to have great advantages, which were accentuated when demand grew sufficiently to support the building of pipelines for the economical transport of crude oil from the coast. At the end of the 1950s pipelines from both Wilhelmshaven and Rotterdam reached the area, which rapidly overtook the north to become Germany's major refining centre, with at one time nearly 60% of total capacity. What had been the power-house of Germany was now the target for massive energy imports.

The obvious next move for the oil companies was to attack the growing markets of South Germany. From the north the Rotterdam–Rhine pipeline was extended to a refinery near Frankfurt. South of this point it is economically more attractive to rely on pipelines from French and Italian Mediterranean ports, the use of which saves 2,000 tanker miles on voyages from Suez. The first to arrive was the South European pipeline from Lavéra near Marseilles to Strasbourg and Karlsruhe. The latter was selected as a major refining centre because of its situation in the densely-populated Rhine valley, as well as the existence of excellent motorway and rail links and indeed the Rhine itself for widespread distribution in southwest Germany and Switzerland. Northern extensions of the South European line supply refineries at Speyer and Mannheim. A further extension runs eastwards to supply South Germany's second major refinery concentration at Ingolstadt and near-by Neustadt on the Danube. The same group of refineries is the principal objective of two transalpine pipelines, an Italian line from Genoa and the giant TAL line from Trieste. Ingolstadt has the advantage of lying midway between the two major Bavarian markets of Munich and Nürnberg, with good motorway and rail connections. In the three years 1960–3 South German refining capacity expanded from nothing to a third of West Germany's total, and because of the advantage of transport by pipeline, oil prices fell by about a quarter. The benefit to the expanding South German economy was substantial; so too was the blow to the distant Ruhr and Saar coalfields, which could not match such prices.

The division of Germany has had a significant effect on the subsequent development of oil supply. East Germany has only minor home sources of oil and natural gas, and at first relied heavily on the wartime plants based on brown coal. More recently the country has been linked to the pipeline that brings Soviet oil across Poland to a large refinery at Schwedt on the Oder, with an extension to the Leuna chemical plant near Halle.

Electricity. About 80% of electricity produced for public consumption in West Germany is generated from coal, including about 25% from brown coal. Water power contributes about 13%. The use of oil is restricted by official measures to preserve the power station market for coal. A unified power network covers the whole country, allowing the base load to be provided as much as possible by the economical brown-coal plants of the Cologne field and the run-of-stream water-power stations of South Germany and the Alps. The more expensive Ruhr plants can then be used as demand rises, and finally water-power plants with reservoir storage brought in to meet peak demand. During the summer snow-melt period power is imported from Austria and Switzerland, but in winter the flow is reversed. Like many advanced industrialized countries West Germany has begun to develop atomic power. At first, most of the plants were in South Germany, because of the high price of coal there caused by distance from the Ruhr. As generating costs in atomic power stations have come down, so the plants have been able to move ever nearer to the Ruhr, and there are now a number in existence or under construction in the northern part of the country.

East Germany was left after 1945 with brown coal as almost a sole source of energy, and power plants reduced to a third of prewar capacity by damage and dismantling. Output rose again in the postwar years, especially through the building of new plants on the expanding Lower Lusatian brown-coal field, but it never caught up with the rapidly increasing demand. This high degree of reliance on brown coal as a source of electricity explains East German interest in the building of atomic power stations. East Germany is a major source of uranium, but the ore has been exploited primarily in the interests of the U.S.S.R., which supplies the fuel needed for the East German atomic stations.

Gas. In the past West German gas supplies were derived from coal. From the coke ovens of the Ruhr a gas grid radiated as far north as Hanover, as far south as Mannheim, where it linked with a smaller grid based on the Saar. Outside the radius of these schemes towns mostly had individual gasworks, based on transported coal. As in other countries gas now comes increasingly from a petroleum base. In South Germany the development of the new refineries has permitted the creation of a gas grid, replacing the old town gasworks, and based on a trunk main running from Kassel to Freiburg. West Germany has modest supplies of home natural gas; the most important source is the Emsland field, with smaller supplies in the Rhine Rift Valley and the Alpine Foreland. Much of the natural gas is used as a raw material in the chemical industry. With the development of a trunk main carrying imported gas from the Netherlands Schlochteren field southwards across Germany the energy pattern is likely to change yet again.

For gas supply East Germany has hitherto looked mainly to brown coal. A gas grid has been under development, based on coking and complete gasification plants in Lower Lusatia. In East Germany also increased reliance on imported petroleum and possibly on imported natural gas seems likely.

THE MINERAL BASIS

Iron Ore. West Germany is not rich in metallic mineral resources. Home iron ores meet only about a tenth of the requirements of the iron and steel industry, measured by the iron content of the ore. Until recent years the principal deposits worked were the vein ores in the Devonian rocks of the Siegerland and adjoining parts of the Rhenish Uplands, but today the main supply comes from the Cretaceous ores of the Harz Foreland. These ores are very lean (22–32% iron) but occur in beds of 10–30 m/30–100 ft in thickness, and so can be economically worked in open and deep mines. The largest single source is the Lower Cretaceous deposit at Salzgitter. Thanks to exploration for oil, it is now known that enormous reserves of moderately rich (38–42% Fe) Jurassic Dogger ores exist at workable depths beneath the Northern Lowland. Lesser deposits of sedimentary iron ores are worked near Osnabrück (Cretaceous), near Amberg in the Upper Palatinate (Cretaceous) and near Freiburg-im-Breisgau (Dogger).

Unfortunately for German ore mining, Ruhr furnaces prefer to use rich imported ores, which require less coal to smelt and which enable the capital cost of the blast furnaces to be spread over a much greater throughput of iron. In consequence most of the mines that existed at the end of the war have now closed.

The largest single source of imported ore is Sweden, but increasingly large supplies now come from Latin America (especially Venezuela and Brazil) and from Africa (especially Liberia). Of somewhat lesser importance is France, which still supplies considerable quantities of lean Lorraine ore.

Other Metals. The Harz and the Saxon Ore Mountains were in medieval times famous throughout Europe for the mining of non-ferrous metals. After the close of medieval times the industry collapsed under the impact of technological difficulties and competition from the New World. There have been periodic revivals since, the last during the Second World War and the subsequent period of shortages, but in West Germany a renewed wave of mine closures began in 1957.

Lead and zinc ores of the Rhenish Uplands and the Harz meet about a third of West German requirements of lead and about 80% of zinc. Pyrites ores from the Sauerland and the Upper Palatinate are primarily worked for sulphur, but also yield zinc and iron. Small quantities of copper are obtained from the Harz. There are uranium deposits in the Fichtelgebirge, just over the border from the Ore Mountains, in the Black Forest and on the fringe of the Saar.

In East Germany the centuries-old Mansfield mines, on the eastern fringe of the Harz, are still yielding copper ores. In the Ore Mountains and adjoining Thuringia intensive prospecting associated with the working for the U.S.S.R. of the greatest uranium field in Europe led to the discovery of many other minerals. The ancient mining town of Freiberg is the main centre for lead and zinc mining, and nickel ores are worked and smelted in the Saxon Hills north of Zwickau.

Potash and Common Salt. Germany is the major world producer of potash, and has all the salt needed for chemical and culinary purposes. The main salt and potash deposits occur in the Zechstein rocks wrapping round the Harz, beginning at the Werra river in Hesse, swinging through Thuringia and east of the Harz, before returning westwards along the Harz Foreland to Hanover and the Leine valley. West Germany has minor salt and potash deposits of Tertiary age beneath the Rhine Rift Valley, and salt is also obtained from the Lower Rhineland, the Neckar basin and the ancient mines of Berchtesgaden. The division of Germany also divided the salt and potash deposits, with most of the potash mines falling to East Germany. Since 1945 West German output has been raised to the level of the entire *Reich* in 1939. About 40% of potash output is exported, giving West Germany about a fifth of the world market.

Other Non-metallic Minerals. Both West and East Germany have supplies of the spar minerals needed by the steel and pottery industries. They occur principally in the hills of the Upper Palatinate and their continuation through the Vogtland to the Ore Mountains. The same area provides kaolin, but not enough to meet all home requirements. Pottery clays are plentiful, and there is even an export of refractory clays, especially from the Neuwied Basin. West Germany is a major producer of graphite, from one mine near Passau; half is exported. Gypsum and anhydrite for the building industry are available from the Trias of Franconia and the Zechstein of the Harz fringe in both West and East Germany. The latter also uses anhydrite as a source of sulphur. The location of cement manufacture has hitherto depended as much on coal transport as on the availability of limestone. Major centres are the Münster Basin northeast of the Ruhr and the northern end of the Rhine Rift Valley. The great variety of building stone available in the Central Uplands has contributed greatly to the character of the historic German towns and villages, from the gleaming slate roofs of the Sauerland to the red sandstone churches of the south.

METAL INDUSTRIES

Iron and Steel. West Germany is the fourth world producer of steel, having taken third place from Britain in 1955 only to be overtaken by Japan in 1964. The German steel industry accounts for about 45% of the output of the six founder-members of the European Coal and Steel Community, and is nearly twice as large as that of the second biggest producer, France.

Iron and steel capacity is located mainly on the coalfields, especially in the Ruhr, which provides 65% of West German steel supplies. The German steel industry has always been characterized by very large vertically organized firms, uniting coal and iron ore mines, coke ovens, iron and steel capacity and diverse forms of engineering. Most firms were based on the Ruhr, and their names like Krupp and Thyssen are known throughout the world. The concentration movement culminated before the war with the formation of the great steel trust known as *Vereinigte Stahlwerk*, which controlled about 60% of Ruhr steel and about a third of its coal and coke output. The trust was not particularly successful as a business enterprise, and was dismantled by the victors after the Second World War. Subsequently German steel plants have been re-grouped into a number of combines, the largest being Thyssen in the western Ruhr. Imported ore for the Ruhr must be transhipped at Rotterdam, Emden or Bremerhaven, but good waterway connections run direct to the plants, which have the advantage of local coal supplies and an enormous local market.

Orefield plants are not common in Germany; there are a few small works on the Sieg-Lahn orefield and in Bavaria, but

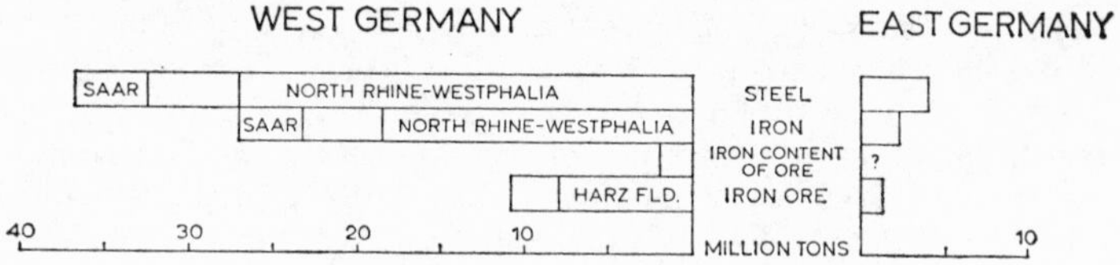

FIG. 31. Output of the iron and steel industries.

the most important unit of this type is at Salzgitter, in the Harz Foreland. At a time when the giant ore carrier and the availability of cheap American coal are making the advantages of coastal location for iron and steel production ever more apparent, Germany has only one unit in this category, at Bremen. Even here large modern ore carriers must dock downstream at Bremerhaven. By the mid-1960s the German steel industry was severely affected by competition from the modern coastal plants of her Common Market partners. Ruhr coke had to be subsidized to reduce the cost disadvantage of German steel, and competition was reduced by the grouping of plants into giant sales syndicates. Further consolidation of the industry appeared inevitable.

East Germany lacks coking coal and has little iron ore, and emerged from the war with iron-smelting capacity only at one derelict plant in Thuringia. Additional blast furnaces have since been erected, notably the plant at Eisenhüttenstadt on the Oder, using Polish coking coal and Russian ore. Steel-making capacity has recently been added. Additional steel capacity is found at scattered plants located near the markets of Berlin and Saxony, based on scrap and imported pig iron. In spite of considerable increases of output over prewar figures, iron and steel production is not a major branch of the economy (Fig. 31). Great reliance is put on imports, especially from the Soviet Union. Special steels for East Germany's advanced engineering industry are produced at Freital near Dresden and Döhlen near Leipzig.

Engineering. The building of machinery must be regarded as West Germany's greatest industry, employing more workers than any other and leading in the value of its exports. West Germany, for example, is the leading European producer, and the world's second producer, of machine tools, that key product for modern industrial development. The building of the heaviest machinery, such as steel rolling mills, is naturally linked with steel production, and so is concentrated on the coalfields, especially the Ruhr. The same is true of the allied heavy constructional industry, building bridges, port installations and the like. The production of medium and light machinery, like German industry in general, is dispersed among a number of centres. The Rhine–Ruhr region outside the Ruhr coalfield is important, but so too are the Rhine–Main region, industrial Württemberg and many other industrial concentrations and individual towns of West Germany (Fig. 32). There are numerous examples of regional specialization, such as the manufacture of textile machinery in Württemberg and the Lower Rhinelands, or the clock and precision engineering industries of the Black Forest and its fringes.

An allied and very prosperous branch in the engineering sector of industry is the manufacture of metal goods other than machinery. Once more the industry is dispersed among many industrial regions and towns, and there is often a high degree of regional specialization, perhaps with a single town devoted to a single product. Just south of the Ruhr, for example, Solingen is Germany's principal cutlery centre, neighbouring Remscheid predominates in hand tools and Velbert is the capital of lock making.

Medium and light engineering is of long standing in East

Germany, and textile machinery, office equipment, cameras, microscopes and astronomical equipment are still important and typical exports. After 1945 Communist industrial planning threw the emphasis much more on heavy machinery and machine tools, but there is no single concentration to compare with the Ruhr. Instead heavy engineering is scattered, in the Karl-Marx-Stadt (Chemnitz) district of Saxony, the brown-coal fields of Central Germany and Lower Lusatia, at Magdeburg, Berlin and other towns. Machinery of one sort or another is East Germany's most important export.

Vehicles. West Germany is the leading European car producer, and the second producer in the world. For the most part car manufacture has grown up outside the older centres of heavy industry, being one of the principal causes of growth in the newer industrial concentrations such as the Rhine–Main region or the Stuttgart agglomeration.

In the postwar years the great success story was that of Volkswagen, the 'peoples' car', produced in Germany's largest single car plant set up by dictatorial edict in open country at Wolfsburg, near Brunswick. A new town had to be created to house the workers, and following the division of Germany the location, from being central, became rather an isolated one. Labour shortage at Wolfsburg drove the firm to disperse production to various larger towns, including Hanover (commercial vehicles), Brunswick (engines), Kassel (components) and even to Ingolstadt far away in the south (assembly). The other large producer in northern Germany is Ford, exceptional in its situation in the 'old' Rhine–Ruhr industrial region. By far the largest part of the industry is in South Germany, centred especially on Stuttgart. The American Opel firm has its principal plant in the Rhine–Main region. In South Germany is the great 'quality' firm, Mercedes-Benz, with a group of plants centred on the Stuttgart conurbation. Most of the smaller and specialized car firms are also in the south, at Munich, Heilbronn, Stuttgart and elsewhere.

The larger car firms also produce commercial vehicles, but there are some specialized producers also, usually subsidiaries of major engineering firms. Another obvious extension of the motor vehicle industry is into the manufacture of tractors; one of the largest producers is a Cologne firm that also manufactures commercial vehicles. Agricultural machinery on the

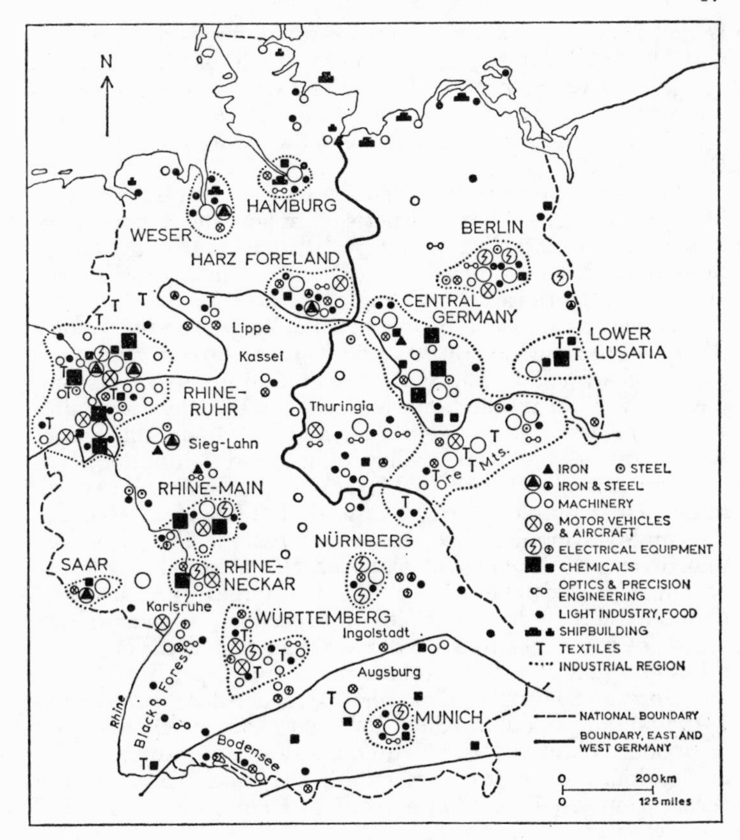

FIG. 32. Industrial regions.

other hand is more often produced separately at rather rustic locations, such as Düren in the Lower Rhinelands, Harsewinkel near Bielefeld or Marktoberdorf in the Allgäu.

The vehicle industry has in recent years made a major contribution to economic growth, both of West Germany as a whole and of those regions, mostly in South Germany, that have a large concentration of car plants. The impact is transmitted to a wide range of industry through component suppliers, many of which are in the same regions. Of the two largest instrument suppliers, for example, one is at Frankfurt and the other at Stuttgart, where much of the electrical equipment for motor vehicles is also manufactured. Castings and small metal parts, on the other hand, often come from the 'traditional' industrial regions like the Mark, south of the Ruhr (pp. 233–4).

The expansion of the motor industry and its related plants has been so great that shortages of space and labour have forced firms to establish branch plants outside the agglomerations in which they developed. Daimler-Benz, for example, while keeping research and engine production in Stuttgart, has moved its car assembly lines to Sindelfingen, on the western fringe of the agglomeration, where rural labour can more easily be attracted. The same firm has transferred its commercial vehicle production right out of Württemberg altogether, to Mannheim, Gaggenau and Wörth in the Upper Rhine Valley. The Rhine valley offers good communications and easy access to Common Market neighbours, while Wörth in particular is able to draw on the pool of labour available in the 'underdeveloped' Saar–Palatinate region. The firm even took over an existing car plant at Düsseldorf, in order to obtain its skilled labour force. The two large American companies exhibit similar examples of dispersion. It is very much a sign of the times that each has selected a declining coal-mining region as a likely source of labour, Opel at Bochum and Ford at Saarlouis. Each, like Mercedes-Benz, is attracted to the labour pool of the Saar–Palatinate region, Opel with a component plant at Kaiserslauten and Ford, as already noted, at Saarlouis. Each firm has established links that run even across frontiers, Ford with a plant at Genk in Belgium, and Opel with one at Antwerp.

Before the war the area that is now East Germany had a number of important motor plants, but since partition the industry has suffered from difficulties in component supply and possibly from a lack of interest on the part of the authorities in private car production. The most important car-producing combine unites various plants at Karl-Marx-Stadt (Chemnitz) and Zwickau; a second producer is at Eisenach. Four works produce commercial vehicles, at Zittau, Werdau, Karl-Marx-Stadt and Ludwigsfelde, south of Berlin. Under 'Comecon' specialization agreements, heavy lorries are supposed to be imported from Czechoslovakia and buses from

Hungary. Tractors are made at Schönebeck on the Elbe, and motor bicycles at Zschopau, south of Chemnitz, and elsewhere.

The German aircraft industry was entirely destroyed as a consequence of the war. In West Germany a modern aerospace industry has been reconstituted, with considerable U.S. participation. There are two main groupings of plants, one in the north at Bremen and Hamburg, and one in the south at Munich, Augsburg, Friedrichshafen and elsewhere. Jet engines are made at Munich. The only East German aircraft plant, at Dresden, was closed in the late 1950s as part of 'Comecon' rationalization measures.

Shipbuilding. Until 1948 West Germany was forbidden to build ocean-going ships, yet within a few years the country was battling with Britain and Sweden for second place in world shipbuilding to Japan. Hamburg is the largest single centre, with important yards also at Kiel, Bremen, Emden, Lübeck and Flensburg. As in most European countries, the industry has gone through a period of difficulty, largely as a result of Japanese competition, with some closures and a generally depressing effect on the economics of the shipbuilding towns.

East Germany has made a remarkable effort to create a shipbuilding industry almost from nothing. Yards at Stralsund, Rostock, Warnemünde and Wismar have been laid out and equipped on the most modern lines, and the labour force increased many times over. Specialization agreements among the 'Comecon' countries enable East Germany to concentrate on the series production of a limited range of vessels, notably deep-sea trawlers, fish-factory ships and freighters of 10,000–12,000 tons. Until about 1952 the industry sold almost exclusively to the U.S.S.R., often at well below world market prices, but a substantial East German merchant marine has subsequently been equipped.

Electrical Equipment. West Germany accounts for about half of the electrical equipment produced by the six original Common Market partners. Before the war about half of the German industry was in Berlin, about equally divided between the western and eastern sectors. Following wartime destruction and postwar dismantling, the West Berlin electrical industry was reconstructed, but many Berlin and East German firms transferred most or all of their activities to the more settled conditions of West Germany, where the explosive recent growth of the industry has been concentrated.

Although there are scattered electrical plants throughout northern Germany, notably in the Ruhr, the main centres of this growing industry are in South Germany. The largest and longest-established plants, especially those making heavy equipment such as generating sets and switchgear, are located in the major population agglomerations, Stuttgart, the Rhine–Main complex, Munich, Nürnberg–Erlangen–Fürth and Mannheim. Even more noticeably than in the car industry, recent years have seen a considerable dispersion of the industry from the agglomerations to rural areas in search of labour. Many villages in the hills of Hesse, for example, have small branch plants of electrical manufacturers from the Rhine–Main area, where women can work at the assembly of components on a part-time basis. The same is true of the Franconian hills north of Nürnberg or the Palatinate west of Mannheim. New plants in the rapidly developing electronics industry, with its light and high-value products, are also well dispersed, frequently to pleasant towns within reach of a university, such as Mainz, Konstanz or Sindelfingen near Stuttgart.

Great strides have also been taken in East Germany, where there was no heavy electrical capacity after the war. Before new power stations or electric locomotives could be built manufacturing capacity had to be created, mostly from the ruins of the dismantled Berlin plants. As a country with a high level of technology but a shortage of labour East Germany has put great stress on the development of electronics and automation. These developments have made electrical equipment manufacturing the fastest growing industry in East Germany, and a major contributor to the export trade.

OTHER INDUSTRIES

Chemicals. The modern chemical industry was in many ways a German creation. In 1945 the industry was divided, about two-thirds falling to the share of West Germany. In both parts of Germany postwar growth has been spectacular, especially in fields like plastics and synthetic fibres.

West Germany has good supplies of a number of raw

materials needed in chemical production, notably salt, potash, pyrites and some natural gas. Water power in the south and brown coal in the Rhinelands provide power for the electro-chemical processes. Until the Second World War the major basis of the industry was Ruhr coal. It was on the basis of coking by-products, for example, that before the First World War the German chemical industry built up a monopoly in the supply of synthetic dyestuffs. The plants of this essentially coal-based chemical industry were primarily aligned on the Rhine, in the Rhine–Ruhr, Rhine–Main, Rhine–Neckar and Basel regions. The Rhine brought coal, coke and tar from the Ruhr, carried imported materials like phosphate rock, provided process water and allowed the disposal of effluent.

The postwar period has seen a major change from a coal-based industry to one in which oil is not only a source of energy but the raw material base for two-thirds of the industry's output, including all the synthetic fibres, the modern plastics, detergents, synthetic rubber, paints and varnishes and most of the nitrogen fertilizer. The new basis has not involved major changes in the location of existing plants, since the dense concentrations of population and industry in the Rhine–Ruhr, Rhine–Main and Rhine–Neckar regions were rapidly served by pipelines and refineries. Even where new products and new processes have demanded the construction of entirely new plants, the Rhine has maintained its attraction. On the Lower Rhine from Wesel to Bonn, on the Upper Rhine from the Main confluence to Karlsruhe, the river has now a chain of oil refineries and plants of the chemical, plastics and fibres industries.

South Germany away from the navigable Rhine has smaller groups of plants, notably those based on the hydro-electricity of the Alpine Foreland and the Rhine between the Bodensee and Basel. The arrival of pipelines and refineries in this region is leading to expansion and diversification of the industry. The same is true of the Saar, where the new Klarenthal refinery is the basis for joint Franco-German petrochemical developments to augment the existing coal-based chemical industries of the Saar and Lorraine coalfields. With the development of the Common Market, links across frontiers have become increasingly important; heavy German investment, for example, has gone into a major new complex of petroleum-based chemical plants at Antwerp in Belgium.

In East Germany also chemical expansion has been considerable, and the industry is by value of product the greatest in the country. Salt, potash and various non-ferrous metals provide important raw materials, but the essential base until recently was brown coal, as a source of electricity and as a raw material. Both the electrochemical industry and plants based on the distillation and hydrogenation of brown coal are found on the Central German brown-coal field, the main centre of the chemical industry. Chemical production on a brown-coal base was even extended in the 1950s, when large projects for producing metallurgical coke and chemicals from the coal of Lower Lusatia were initiated. With the opening of the crude oil pipeline to Schwedt the East German chemical industry began to follow the international trend towards the use of petroleum as a base for chemical production. The Leuna chemical complex on the Central German field has been greatly extended and linked to the Schwedt refinery by pipeline. Although fibre production has been dispersed to Thuringia and the Oder, it appears that the main location for the chemical and plastics industries is to continue to be the Central German field (Fig. 58).

Textiles. In Germany, textile mills are not closely grouped on coalfields, as in Britain, but dispersed among numerous towns and villages. In a united Germany, each of the textile regions had its own specialities, for example worsteds and fine stockings in Saxony, linen and woollens in Lower Lusatia, cotton and silk in North Rhine–Westphalia, cotton and knitted goods in Swabia, or woollens in Bavaria. With the division of Germany, both parts of the country have tried to become self-sufficient in all branches of production. This, together with the increasing use of synthetic fibres, has done much to break up the old pattern of specialization. Many textile manufacturers from East Germany and Bohemia set up anew in West Germany, not always at the traditional textile locations. The same is true of the clothing industry. Berlin in particular lost much of its predominance in the fashion industry to new centres at such large West German cities as Düsseldorf or Munich.

West Germany is the largest manufacturer of cotton yarn and cloth of all the six founder-members of the Common Market, but is second to France and Italy in wool and worsted. In view of the strength of the West German chemical industry, it is not surprising that the country also predominates in fibre production. A feature of postwar development has been the increasing use of knitted fabrics, production of which is strongly localized in Württemberg. The postwar years saw great increases in textile output, but from about 1952 the industry was in difficulty through foreign competition and the loss of traditional export markets, and there were many mill closures. The jute industry went into a particularly sharp decline. In East Germany the textile industry like all consumer-goods industries was rather out of favour in the postwar years, but remains of considerable importance.

WEST GERMAN INDUSTRY SINCE 1945

Reconstruction and Adaptation. In 1945 the towns and industries of Germany lay in ruins. In order to remove any possible military capacity numerous key industries were forbidden entirely, and production generally ordered to be scaled back to three-quarters of 1936 levels. Steel output was to be 5·8 million tons, a mere 30% of the 1936 figure. Industrial plants surplus to these very low levels of activity were to be dismantled for reparations deliveries to territories formerly occupied by Germany, notably the U.S.S.R. In fact, West German production remained at 35–40% of the 1936 level for the first three postwar years because of the almost total collapse of the whole economy. Money lost its function as a yardstick of values, and not much progress could be expected in an economy where the most reliable currency unit was the cigarette, worth nine shillings at the nominal rate of exchange.

At the same time Germany was divided. For 100 years the country had been an economic unit; the various regions had come to specialize in the goods and services that they could produce most economically, exchanging them for the specialized products of their neighbours. Considered broadly, West Germany predominated in coal mining, in chemicals based on coal, in steel and in heavy industry, while East Germany specialized in brown-coal mining, the generation of electricity and the manufacture of chemicals based on brown coal, in the assembly of all sorts of complex machinery and equipment ranging from motor cars to microscopes, and in many consumers' goods.

The division of the country sharply reduced this degree of

specialization and interdependence, and when economic activity eventually revived, two independent economic units were created out of the ruins of the old. Of the two, West Germany had the advantage. Being the larger, it tended to have the greater diversity in its economy. Above all it had Ruhr steel and heavy engineering, however much damaged, and thus the prospect of making the vital machinery needed for industrial reconstruction. The process of replacing supplies formerly received from the eastern parts of Germany was made easier by the flight to West Germany of many industrialists, who used their skill to start afresh. The arrivals ranged from great Berlin electrical manufacturing firms to individual Germans expelled from Czechoslovakia, who brought with them the secrets of their 'Bohemian' glass, jewellery and textile trades. Very frequently small refugee businesses were installed in former military camps or munitions dumps, some of which have remained as industrial estates, often with new 'refugee towns' beside them, like Neugablonz near Kaufbeuren in Bavaria.

Economic Miracle? The determination of the western Allies to reduce and dismantle West German industry did not long survive in the face of their growing desire to see a poverty-stricken country once more an independent, self-supporting and properly anti-Communist member of a revived Western Europe. Far from being condemned as after the First World War to weary years of reparations payments, West Germany was soon in receipt of millions of dollars in Marshal Aid payments from the United States. For the ordinary German the new era can be precisely dated to the currency reform of 20th June 1948, which overnight filled with food and consumers' goods shop windows that had stood empty for years.

As compared with the troubled years of the Weimar Republic, what followed seemed indeed an 'economic miracle', and for that matter a political one. Between 1948 and 1965 industrial production increased six-fold, the rise being dramatic in the early years, continuing thereafter with substantial annual growth rates. Satisfaction with this economic achievement brought a degree of political stability that contrasted markedly with the years following the First World War, yet the record must be viewed in proper proportion. Very similar growth rates were achieved by other European countries, notably

Italy and Austria, while Japanese expansion was even greater. There were certainly some special factors at work, notably the refugees, who from being initially a burden became a valuable addition to the labour force. The stopping of the flow of East German refugees in 1961, followed by a period of faltering expansion in world trade, seemed to usher in a period of less confident progress in West German industry.

While all these changes were going on, East Germany was not static, but the peculiar political circumstances there brought about economic developments so different from those of West Germany, that they must be given separate consideration in Part Five of this book.

European Unity. In the postwar period it becomes increasingly unrealistic to describe the industry of Germany in isolation from her Common Market partners. The effects of a wider market were first seen in the Coal and Steel Community, where national measures to protect individual producers were vigorously attacked. Germany was no longer able to keep Lorraine coal and steel out of the Ruhr's South German markets. It was also no longer possible to give specially low freight rates to help iron ore move from German mines to the Ruhr furnaces, or Ruhr coal move to outlying steel centres in the Rhenish Uplands or Bavaria. The general effect was to make life more difficult for the outlying producers, and to hasten the closure of the German ore mines.

The impact of the Common Market on industrial location is less easy to distinguish. The initial effect seems largely to have been psychological; trade between the six original members began to increase at a faster rate than trade with non-members even before the first tariff reductions on manufactures. One very noticeable tendency has been for German firms to establish strong links across frontiers; examples from the motor vehicle, steel and chemical industries have been noted above.

Structural Change and Regional Growth. Until about 1958 it was still possible to think of German industry primarily in terms of coal and steel, with the Ruhr as the great powerhouse in the centre of things. Now coal is in decline, together with many former staple industries such as shipbuilding. The oil pipelines reach inwards from the coasts to being new sources of imported energy even into the Ruhr itself. Industrial growth now derives from a completely new set of industries: oil refining, petrochemicals, plastics, synthetic fibres, motor vehicles and electrical equipment manufacturing. Fortunately these growth industries are not unrepresented in the Rhine–Ruhr area, but they are much more characteristic of the 'newer' industrial agglomerations. It is particularly in South Germany, especially in and around Stuttgart, that one finds the greatest increases in industry, wealth and population (Fig. 33).

The new growth industries are not tied locationally to coal or other home-produced raw materials. Industries like car assembly or the manufacture of electrical equipment are likely to choose locations where there is a large pool of labour, where there are good communications with suppliers of materials and components and where there is a large local market. All these considerations point to a location in or on the fringe of one of the expanding agglomerations of industry and population, the *Verdichtungsgebiete* (pp. 108–10). When it is also remembered that there has been a decisive shift in the occupational structure in favour of the service sector, which is strongly represented in the great centres of population, then the rising significance of the *Verdichtungsgebiete* for industrial location can be appreciated.

Structurally each of these agglomerations has at its heart one or occasionally more than one major service centre, concerned with retail and wholesale distribution, services of all kinds, administration and transport. Both industry and population are tending to move out from such central areas, with their lack of space and high land values. While many of the older industrial plants still remain embedded in the working-class quarters close to the centre, there is a marked tendency for modern industry to settle on the urban fringe, where communications are easier and rural labour can be drawn in. There is no sharp ending of the agglomeration; the services provided by the regional city combine with the characteristic rural commuting pattern of Germany to spread urban influences deep into the surrounding countryside.

Development Regions. If prosperity is increasingly concentrated into the *Verdichtungsgebiete* it follows that there will be other areas that are falling behind in the race. This can be assumed to be true of all purely rural areas, for the value of output per head in German agriculture is far less than in industry. Beyond this there are certain areas of particular difficulty. Sometimes physical geography is the cause, as in some of the massifs of the Central Uplands, such as the Eifel or the Bavarian Forest. Very different areas of physical difficulty are provided by the

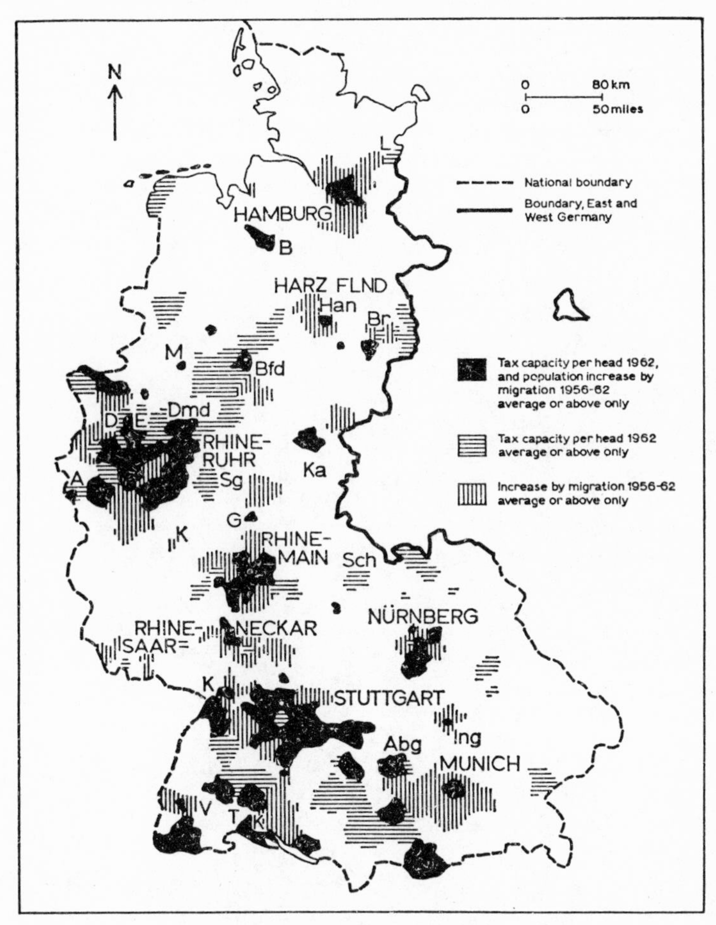

FIG. 33. The geography of prosperity: areas of West Germany with real estate tax and population growth above average.

West Germany, 1965

	TURNOVER (thousand million Dm)			LABOUR (thousands)			GROWTH (1965 index: 1958 = 100)	
1	Food and drink	45·4	1	Machinery	1,084	1	Plastics processing	365
2	Machinery	38·6	2	Electrical equipment	974	2	Chemical fibres	350
3	Chemicals	33·7	3	Textiles	547	3	Oil refining	318
4	Electrical equipment	31·6	4	Chemicals	531	4	Chemicals	215
5	Vehicles	26·8	5	Vehicles	514	5	Vehicles	203
6	Iron and steel	20·9	6	Food and drink	481	6	Oil and gas	202
7	Miscellaneous metal goods	15·0	7	Coal mining	426	7	Electrical equipment	191
8	Textiles	20·9	8	Miscellaneous metal goods	418	8	Glass	186
9	Oil refining	12·5	9	Clothing	398	9	Non-ferrous founding	186
10	Clothing	12·2	10	Iron and steel	359	10	Electricity generation	180

East Germany, 1965

	GROSS INDUSTRIAL PRODUCT (thousand million M)			LABOUR (thousands)			GROWTH (1965 index: 1955 = 100)	
1	Chemicals	15·1	1	*Machinery	386	1	Electrical manufacturing	327
2	Food, drink, tobacco	11·9	2	Textiles	281	2	Miscellaneous metal goods	289
3	Machinery	10·4	3	Chemicals	281	3	General machinery	286
4	Electrical equipment	7·8	4	Electrical equipment	232	4	Precision engineering and optical	269
5	Textiles	5·6	5	Food, drink, tobacco	200	5	Building materials	243
6	Vehicles	5·5	6	Mining	190	6	Heavy machinery	235
7	Metals	4·3	7	Vehicles	144	7	Vehicles	229
8	Mining	2·6	9	Wood products	141	8	Chemicals	223
9	Wood products	2·4	9	Iron and Steel, etc.	112	9	Electricity generation	211
10	Precision engineering and optical	2·1	10	Precision engineering and optical	102	10	Food, drink, tobacco	163
			*	General machinery	204			
				Heavy machinery	182			

peat bogs of the Emsland and the marshes of the northern coast. A second type of problem is provided by remoteness from the main centres of economic activity. Throughout the eastern part of the country this has been accentuated by the division of Germany, which has broken down many former links. Particularly severely affected are the Frankenwald, formerly linked with the Central German textile industries, and Hamburg, which has lost its Elbe hinterland. The position was made worse by the coming of the European Economic Community, which tended to draw industry and population towards the central Rhine–Rhône axis, accentuating the disadvantages of the West German border areas.

Under the Common Market treaty arrangements, assistance to particular industries is forbidden, as being contrary to free competition. Fortunately it is also recognized that there are grave economic and political dangers involved in allowing some regions to fall too far below the general level of welfare, so that efforts to foster their development are permitted. An area about 40 km/25 miles wide along the boundary with East Germany is given federal subsidies to compensate for disruption and isolation. This area and also the other development regions benefit from efforts to make them more attractive to industry. These efforts take two main forms, the improvement of the 'infrastructure' (roads, water supplies, electricity, educational facilities and the like), and the granting of credits to attract industrialists.

Since West Germany is a federal state, the constituent *Länder* can also assist problem regions, within the limit of their resources. Among special schemes initiated by the *Länder* are the 'Emsland Programme', to upgrade the dreary peat bog area along the Netherlands boundary, the 'Coast Programme' to counter flooding and improve the agricultural structure along the coast of Lower Saxony and the 'Northern Programme' to improve agriculture and establish service industries in the remote area of northern Schleswig-Holstein. A further Federal Government measure in 1959 was the initiation of the 'Central Points Programme', an attempt to develop selected small country towns as growth points for industry and services, and so do something to counteract the pull of population towards the *Verdichtungsgebiete* (Fig. 34).

One last type of problem region has generally high incomes and dense population, but is menaced by changes in the structure of industry. The Münsterland and the Frankenwald regions, for example, were deeply affected by the crisis in the textile industry, but their problems were on a small enough scale to be met on a fairly local level. Of an entirely different order are the decline in coal and the crisis in steel. The Ger-

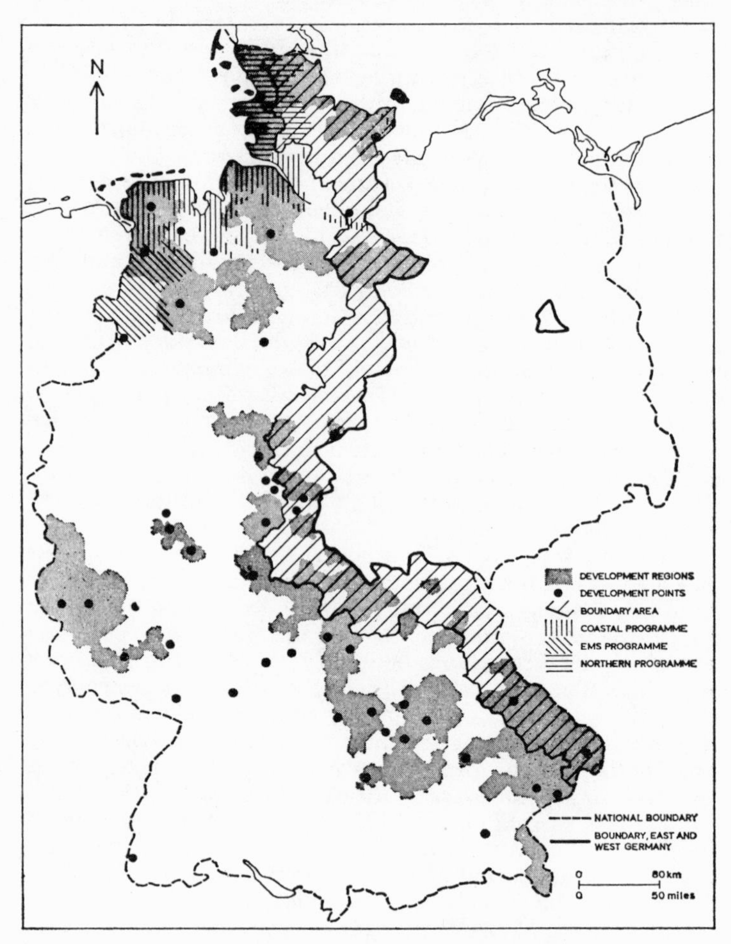

FIG. 34. Development regions of West Germany.

man government measures to check the decline in coal consumption by a tax on fuel oil and by various other forms of aid may be regarded as an attempt to bring about a more orderly adaptation of regional industrial structure on the coalfields. The same may be true of the subsidization of coke for the steel industry. *Land* and local administrations have also been busy in attracting new industries, like the Opel motor plants at Bochum in the Ruhr. It is indeed fortunate that the Ruhr coalfield is embedded in the large and varied industrial region of North Rhine–Westphalia, which in turn is situated on the major Rhine axis of growth within the Common Market. Industrial conversion may have locally severe effects, but the prospects are far from hopeless. Even the Aachen and Saar coalfields, although away from the Rhine, may find that their frontier situations offer them great opportunities in the wider frame of the European Economic Community.

SUGGESTIONS FOR FURTHER READING

T. H. Elkins, 'The brown coal industry of Germany', *Geography*, 38, 1953, pp. 18–29.

N. J. G. Pounds and W. N. Parker *Coal and steel in Western Europe* (Faber and Faber), 1957.

G. Stolper *et al.*, *The German economy: 1870 to the present* (New York: Harcourt, Brace and World), 1967.

United Nations, 'Structural adaptation in Eastern and Western Germany', *Economic Bulletin for Europe*, 8, 1956, pp. 45–89.

Chapter 10

COMMUNICATIONS AND TRADE

RAILWAYS

The first railway line in Germany was opened in 1835 to link the adjoining towns of Nürnberg and Fürth. By the end of the 19th century the network as we know it today was essentially complete, with a density of lines practically equal to that of Britain, and only exceeded in Europe by Belgium.

Three great industrial regions, the Ruhr, Central Germany and Upper Silesia, dominated prewar German goods traffic by the weight of coal and heavy industrial products they despatched, and by the raw materials and food that they received. Because all three coalfields are in the Hercynian Foreland belt, with the fourth great traffic centre of Berlin not far to the north, traffic in prewar Germany was dominated by east–west movements. The principal south–north route followed the Rhine valley, intersecting the Hercynian Foreland axis in the great traffic node of the Ruhr. In passenger traffic, a similar predominantly east–west pattern was seen, this time with the main routes radiating from the capital, Berlin, and the most important of them running westwards to intersect the Rhine valley route at the great international passenger junction of Cologne.

Before 1945, the main motive power was steam, but electrification had made progress in three regions. In Central Germany a network using electricity generated from local brown coal linked Magdeburg, Leipzig and Halle, and reached southwards up the Saale valley as far as the Bavarian boundary in the Thuringian Forest. A second network existed in Silesia, and a third in southern Germany, using power generated from the Alpine rivers. This continued the electrified lines of Austria northwestwards to Munich and Stuttgart, and northwards through Nürnberg to link with the Central German system (Fig. 36).

West Germany. The postwar division of Germany brought fundamental changes to the pattern of rail traffic, owing to the

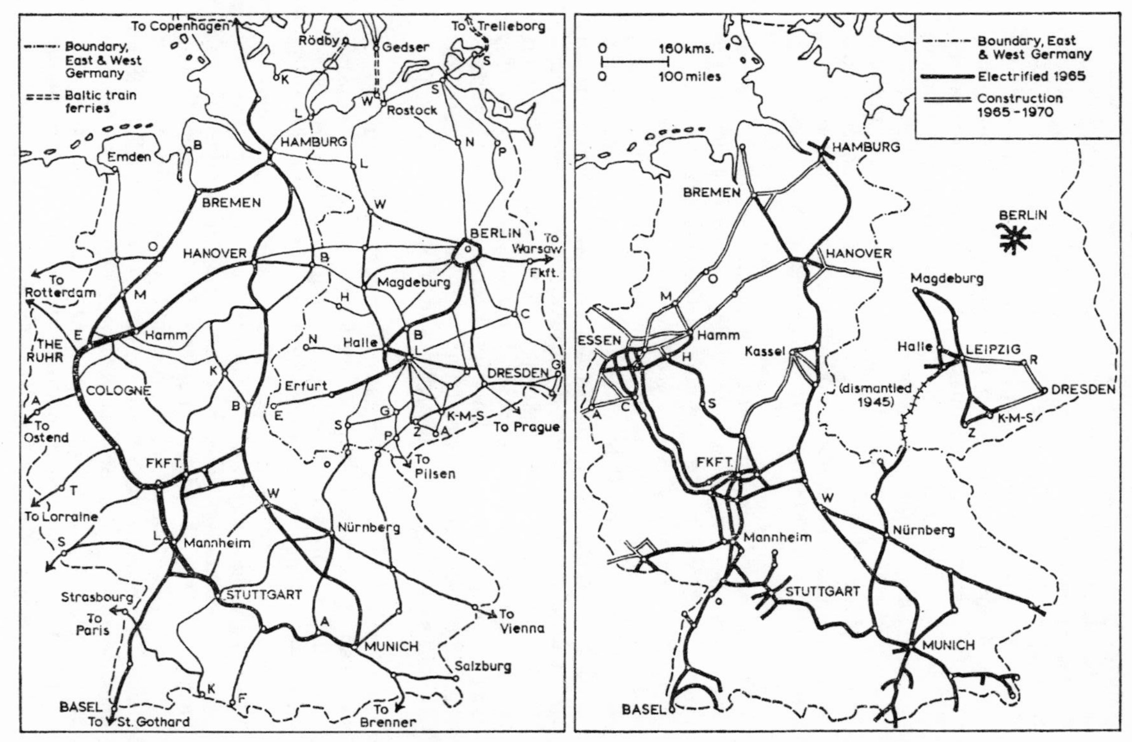

FIG. 35. Principal rail routes of postwar Germany.

FIG. 36. Electrified lines.

restriction of crossings into East Germany to seven points only, and the decline of trade between the two parts of the country. Traffic on the east–west routes across the East German border became a mere trickle, mainly passing to and from West Berlin. As West Germany replaced supplies of food and raw materials formerly obtained from eastern Germany with imports from abroad, so the routes running southwards from the North German ports through Hesse to southern Germany acquired an altogether new importance (Fig. 35). In the north a new Scandinavian ferry link has had to be provided to avoid the use of East German ports. The German island of Fehmarn has been linked to the mainland by a bridge, and the new ferry introduced from Puttgarden to the Danish port of Rödbyhavn on Lolland.

The increased emphasis on north–south links is also seen in the extension of main-line electrification out of the Alpine water-power region. One main electrified link runs northward through Hesse to the North German ports. A second route, double or even triple in places, follows the Rhine to the Ruhr, the Netherlands and Belgium, with further extensions to the North German ports. An important addition to the electrified system runs from the Rhine–Main region across the Rhenish Uplands to Hagen. As the shortest route between the Ruhr and South Germany it is much used for goods traffic. While this electrification of the main lines has been going on, thousands of kilometres of minor lines have been closed, rendered unprofitable by the great growth in road traffic.

East Germany. The East German railways suffered from extensive war damage and dismantling for reparations. The losses were all the more serious in that the industrial regions of East Germany are not well served by waterways. As in West Germany the restoration of the system has been considerably affected by the division of the country, as well as by the new political orientation. The heaviest traffic is in the Central German industrial region and on the links from there to Berlin. The once busy routes westwards and southwards into West Germany are now little used, except for West Berlin traffic. From Berlin two major links connect with East Germany's new trading partners. One carries U.S.S.R. traffic eastwards to the Oder crossing at Frankfurt, the other runs northwards to the enlarged ocean port of Rostock. An outer ring has been completed to enable both goods and passenger traffic to avoid West Berlin, although the international expresses linking eastern and western Europe still run through. The electrified system in Central Germany has for the most part been restored and is in process of extension.

INLAND WATERWAYS

Modern industry reached Germany with the railway age; there was no preceding canal age, as in Britain, although a few canals had been constructed as early as the close of medieval times. Even on the mighty Rhine, traffic was hampered until well into the 19th century by both physical and human barriers. The physical obstructions were removed by the engineers who blew up the rock bars of the Rhine Gorge, or straightened and confined the stream in its Rift Valley and Northern Lowland sections. The human obstacles, provided by the scores of toll stations that were the curse of Rhine navigation, were progressively removed by the unification of Germany.

The canal system being the product of our own century, its scale is appropriate to modern needs. All new canals in West Germany are constructed to take the standard European 1,350-ton barge, and where necessary older canals are being brought up to this standard. Naturally the Rhine is in a class by itself, carrying three-quarters of all West German waterways traffic, and capable of taking 2,000-ton barges right through the Central Uplands to the fringe of Alpine Europe at Basel. Over 80% of the barge fleet is self-propelled. Only on the Rhine has this trend been modified by the growing use of pusher units as the most efficient and labour-saving form of mass transport. Sea-going coastal vessels can also be used on the Lower Rhine.

The trunk from which the German waterways branch is the Rhine, which dominates the water traffic not only of Germany but of the other Rhine states as well. It is scarcely surprising that the busiest section of the river is between the Netherlands ports and the Ruhr coalfield. The ports on the Rhine front of the Ruhr are concerned with the unloading of bulk commodities like ores, grain and timber which have been transhipped from ocean-going vessels at the mouth of the Rhine.

Not all the traffic from Netherlands ports terminates at the

Ruhr; some passes on upstream, joined by Ruhr coal, refined petroleum and Rhenish brown-coal briquettes moving to

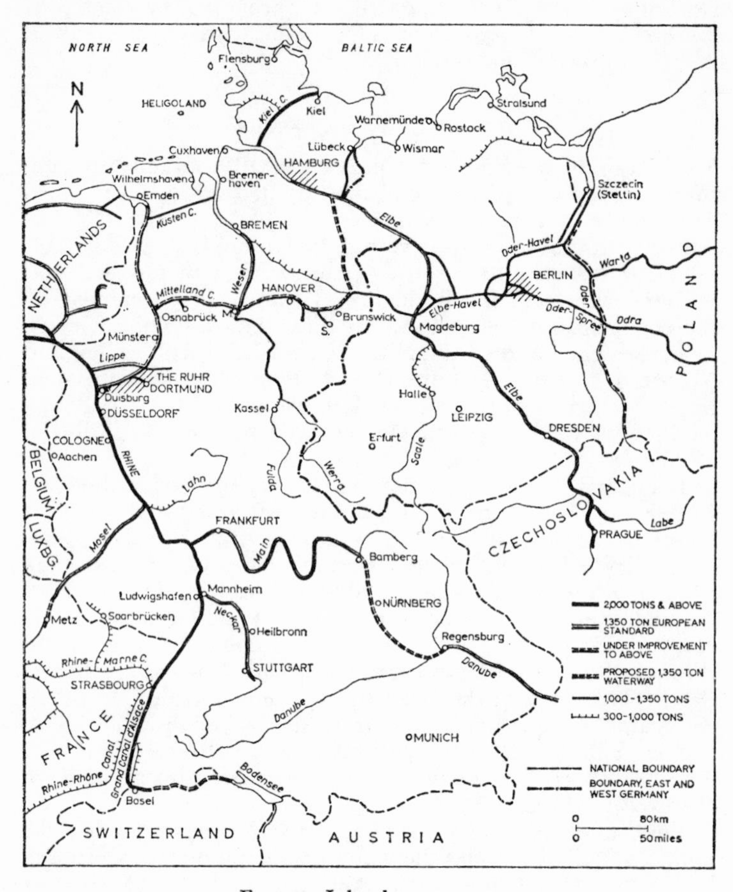

FIG. 37. Inland waterways.

markets further south. Ports above the Ruhr are mainly concerned with unloading these bulk goods, and so the volume of traffic declines until Basel is reached.

The constricted Middle Rhine section through the Rhenish

Uplands is a difficult one, due to the greatly increased water speed in times of flood, and delays when rock bars are exposed at low water. Basalt stone, pumice (Bims) and other building materials are loaded in this section. The stretch of the Upper Rhine from Bingen to Strasbourg is again more placid: the greatest port is Mannheim-Ludwigshafen, which receives coal and raw materials for its chemical industries and for distribution in southern Germany. With the development of refining Karlsruhe has become an oil port. Improvements to the difficult section above Strasbourg had by 1931 enabled full-scale barges to reach Basel, which thereafter became one of the greatest ports on the river. Meanwhile beginning in 1927–32, but especially after the Second World War, the French began the construction of the lateral *Grand Canal d'Alsace*. Intended primarily for the generation of electricity, the canal provides a greatly improved waterway for Rhine traffic. Not unnaturally the Germans objected to a system which threatened to leave Baden on a backwater, cut off from the main Rhine traffic. Accordingly, from Breisach (near Freiburg) northwards to Strasbourg the lateral canal is replaced by a system of loops, which at first follow the existing Rhine before swinging onto the French bank to pass through a power station and then back to the Rhine again. Rhine navigation ceases just above Basel, although there are distant prospects of a continuation to the Bodensee, where there is already a lively passenger traffic.

The principal tributaries have been improved to take the standard 1,350-ton barges by the building of barrages, which also provide electric power. The Main has been canalized to Bamberg, and the Neckar to Plochingen, south of Stuttgart. These new waterways have become particularly significant for the carriage of bulk commodities like gravel, coal, petroleum products, cement and fertilizer to road distribution depots established at the various inland harbours. The latest Rhine tributary to be improved is the Mosel. The project is of little benefit to Germany, except in a small way by the generation of some electric power. It was part of the price paid by Germany for the return of the Saar, and enables 1,350-ton barges to reach the Lorraine industrial region in eastern France.

In spite of the disadvantage of its Alpine régime (p. 40), the Danube below Regensburg has been considerably improved by the regulation of the low-water channel and by the erection of barrages in the rocky narrows where the Danube is incised into the fringe of the Bohemian massif. Traffic has increased greatly over the prewar figure owing to the downstream movement of coal to the Austrian steelworks at Linz and the upstream movement of oil, bauxite, pyrites and other bulk products of the Danubian lands. At the moment the Danube is isolated from the rest of the German waterways system and awaits the completion of the Rhine–Main–Danube link. Work is in progress on the canal section of the route which runs southwards from Bamberg past Nürnberg and then with a formidable 400 m/1,300 ft rise through a gap in the Franconian Jura to the Altmühl and so to the Danube at Kelheim. When this link is complete there will be an uninterrupted waterway across Europe from the North Sea to the Black Sea.

The Rhine is linked through the Ruhr coalfield to the canal system of the Northern Lowland by the 1,350-ton Rhine–Herne and Lippe canals. The ports of these canals were primarily concerned with coal loading, but the receipt of building materials and the despatch of petroleum products are also of some importance. The northern link is continued by the heavily overloaded southern section of the Dortmund–Ems canal. This canal, completed in 1899, was intended to divert Ruhr traffic to an all-German route to Emden. This object has not been achieved, partly because hitherto the canal has not been able to take standard Rhine barges. To meet this difficulty enlargement is in progress.

The Mittelland canal links the West and East German canal systems along the line of the Hercynian Foreland, serving on the way the Harz Foreland industrial region. The western end of this canal is also overloaded, and enlargement is necessary. Further east the canal has been affected by the division of Germany; traffic tapers off miserably as the East German border is approached.

At Minden the canal crosses the Weser, which provides a 1,350-ton route to the Weser ports, which can also be reached from the Dortmund–Ems canal by means of the Küsten canal. Thanks to these two routes Bremen, traditionally a rail port, has greatly increased its inland water traffic. By contrast, movements to and from the traditional waterways port of Hamburg have remained consistently below prewar figures.

The Elbe is an indifferent waterway, on which for much of the year low water prevents barges being fully loaded, but the main reason for its decline is the division of Germany. There are now proposals for the construction of a north–south canal running entirely within West German territory, linking the Elbe above Hamburg with the Mittelland canal and so with the rest of the West German waterways system. Further north the Kiel (Nord–Ostsee) canal was completed in 1895 to allow the passage of the German battle fleet from the Baltic to the North Sea. It is primarily a ship canal, but carried some inland water traffic between the Elbe and Kiel.

In East Germany, the ice-margin trenches (*Urstromtäler*) have facilitated the construction of east–west links between the main rivers. Berlin is well served by the canals which link the Elbe and Oder, but the Central German and Lower Lusatian industrial regions have to rely mainly on rail and road transport.

ROADS

In recent years, roads have come to carry a large proportion of goods moved, especially over the shorter distances. The backbone of the road system is provided by the motorway (*Autobahn*) net, initiated for military purposes in the 1930s. The centre of the system as originally designed was the incomplete ring road around Berlin, from which motorways radiated to the various regions of prewar Germany. Once again the principal east–west road ran from Berlin along the line of the Hercynian Foreland to the Ruhr. Here it swung south to follow the second main axis, the Rhine valley, to southern Germany.

As already noted, the postwar division of Germany caused a great increase in the north–south traffic between the North German ports and South Germany. There was a particularly urgent need to aid Hamburg, which having lost its Elbe hinterland was being forced to rely on extremely poor roads across the sandy Lüneburg Heath. There was therefore an urgent need to complete the motorway from Hamburg to Hanover and on through Hesse to the Rhine–Main region and South Germany. One of the most interesting recent projects is for a new motorway on the west bank of the Rhine, doubling the existing one on the right bank. The West German motorway system is now firmly tied with the systems of neighbouring countries, so that it is now possible for example to drive by

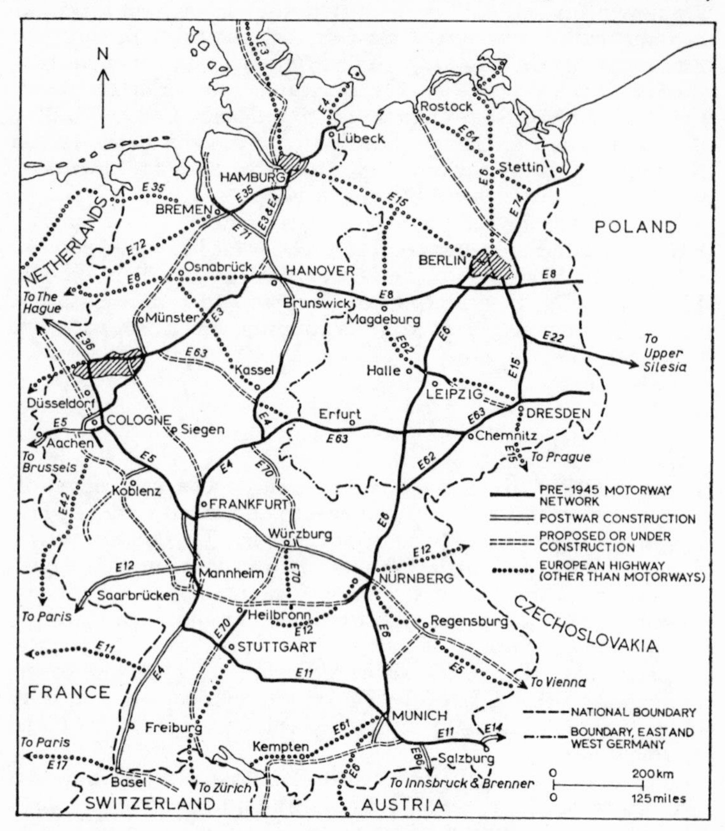

Fig. 38. The Autobahn system.

motorway from Amsterdam to Vienna. Most of the West German motorways are also part of the system of 'European' highways, although a very few links in the E-road system still have to be provided by ordinary main roads (Fig. 38).

The lengths of motorway inherited by East Germany give

reasonable links between Berlin and the east and south of the country. Motor transport, particularly private motor transport, has not hitherto received a very high priority in East Germany, which relies heavily on trains for long-distance movements. Extensions to the motorway net have therefore not appeared urgent. There have for some years been proposals to construct a motorway from Berlin to the ocean port of Rostock, which would also help the economic development of the north. The linking of Leipzig and Dresden is perhaps a more immediate prospect.

CIVIL AVIATION

Air transport became of particular importance in postwar Germany because of the peculiar position of West Berlin as an 'island' in East German territory. Flights along the three air corridors allocated for air journeys from Hamburg, Hanover and Frankfurt to Berlin are not subject to control by the East German authorities. In consequence air transport is the normal means of movement for passengers and for the more valuable or perishable types of freight. Indeed, for nearly a year of blockade from June 1948 onwards, West Berlin was entirely supplied with food and fuel by the 'Air Bridge' from West Germany. Curiously West German planes are barred from the profitable Berlin traffic, although the national airline *Lufthansa* has grown to major importance since it resumed operations in 1955. The East German line *Interflug* dates from the same period. To serve international traffic East Germany has constructed a new airfield at Schönefield, southeast of Berlin.

TRADE

Germany's foreign trade, and trade between West and East Germany, came almost to a standstill in the postwar period of economic depression. As trade recovered, the division of Germany caused it to flow in a very different pattern from before the war.

Even before 1939 only about one-third of West German trade was with the part of the country that is now East Germany. The loss of East German potash, brown coal, food and specialized manufactures was initially disturbing, but the country of the 'economic miracle' was able to replace them either by expanding home production or by imports. In marked contrast to the strivings for national self-sufficiency that marked the immediate prewar period, West Germany

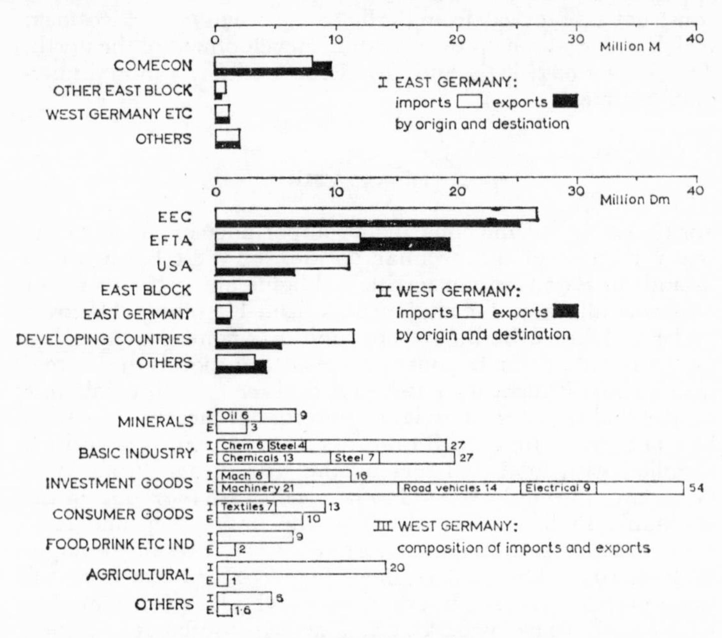

FIG. 39 Foreign trade.
The numbers on graph III are percentages of total imports or exports.

turned to the outside world, becoming the greatest trading power after the United States. A feature of recent years has been the development of increasingly close ties with neighbouring countries of the European Economic Community. Trade with East Germany is not officially counted as foreign trade, and tends to fluctuate with the political situation.

In composition East Germany's trade is similar to that of West Germany; the main need is food for the people and raw materials to sustain a rising industrial output. Accordingly the principal imports are coal and coke, oil, ores, metals, timber, grain and vegetable oils. To keep industry efficient it is also necessary to import new types of machinery and industrial 'know-how', mainly from the West. The most important East German exports are industrial machinery (about 35% of total exports), followed in second place by chemical products. Clothing, textiles, glassware, electrical equipment, optical and precision instruments, ships, toys and musical instruments are all important. The pattern is clearly that of an advanced industrial country having few indigenous raw materials.

The direction of East German trade is now quite different from that of West Germany. Three-quarters of total trade is with the countries of the 'socialist camp', predominantly the European communist countries united in the 'Council for mutual economic assistance', known in the West as COMECON. The object of COMECON is to arrange for industrial specialization by the member countries, who are then expected to export their specialities in exchange for goods that they could only produce uneconomically. As a highly industrialized country in an association most members of which are still very much on the road to development, East Germany has a key position. In particular it is the largest machinery exporter to all the communist countries.

Within COMECON the lion's share of trade is with the U.S.S.R. Almost half of East Germany's total external trade is with this one country, which is the principal supplier of raw and semi-finished materials of all kinds. In return East Germany supplies advanced industrial equipment, chemicals, ships and consumer goods.

Before the war, the area that is now East Germany depended on West Germany for at least half its total trade, so that the effects of partition were serious, much more so than for the larger and more diverse economy of West Germany. Under the present trading arrangements East Germany receives machinery, chemicals, fertilizers, coal, steel and a variety of other commodities essential for her economy. Brown-coal briquettes, textiles and clothing are among the exports. An important aspect of inter-German trade is the supply of West Berlin with some heavy commodities like briquettes, motor fuel, gravel and cement, as well as with services ranging from the haulage of trains to the disposal of sewage. Unfortunately most of the city's requirements still have to be hauled 160 km/100 miles or more from West Germany. There is no doubt that the East German government regards inter-German trade as far too small and in fact deliberately restricted by West Germany for political reasons.

PART FOUR
THE REGIONS OF WEST GERMANY

Chapter 11
BADEN-WÜRTTEMBERG

THE NATURE OF SOUTHERN GERMANY

Southern Germany is cut off from the remainder of the country by a wooded upland barrier formed by the Rhenish Uplands, the forested plateaus of Hesse, the Thuringian Forest and the Bohemian Massif. The barrier is in most places wide enough to develop a human geography of its own, so that it is a transition zone rather than a line. Politically this zone is represented by the postwar *Länder* Hesse and Rhineland-Palatinate, and by the Saar (Chapter 13). Even the relatively narrow Thuringian Forest is not a perfect 'natural' boundary, for Thuringians have settled on its southern side.

Physically, southern Germany has three main regions: the Rhine Rift Valley and its adjoining uplands, the South German Scarplands (divided into the Main and Neckar basins) and the Alpine Foreland. Three main German tribal groups occupied this country, each substantially cut off from the others by forests. In the southwest, the Alemans or Swabians occupied the southern Rift Valley, the Neckar basin and the adjoining Alpine Foreland; in the southeast the Bavarians occupied the Danube valley and the major part of the Alpine Foreland; and in the north the Franks held the Main basin, the country still known as Franconia. After centuries of political fragmentation, the old units were restored in part after 1945. In the southwest *Land* Baden-Württemberg occupies most of the old Alemanic territory, while in the southeast Bavaria not only includes the old heartland on the Alpine Foreland but extends north of the Danube to include Franconia. Only the transitional northwest was left illogically divided by the postwar settlement.

Southern Germany shows many differences from the north and east of the country. It is old-settled land, where the fertile, early-cleared areas bear large villages which still retain a pattern of hedgeless strip fields around them, although the former cultivation in common has mainly disappeared. Repeated division among heirs has made holdings smaller and smaller, and increasingly divided into scattered strips, bringing about the surprising situation that some of the poorest peasants are found on the richest, early-settled land. Such areas contrast markedly with the higher and poorer country occupied later during the medieval clearing of the waste. Here settlement in isolated farms or hamlets is normal, the farm land is usually in compact fields rather than dispersed in strips.

Southern Germany falls into a number of clear physical regions, which because they have responded individually and distinctively to the various economic and social factors acting on the area, have considerable validity also in human geography. Nevertheless, some sources of local geographical distinctiveness do not reside in the physical landscape, but are of a social or political nature. Particularly is this true of the effects of the political fragmentation that emerged in medieval times, especially in the southwest.

The territories were formative geographically because their lords made laws affecting, among other things, taxation and inheritance. On the system of inheritance largely depended whether a village would through repeated subdivision of holdings become a large agglomeration of poor peasants or remain a small group of substantial farmers, handing down their lands intact to one son. Contrasts of this nature can still be seen in the course of a few miles' journey in southern Germany or Hesse, with the crossing of the boundary of one of the former territories.

After the Reformation the rulers of the territories attempted to determine the religions of their subjects, and religious adherence has certainly had some effect on attitudes to capital, interest and economic advance. It is perhaps no accident that Protestant Württemberg was a pioneer in the development of modern liberal capitalism and industry in southern Germany. The territorial rulers were also great founders of the towns that are strewn so freely over southern Germany. They were founded as capitals, like Karlsruhe, or to defend the boundaries of territories, like Freiburg, or simply as sources of tax income and market dues. Some failed, and remain today as little more than villages, others found prosperity. That they did so often depended on the success of the lords and territories that gave them birth. It was the rise of Württemberg that determined that Stuttgart should be the regional capital of the southwest, rather than the older free city of Esslingen or any one of half a dozen equally suitable candidates. Similarly the fortunes of Munich have been linked with the rise of Bavaria, and Karlsruhe with Baden.

Traditionally southern Germany is a country of small farmers and numerous small market towns, with a generally Roman Catholic and frequently conservative population. Great concentrations of heavy industry are lacking, except in the marginal Saar. The very density of rural population has however served to attract the modern, lighter forms of industry, usually textiles to begin with, and subsequently the manufacture of machinery, electrical and electronic equipment and, on the Rhine, chemicals. A change to a fundamentally industrial society was first carried through in Württemberg and in parts of the Rhine valley, but since 1945 industry has pursued sources of labour throughout the region, most notably in rural Bavaria. Today new forms of geographical relationships are spreading through the traditional countrysides, based on the expanding agglomerations, the *Verdichtungsgebiete*. It is these great urban concentrations of population and of economic power that today form the major geographical features of southern Germany.

THE BLACK FOREST

The Rhine from Basel northwards to Bingen flows for some 300 km/180 miles through the elongated lowland of the Rhine Rift Valley, bordered on either side by the upland massifs of the Vosges, Black Forest, Haardt and Odenwald. In spite of their apparent diversity, all these regions were formed in the Tertiary earth movements from a single Hercynian massif, which with its cover of Secondary rocks was gently upfolded along an axis marked by the present course of the Rhine. The axial zone developed weaknesses, and a belt of country some 30 km/20 miles across was let down between fault lines to form the Rift Valley. The remnants of the Hercynian massif to either side were left tilted, with a steep fault-line scarp slope looking inwards over the Rift Valley, and a gentle slope descending to the scarplands on either side (Fig. 41).

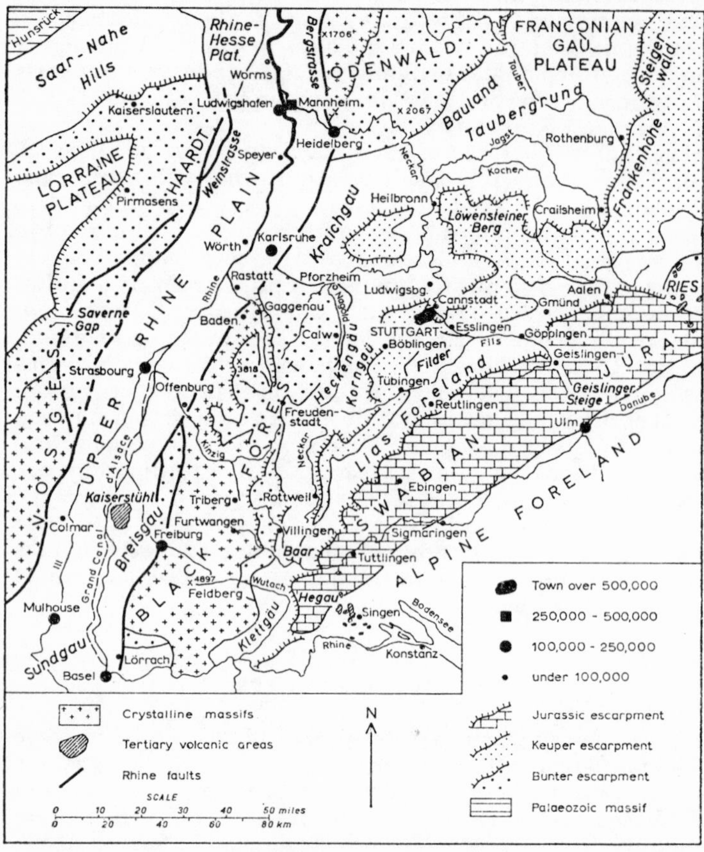

FIG. 40. Baden-Württemberg.

These bordering highlands of the Upper Rhine reach their greatest elevation of over 1,200 m/4,000 ft in the south, where they are nearest to the Alpine folding. The maximum degree of elevation by reference to the crystalline basement rocks beneath the Rhine Rift Valley is about 5 km/3 miles, but 3 km/2 miles of this is masked by the Tertiary fill of the rift. The cover of Secondary rocks has been stripped off the massif to reveal the granite and gneiss beneath. A striking series of erosion surfaces provides generally accordant skylines. While the gentle eastward descent of the tilted block is only moderately dissected by the Danube headwaters, the Rhine tributaries, operating to the lower local base level of the Rift Valley, have deeply fretted the west and south. At one point the aggression has cut right across the Forest, for the upper Kinzig was once a Danube tributary. The massif was high enough to have attracted some Pleistocene glaciation. The southern Black Forest bears signs of some short valley glaciers, while further north cirques, now often lake-filled, are more characteristic features. Regional variations in the height of cirques have been used in an attempt to prove that upward movement and deformation of the massif has continued even in post-glacial times.

Settlement of the Black Forest began with the medieval forest clearances, from about the year 1000 onwards. The settlement was characterized by strong control exercised by the territorial lords, backed up by monks of the Cluniac reform movement, who established many new monasteries within the Forest. For the lords the incentive lay in carving from the forest a unified territory, with undisputed lordship over all men and lands within it, in contrast to the hopeless confusion of rights that had developed in the old-settled areas surrounding. The best-known example is provided by the Zähringen family, which moved from the Swabian Jura to organize the agricultural settlement of much of the central Black Forest. The Zähringen Dukes defended their new territory by establishing peripheral castles or towns, notably Freiburg, Offenburg and Villingen.

The central Black Forest is the realm of the typical isolated Black Forest farmhouse. Immense wood-shingled roofs sweep down to low, broad eaves as a protection against the heavy snows of winter. Man and beast share the same building. Chains of these farms follow the valley side with the most favourable orientation (*Sommerhalde*), their lands climbing the slope behind in broad 150–300 m/500–1,000 ft wide holdings. The lower slopes are mostly in grass, but there are periodic breaks for arable cultivation (*Feldgraswirtschaft*). Woodlands clothe the steeper upper slopes, above which the open grass lands of the summits are used to pasture young stock in summer. As in most of the upland areas of Germany, arable cultivation is proving increasingly uneconomic and is being steadily abandoned in favour of specialized livestock enterprises based on permanent grassland.

Roughly along the line of the Kinzig valley the crystalline rocks disappear northwards beneath monotonous plateaus of Middle Bunter Sandstone, only occasionally broken by a narrow valley. Because of the high rainfall (reaching to nearly 2,000 mm/80 in) soils are podsolized, and on the higher flatter surfaces blanket bog has developed. Elsewhere there are vast forests of sombre spruce. The northern Black Forest is a lonely negative region between the densely-peopled Rhine and Neckar lowlands. The only interruption to the forest cover is in the east, towards the Nagold, where the plateau is covered by clays of the Upper Bunter. This slightly more favourable area was cleared in the Middle Ages by the lords of Calw, who established there a conspicuous group of linear *Waldhufendorf* settlements.

As in many upland regions, the inhabitants have been forced to develop industries in order to live, and these originally used local raw materials, especially the abundant timber and water power. The timber industry is still widely dispersed at numerous water-power sites in the valleys of the Forest, but the larger wood-using concerns like furniture factories and pulp, paper and rayon mills seek better communications on the fringes of the massif.

Even before the arrival of modern industry, the Black Forest developed a reputation for wood carving and the making of cuckoo clocks. Out of this grew the modern clock, precision engineering and optical industries, typical of mountain regions because the raw materials are easily transported, great amounts of fuel are not needed and a skilled labour force is highly important. The main centres are partly within the forest, as *Triberg* and *Furtwangen*, but the industry has also spread over the Gäulands to the east, notably to Villingen. Textile manufacture is also typical, especially in the south, where cotton and silk working have spread northwards from Switzerland. Here, too, electricity generated from the Rhine is the basis of the manufacture of fertilizers, aluminium and other chemical and metallurgical products. Characteristic of an upland situation is also the jewellery industry of *Pforzheim* (87), on the north-eastern fringe of the forest. The town also has an important electrical equipment industry.

Finally it must not be forgotten that the Black Forest is one of Germany's most popular tourist regions. The tourist industry has in places considerably modified the settlement pattern by adding between the Black Forest farmhouses strings of guest houses, cafés and hotels. The road system has been considerably improved, and special scenic routes created.

Kraichgau and Odenwald. The Bunter Sandstone of the northern Black Forest continues to dip northwards until it disappears beneath the Muschelkalk rocks of the Kraichgau depression, a zone of downwarping in the underlying Hercynian rocks. Beyond this the Sandstone rises once more to form another forested upland, the Odenwald, which in structure and land use resembles the northern Black Forest. One of the most spectacular features of the Odenwald is the course of the Neckar, which in making its way to the Rhine ignores the wide-open Kraichgau gap and instead cuts a narrow valley 500 m/1,600 ft deep through the extreme south of the massif. Just at the mouth of the valley, hemmed between river and wooded slopes, lies the university town of *Heidelberg* (125). On a terrace of the Neckar above the town lies one of the most famous ruins in the world, the remains of the immense Renaissance castle built by the Electors Palatine, mainly in the 16th and early 17th centuries, and destroyed by the French in 1689. Heidelberg owes its prosperity to its attractions as a tourist centre, to its university and to the light and medium industries that have developed on the Rhine plain below the town. Industrially and residentially Heidelberg has to be regarded as the third town after Mannheim and Ludwigshafen in the Rhine–Neckar agglomeration.

THE UPPER RHINE PLAIN

Between the bordering uplands, the floor of the Rhine Rift Valley is occupied by the Upper Rhine Plain. There is rarely a direct fall from upland to plain; the faulted sides are splintered and stepped, providing an intermediate foothill belt of Secondary rocks. Orchards, vineyards and gardens cling to the slope beneath the forested hills, where very early settlement has left a chain of villages and medieval towns. Often the villages almost merge into one another, as in the *Bergstrasse*, bordering the Odenwald. Similar vine and fruit land enfolds the volcanic mass of the Kaiserstühl (557 m/1,827 ft), that springs so suddenly from the Rhine near Freiburg.

The Tertiary rocks, that fill the trough of the Rift Valley, outcrop only in restricted areas in the north and south and intermittently along the sides. Elsewhere, continued sinking has caused them to be buried beneath the gravels of the Ice Age, now dissected into terraces. Where the terrace gravels are covered with loess, they have extremely fertile soils, but where wind operating on unprotected sand and gravel spreads

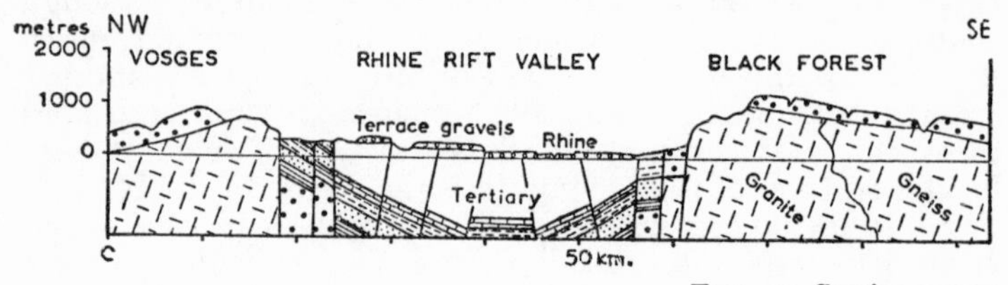

FIG. 41. Section across

in the immediate post-glacial period created sand dunes, forest generally remains.

Into the terraces the Rhine has carved its present flood plain. In its natural state, the river meandered in a constantly changing and divided course, but was in the 19th century straightened and confined between embankments, allowing large areas of lime-rich alluvium to be reclaimed for arable cultivation. From Idstein south of Basel to the Kaiserstühl the Rhine is now deserted by barge traffic, which follows the superior waterway afforded by the French lateral *Grand Canal d'Alsace*. From this point downstream to Strasbourg the navigable channel partly follows the bed of the Rhine, but periodically loops off so that water can pass through the French power stations.

The Rhine Plain is climatically the most favoured part of Germany. January average temperatures never fall below freezing point, and spring sets in early. Summers are warm or very warm (July mean 18·5°–19·5° C/65°–67° F), and fine weather normally continues until the end of September. Rainfall is moderate (500–750 m/20–30 in), with a late summer maximum. These conditions favour the intensive cultivation of the loess and loam soils, and even of the sand areas on the Low Terrace. As well as the normal field crops, there is much specialization in market gardening and the growing of industrial crops of high value, including tobacco. Other specialized crops are sugar beet, malting barley, early potatoes, hops and vegetables such as asparagus.

Naturally, the existence of the Rhine with its water and land routeways has stimulated the growth of cities. It is interesting that the most important medieval towns, which developed out of bishoprics on former Roman sites, are all on the west, or Roman, bank of the Rhine. The largest of these, Strasbourg,

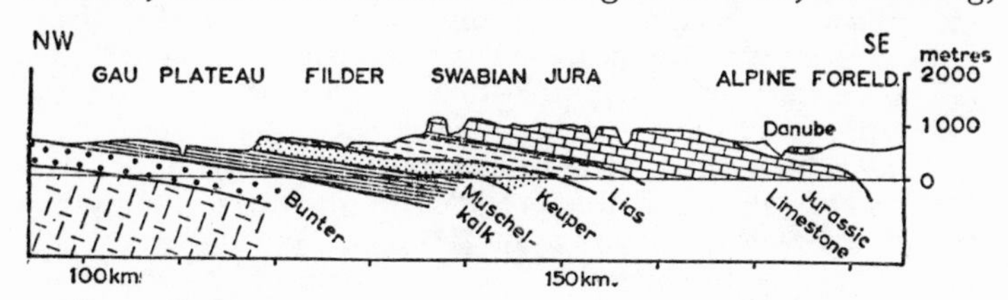

southwest Germany.

controlling the Saverne Gap, and Basel commanding the southern end of the Rift Valley, are now outside German territory. On the German side, the medieval towns were by origin local markets, and so lie back at the junction of hill and plain. Only with the rise of the princely states, and the embanking of the unruly river Rhine, were new fortress and capital towns founded on the plain itself.

North of Basel, the first town on the east side of the Rhine Plain is *Freiburg* (154), in the centre of the Breisgau embayment scooped out of the Black Forest. Freiburg is a cathedral and university town, with a flourishing tourist traffic. Further north a wide plain of forested Rhine gravels gave the Margrave of Baden-Durlach space for his 18th-century palace and radially-planned capital (Fig. 16), supplanting the huddled medieval town of Durlach at the edge of the hills. *Karlsruhe* (253) grew as an administrative and garrison town, railway centre and (from 1901) port on the improved Upper Rhine waterway. As well as engineering plants there were industries related to the agricultural riches of the region (tobacco, brewing) or to the transport opportunities (paper, milling).

With the creation of the combined *Land* of Baden-Württemberg Karlsruhe lost the functions of a capital, yet improved relations with France have so much moderated the disadvantages of a frontier situation that the whole region has achieved a most remarkable growth. Electrical equipment manufacture, formerly in Berlin, now employs thousands of workers, and a variety of other engineering and vehicle plants have been set up. The Karlsruhe district appears to be becoming the main centre of Daimler-Benz commercial vehicle production, with plants at Gaggenau and at Mannheim, but with expansion in future likely to go to a new site at Wörth, just across the Rhine, which is well placed to draw in rural labour from the Palatinate. With the completion of the French oil pipeline from Lavéra Karlsruhe has become the principal oil refining centre for southwest Germany, and this in turn has brought the development of the chemical industry.

The agglomeration of 1½ million people at the confluence of the Neckar with the Rhine provides an interesting example of complete reversal of geographical values. As elsewhere along the Upper Rhine, the older right-bank centres lie back at the edge of the hills, where Heidelberg, controlling the crossing of the Neckar by the *Bergstrasse*, was the capital of the Palatinate. On the west bank the ancient cathedral cities of Worms and Speyer lay well clear of the confluence area, which was liable to heavy flooding and long remained a thinly settled natural frontier zone.

A change in the value of this negative area began after the introduction of cannon into warfare made the stone walls of Heidelberg difficult to defend. *Mannheim* (327) was established in 1606 as a frontier fortress town for the Palatinate. In spite of its girdle of scarps and ditches and bastions and all the elaborate fortifications of the age it was several times taken, and finally destroyed in 1689. From 1720 to 1788 it was the capital of the Palatinate, but the transfer of capital functions to Munich following union with Bavaria was a severe blow. More disadvantageous for the development of the whole region was the partition of the Palatinate between Hesse, Bavaria and Baden in the post-Napoleonic settlement. Even the creation of the post-1945 *Länder* still left the Rhine as a boundary between Rhineland-Palatinate and Baden-Württemberg.

German reunification and the growth of economic liberalism in the 19th century swept away internal customs barriers,

Rhine tolls and the market rights of the ancient Rhine cities, allowing Mannheim for the first time to benefit rather than to suffer from geographical situation. With the regulation of the Upper Rhine Mannheim became a great river port, and for several decades it was the head of navigation. Coal and heavy goods were unloaded for transhipment to all parts of southern Germany. If this function has diminished with the improvement of the Rhine to Basel and the Neckar to Stuttgart, the Mannheim harbours still provide most attractive sites for industry. The principal branch is now the construction of machinery and vehicles, notably in what is claimed as Europe's largest omnibus plant. Mannheim is also one of Germany's most important centres for the manufacture of electrical equipment. The extension of the oil pipeline from Karlsruhe and the building of a refinery has placed Mannheim firmly into the developing chain of chemical locations between Karlsruhe and the Main.

Mannheim really forms one town of half a million people with *Ludwigshafen* (177) across the Rhine, founded by Bavaria as a competitor in 1843. This 19th-century 'new town' is dominated by one industry, chemicals. An immense plant stretches for 6 km/4 miles along the Rhine, producing fertilizers, dyestuffs, plastics and an enormous range of other products. Originally based on water-borne Ruhr coal, coke and by-products, the plant now relies predominantly on petroleum products drawn from the Mannheim refinery across the river.

Mannheim and Ludwigshafen have spread their influence far over the Rhine plain, turning scores of villages into dormitory settlements for industrial workers, while the managerial classes take refuge in the heights of the Bergstrasse or at Heidelberg. The chemical industry has had to find new Rhine-side sites in formerly sleepy Worms and Speyer. Even remote areas like the southern Palatinate have been drawn in through the establishment of branch plants, notably by Mannheim electrical firms, to tap the last reserves of rural labour.

THE SOUTH GERMAN SCARPLANDS

The scarplands of southern Germany provide a kind of mirror image of the Paris Basin of France. Just as the scarplands of Lorraine dip westwards away from the Vosges, so the scarplands of southern Germany dip eastwards and southeastwards away from the Black Forest and Odenwald-Spessart, with successively Bunter, Muschelkalk, Keuper and Jurassic rocks outcropping. In Germany, however, the regularity of the basin is broken, for beyond the Jurassic escarpment, along the line of the Danube, the secondary rocks have been caught in the violence of the Alpine folding and are carried rapidly down beneath the Tertiary deposits of the Foreland (Fig. 41).

The South German Scarplands are crossed by a major flexure, which prolongs eastwards the depression of the Kraichgau. Along this line, the Keuper sandstone escarpment takes a great leap westwards to the neighbourhood of Heilbronn, dividing the scarplands into two contrasting sections, one drained by the Neckar, the other predominantly drained by the Main. This forested barrier is of human importance also; through it ran the Roman frontier, the *Limes*, shutting off the barbarians to the east (Fig. 5). The same line divided the lands of the Alemans or Swabians in the Neckar basin from Franconia, settled by the Franks. This contrast between Neckar and Main, Swabia and Franconia, is the basis of a fundamental two-fold division of the scarplands.

THE NECKAR LANDS

The Gau Plateaus. The Secondary rocks of the scarplands radiate like the spokes of a fan from the southern end of the Black Forest (Fig. 40). As they extend northwards the various rocks become less tilted, their outcrops broader, lower and more plateau-like; by the time Franconia is reached the Triassic outcrop is over 160 km/100 miles across.

The Bunter Sandstone that wraps around the crystalline core of the Black Forest dips eastwards beneath the second member of the Trias, the limestone known as the Muschelkalk. The escarpment of the Muschelkalk is not usually very impressive. Its dip slope has been trimmed in a series of erosion surfaces, the *Gaufläche*, which are probably of Pliocene age. The general impression is of a gently rolling landscape, with numerous shallow dry valleys and an absence of surface water. Especially towards the east, the limestone is often covered with a veneer of Keuper clay, and there is a widespread cover of loess, yielding brown forest soils, now almost completely arable. A second landscape element is provided by the deeply-incised, meandering valleys of the few major streams that cross the limestone.

The Gau plateaus are not uniform. The western edge lacks loess cover, and so is stony and not particularly productive. The stones turned up by the plough are thrown to the edge of the strip fields, forming banks crowned with brushwood, hence the name *Heckengau*. Contrast is also provided by the northward descent and broadening of the outcrops. The southern plateaus, being the highest, have much grazing land. In the extreme south the *Klettgau* has been deeply dissected by tributaries draining southwards to the Rhine. One of these, the Wutach, has achieved a spectacular right-angle capture of one of the former headstreams of the Danube. The *Baar*, being drained to the Danube, is much less dissected. The really typical Gau country begins with the *Oberes Gau* or *Korngau*. It is continued by the *Kraichgau* and *Bauland* into Franconia.

These lower Gau plateaus sheltered in the lee of the Black Forest have temperature régimes nearly as favourable as those of the Rhine Rift Valley. Climate, and the soils formed on the loess, have enabled the development of an almost purely arable farming. The quality of land use, however, reflects not only agricultural potential but the settlement forms and social structure of the inhabitants, for the Gau plateaus show as perhaps no other area of Germany the consequences of long-continued subdivision of holdings.

These are old-settled lands, with the *-ingen* place-names of the German settlement of the 3rd to 5th centuries. The original settlements seem to have been small, and the adoption of the open-field system a reaction to increasing population. Until the beginning of the 19th century the villages were still surrounded by great fields each bearing the same crop, irrespective of ownership. Beyond lay the remaining commons, to which the village herdsman would lead out the animals every day. In the 19th century an important adjustment came into the system with the introduction of the practice, still usual, of stall-feeding animals instead of pasturing. The fallow field came to be used for growing fodder crops, and the commons, no longer needed, were divided into additional strips and added to the arable land, which now stretched more continuously over the Gau plateaus than ever before.

There is some evidence that the growth of the Gau villages

to their present size, with populations measured in many hundreds, may have taken place only in the last few centuries, facilitated by the inheritance and land-tax laws of the state of Württemberg. As a result of repeated subdivision only one or two holdings in a village will have the 15–20 ha/40–50 acres needed to occupy a full-time farmer, and it is by no means impossible for such a unit to be divided into over 100 separate parcels. Even the farm buildings have been reduced by subdivision to a special local type, in which all activities, barn, byre and living-quarters are under a single roof.

Most holdings are inevitably too small to support a family, and the breadwinner must seek the employment that is readily available in Stuttgart or the other industrial towns of the region. It used to be held that the holding of land by industrial workers was socially desirable, giving stability and a degree of insurance against times of industrial crisis. Today, after years of high industrial activity, attention is turning more to the system's economic inefficiency. It is, after all, absurd that some of the most fertile land in Germany should be farmed on a ridiculously small scale by men tired after a day's work, or by their wives and children. All too often the form of land use chosen is one requiring the least effort from the owner, not that which will bring the greatest return. Instead of field crops one sees rough grass and scrubby fruit trees, standing in the way of a reorganization of the land for professional mechanized agriculture.

For without doubt this is a rich countryside. The climate permits the growth of a range of specialized crops, tobacco, hops, asparagus and other field vegetables. Above all, a few men with machines could produce great surpluses of wheat, malting barley, maize and beef. This could be a Beauce or an East Anglia if the pattern and scale of land holding permitted. In an area like this, German agriculture is clearly faced with great changes if it is to be fully competitive in the European community.

The Keuper Scarp. The Gau plateau ends southeastwards against the escarpment of the Keuper. The lower clay slopes are in grass and fruit, but the sandstone cap above is under forest, originally deciduous but with much planted conifer. On south-facing slopes the Keuper is frequently devoted to vineyards, planted on terraces held up by sandstone walls.

Since a family used to be able to live off 3 ha/7 acres of vines, compared with 10–15 ha/25–40 acres of arable, the vine-growers' villages along the Keuper scarp and in the Neckar valley grew very large and prosperous. As in the Black Forest, medieval lords established castles and towns to control the fringes of the forests. One such town, in a little valley on the edge of the Schönbuch Forest, was Stuttgart. Only Stuttgart's function as the capital of the successful state of Württemberg can explain the development in this highly inconvenient site of the administrative and commercial centre for all southwest Germany.

The Lias Lands. Between the forests of the Keuper and the scarp of the Swabian Jura is another belt of open farmland on the Lias clays, which are often covered with loess. This is once more a country of village settlement and former open-field agriculture, but there is more grass than on the Gäu plateaus, and very many fruit trees growing among the fields. The principal use of the fruit is for making *Apfelmost*, a popular unfermented drink. The area of Lias known as the *Filder*, downfaulted into the Keuper south of Stuttgart, has as a local speciality the growing of the large cabbages used in the manufacture of Sauerkraut. The Filder today is much invaded by the expansion of Stuttgart from its restricted valley site. At the foot of the Swabian Jura escarpment another feature is provided by the forested iron-bearing sandstone of the Dogger. This has been worked as an ironstone from time to time, but is of much less significance than the Minette of Lorraine.

The Lias foreland of the Swabian Jura well illustrates the extraordinary profusion of medieval towns in southwest Germany. In medieval times this rich area was divided among scores of petty territories, each of which wanted towns for purposes of political consolidation, prestige, defence and trade. The castles of the lords are a conspicuous feature of the Jura scarp and its outliers above the towns. The most important is Reutlingen, a former free city that like near-by Esslingen declined relatively with the rise of Stuttgart.

The Swabian Jura (Schwäbische Alb). The scarplands are closed to the southeast by the imposing scarp of the Swabian Jura. The lower slopes of the escarpment, cut mainly in clay, are relatively gentle. Well watered by springs from the base of the limestone, their deep brown-earth soils are mostly given over to grass and fruit trees. With the oncoming of the limestone the slope steepens, making a double rise through splendid beechwoods to a crest generally well above 700 m/2,000 ft, something like 350 m/1,000 ft above the foreland beneath. Everywhere the escarpment is fretted by powerful springs, feeding the vigorously downcutting tributaries of the Neckar. Many outliers have been isolated and are favourite sites for castles, like Burg Hohenzollern, the ancestral home of the Prussian ruling family. The larger streams have cut back many miles into the escarpment, and the whole landscape is on a grander scale than the gentle Jurassic cuestas of England.

The dip slope of the Jura is some 40 km/25 miles across, substantial enough to be a region in its own right. It is a high, rolling surface of many dry valleys and dolinas, often broken by steep little forested hills that represent former reef knolls in the limestone seas. Astonishingly there are numerous villages at heights up to 750 m/2,500 ft, bearing the *-ingen* place-names of the original Alemanic settlement period. Originally the villages had the same sort of open-field agriculture as on the lowlands to the west, but today the arable area is much diminished. Many of the arable strips are grassed over, and help to support stall-fed dairy cattle; any damp hollow is filled with meadow. Meanwhile the forest is creeping down over the cleared land, planted spruce contrasting with the original beech. These changes are in part an obvious reaction to high rainfall and elevation, but they are stimulated by the industrialization of Württemberg which draws off labour even from the remote villages of the Swabian Jura.

The dip-slope plateau is the scene of a conflict between the somewhat sluggish Danube system and the vigorous Rhine and Neckar tributaries, in which the Danube streams are steadily driven back as their valleys are invaded. The process has created a number of passes across the crest of the cuesta, of which the most important is the Geislinger Steige, linking Stuttgart with Ulm. In its course across the western end of the cuesta the Danube also loses water by seepage; near Tuttlingen it is occasionally dry. The lost water merges at the foot of the dip slope in a powerful vauclusian spring, and flows into the Bodensee and so eventually to the Rhine.

Industry in Swabia. This rich land had by the early 19th century become notorious for rural poverty, owing to overpopulation and farm fragmentation. Only industry could take up the surplus members, but there were no important minerals, and no major waterways to bring raw materials from outside. Yet, in a few decades of the 19th century, Swabia was changed from its rural poverty into one of the most important industrial regions of Germany. This was achieved by selecting industries which could use a large and increasingly skilled labour force, and by relying on products which did not demand the transport of large quantities of bulky raw materials.

The starting point was textiles, and today *Land* Baden-Württemberg (mainly the Neckar basin of Swabia) still accounts for about one-quarter of the West German textile industry. Local specializations include the making of knitwear, hosiery and underwear. Out of textiles grew textile engineering, which developed into the making of machinery of all kinds. Out of this in turn has grown motor vehicle and aircraft construction, and because of the demand for electrical installations for vehicles, a flourishing electrical engineering industry. Baden-Württemberg accounts for about one-fifth of all machine construction, vehicle building and electrical engineering in West Germany.

The fuel and raw materials for Swabian industry have to be brought from other parts of Germany or abroad; only the building of the railways in the years 1850–60 permitted industry to develop. It is not surprising, therefore, that the industrial backbone of Swabia is provided by the main railway line which enters the region at Heilbronn, follows the Neckar to Stuttgart, then crosses the Swabian Jura by the Geislinger Steige on its way to Ulm. Much the same route is followed by the motorway and by the newly canalized Neckar, which brings heavy goods as far as the harbour of Stuttgart.

Here is no dense-packed industrial conurbation like the Ruhr, although Württemberg is Germany's most rapidly expanding region, and has at its heart the Stuttgart agglomeration of 2 million people. Factories often stand in green fields, close to small towns or villages. Many of the workers still retain their tiny patches of farmland, preferring to stay in their villages even at the cost of a long daily journey to work. The villages are swollen by the addition of many new houses, especially for the refugees, who make up a fifth of the population.

Industrial Regions. Coming from the north the first region centres on the gap and bridge town of *Heilbronn* (95). Some of Heilbronn's industries process agricultural commodities from the rich Gäu plateaus, but engineering and the motor vehicle industry are more important, both in Heilbronn itself and in neighbouring towns such as Neckarsulm. The canalization of the Neckar has brought new life to the river port as a centre for distributing heavy commodities to the surrounding region.

The second region centres on *Stuttgart* (633) which, although unimportant in medieval times, has grown as the capital of the state of Württemberg to overshadow all rivals in southwest Germany. This rise took place in spite of its beautiful but highly inconvenient site in a nest of vine-clad Keuper hills, with only one convenient outlet to the main road following the Neckar.

The heart of Stuttgart has been transformed into a modern centre for commerce, banking and all the administrative services needed by the capital of one of the wealthiest of the Länder. The remaining space in the hollow in which Stuttgart lies is taken up by a grid of 19th-century streets. Villa development, especially in the present century, has taken over the orchards and vineyards of the attractive slopes overlooking the city. Since the war, space for workers' housing has had to be found on the Filder plateau above. The building of road tunnels and the development of an electrified suburban railway system have done something to ease the acute traffic problems inherent in this difficult site.

The larger industries of Stuttgart have long had to seek space on the fringes of the 19th-century urban area, either well to the north or in the Neckar valley, where the great Daimler-Benz plant is situated. As the most important centre of the German motor industry Stuttgart has attracted many factories manufacturing vehicle components, electrical equipment and instruments. It is one of Germany's greatest centres for machinery building and the manufacture of electrical and electronic equipment. It is also well known for the manufacture of hosiery, knitwear and women's outer clothing.

There is little available land or labour to support further industrial growth in Stuttgart, so that development takes place on the expanding fringe of the agglomeration. The Daimler-Benz firm, for example, uses Stuttgart for administration, research and engine manufacture. The actual assembly of cars is done in a much larger plant at *Böblingen-Sindelfingen*, well placed for drawing in rural labour from the Korngäu. The same area has a very large new electronics plant. Many other surrounding towns participate in the characteristic industries of the region. The most important is *Esslingen* (83) on the Neckar, in medieval times a free city, the most important in the area. It was overshadowed by the rise of Württemberg and consequently of Stuttgart as its capital. Renewed expansion came in the mid-19th century, when Esslingen began to produce rolling stock and equipment for the new railways. It is still a major engineering centre, with some residual wool textiles and a postwar radio and electronics industry.

The third region is the home of the traditional textile industry, although machine building is now of equal importance. The cotton textile industry developed in the numerous small towns and villages of the Lias foreland of the Jura, and occupied the water-power sites of the valleys cutting back into the scarp. *Reutlingen* (73) is the largest town and organizing centre. Like other textile towns Reutlingen developed the manufacture of textile machinery, and through this engineering in general, especially the fine and precision branches. It also takes part in another Württemberg textile speciality, the manufacture of knitted textiles, which extends southwestwards along the foreland and reaches its greatest intensity in the Jura valleys of the *Ebingen* area. This is a branch of the textile industry that developed markedly after the war; the Ebingen area also produces the necessary machines. The textile region extends southeast up the Filstal, used by the railway in its ascent to the Geislinger Steige. Engineering is of rather greater significance here, especially at *Goppingen* (48).

In addition to the three main regions mentioned, there are various outlying centres. Reached by the Geislinger Steige is the Danube bridge town of *Ulm* (93), with its Bavarian twin Neu-Ulm across the river. It has various engineering and electrical industries, and makes buses and heavy commercial vehicles. Rather further away beyond Ulm is the group of industries on the shores of the Bodensee (p. 205). To the southwest towns like Rottweil and Villingen participate in the watch and precision industries of the Black Forest. Near-by *Tuttlingen* is a large centre of musical instrument making. Some of the most striking recent progress has been east of

Stuttgart. *Schwäbisch-Gmünd* has a traditional specialization in precious metal working and jewellery manufacture, but a new element has been the establishment near *Aalen* of the refugee Zeiss optical works from Thuringia.

Growth and Change in the Southwest. Baden-Württemberg was created in 1952 out of the prewar *Länder* Baden and Württemberg and the small Prussian province of Hohenzollern. It was an area where the economy gained many new branches through the setting up of refuge firms from Berlin, East Germany and Czechoslovakia, notably in textiles, clothing, electrical equipment, optical and precision engineering. The industrial structure enriched in this way proved to be extremely strong in the postwar growth industries, notably motor vehicles, electrical equipment, radio and electronics. The existing chemical industry was able to take up the new processes based on oil, and many new chemicals, plastics and fibres plants were added. A new complex of oil refineries was created on the Rhine.

As a result, the postwar increase of population through the arrival of refugees was perpetuated by a continuing immigration from the rest of the country, attracted by the wealth and opportunities of the area (Fig. 33). Industries spread very widely, even into rural areas, in search of labour, but the most striking geographical development since the war is the mergence of the great agglomerations of population, the *Verdich-Tungsgebiete.* In the north the Rhine-Neckar region centred on Mannheim straddles the boundary with Rhineland-Palatinate. Another such agglomeration appears to be forming about Karlsruhe. Dominating them all is the great Stuttgart agglomeration, with at its heart the political, industrial and commercial capital of this most prosperous and thriving part of Germany.

SUGGESTIONS FOR FURTHER READING

H. EGGERS, *Schwarzwald und Vogesen*, Braunschweig (Westermann-Verlag), 1964.

T. H. ELKINS and E. M. YATES, 'The South German scarplands in the vicinity of Tübingen', *Geography*, 48, 1963, pp. 372–92.

F. HUTTENLOCHER, *Baden-Württemberg*, Karlsruhe (Braun-Verlag), 1960.

Chapter 12

THE BAVARIAN LANDS

FRANCONIA

Bavaria, the West German *Land* with the largest area and second largest population, is divided into three contrasting sections. In the south, the Danube valley and Alpine Foreland have been the homeland of the Bavarian tribal group since the late 5th century (Fig. 6). To this in the 10th century was added the frontier march of the Nordgau or Upper Palatinate, on the borders of Bohemia. The third section, the scarplands of Franconia, was originally the home of a completely separate tribal group, the Franks, and has been Bavarian only since Napoleon's political reorganization of Germany.

The Franconian scarplands are directly continuous with those of Swabia, and made up of the same Triassic and Jurassic rocks dipping off the uplifted Hercynian massifs of the Rhine, but in detail there are important contrasts. The fertile Lias vale at the foot of the Jura scarp is narrow or absent. The fanning out of the various outcrops, begun in Swabia, is continued, so that the Muschelkalk plateaus are much wider, and so, unfortunately for Franconian agriculture, are the expanses of infertile Keuper sand.

Spessart and Gau Plateaus. Like the neighbouring Odenwald, the Spessart consists of a tilted massif of crystalline rocks, mainly covered by forested Bunter Sandstone. The Main breaks through between Spessart and Odenwald in a broad valley, and just before it leaves Bavarian territory is the river port of *Aschaffenburg* (56). Based on the Spessart forests there are extremely important timber, pulp, paper and rayon industries, but these are overshadowed by the making of men's clothes, partly by outworkers living in the poor forest villages. The whole area around Aschaffenburg is developing industrially as it is increasingly drawn into the expanding Rhine–Main economic region.

The Gau plateau, cut in Muschelkalk Limestone and Lower Keuper Clay, is continued from the Neckar in Swabia right across Franconia as far as the headwaters of the Werra in Hesse. In the west, the surface is composed of Muschelkalk alone, poor, dry, stony land rising westwards to a distinct 450 m/1,600 ft scarp. Further east, where a veneer of Keuper Clay and loess covers the extremely even plateau at an altitude

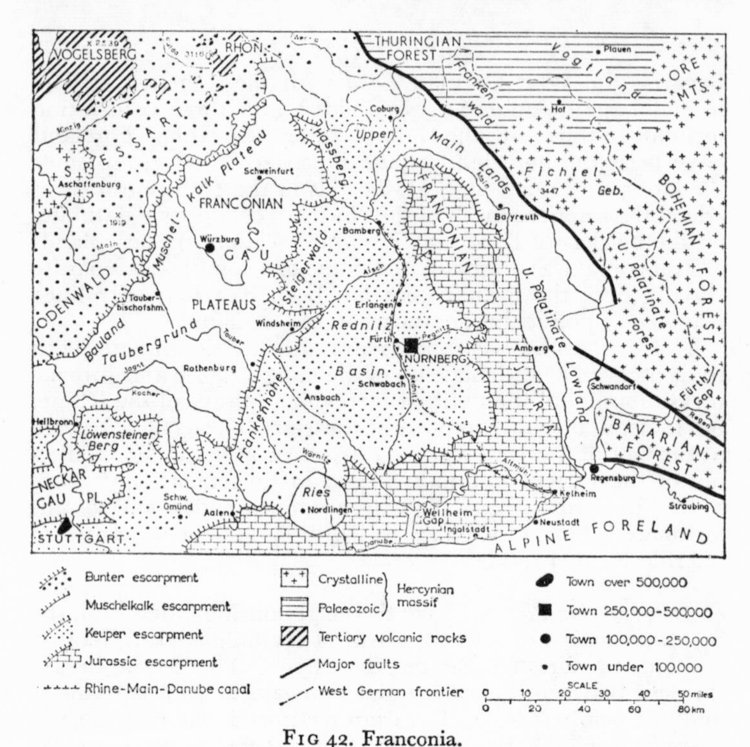

FIG 42. Franconia.

of about 400 m/1,200 ft, the typical Gau landscape appears. The traveller sees only the open arable fields, growing wheat, barley, sugar beet, potatoes and lucerne, stretching on either side as far as the eye can see. There appear to be no villages, nothing except the distant blue line of the Keuper scarp to interrupt the scene. Only when a depression in the plateau is reached is a large nucleated village revealed, clustering around a spring or a well, bearing, probably, the *-heim* place-name of the earliest Frankish settlement. This is the granary of Franconia, and fattens large numbers of cattle on lucerne and other fodder crops. Towns on the plateau are small and few, and industry almost entirely lacking.

The Main Valley. A complete contrast with the rustic peace of the plateau is given by the life and warmth of the valley of the Main. The river flows between steep valley sides of Muschelkalk Limestone. Where these have a southerly orientation, vines grow in pockets of earth retained by laboriously erected and maintained limestone walls. Fruit trees and vegetable gardens cover the lower slopes.

The valley is followed by important rail and road routes linking Nürnberg with Frankfurt and the Rhine. The Main has been improved to take standard 1,350-ton barges to Bamberg, and work is in progress on the Rhine–Main–Danube canal link by way of the Nürnberg industrial region to the Danube. The existence of good communications has permitted some scattered industrial development. Local raw materials are the basis of cement, gypsum, brewing, sugar and canning industries, and there are even a few specialized and famous engineering plants.

Würzburg (121) originated as a bishopric founded about 742. The town lies in the valley, dominated by the magnificent medieval castle of the Bishops, the Marienburg. The 18th-century palace which the brilliant architect Balthasar Neumann built when the Bishop sought more comfortable quarters is one of the glories of German Baroque architecture. Würzburg has with the improvement of the river become an important harbour, and there are printing and engineering works.

Further upstream *Schweinfurt* (59) is the main German centre for making roller- and ball-bearings. They can be made here, far from the Ruhr, because the weight of steel used is small, and the finished bearings are a most high-valued product that can easily bear the cost of despatch all over Germany and to export markets. *Bamberg* (73) with cotton textile industries is economically rather stagnant, in spite of its new harbour on the Main; it still preserves the atmosphere and artistic treasures of an ecclesiastical capital. Into the area around *Coburg* (43) has been concentrated much of the varied small-scale and domestic industry that formerly lay on both sides of the Bavarian-Thuringian frontier. The traditional manufacture of toys, Christmas-tree decorations, perambulators and basket-ware has been reconcentrated on West German territory, where there is access to the established organizing centre of Nürnberg, with its famous toy fairs. Branch factories making electrical components have also been introduced into an economy already quite diverse, so that the area is more prosperous than the neighbouring Frankenwald. At the headwaters of the Main *Bayreuth* (63) is best known for its Wagner festival.

Keuper Escarpment and Rednitz Basin. The Gäu plateaus end eastwards against the Keuper scarp, which rises to 500 m/1,600 ft, and is divided into three distinct sections, Frankenhöhe, Steigerwald and Hassberg (Fig. 42). The scarp is much further from the Jurassic cuesta in Franconia than in Swabia, leaving room for the broad Rednitz Basin. Here there are few spreads of fertile Lias, as found on the Neckar; instead, poor sands of the upper part of the Keuper extend to the very foot of the Jura. This is by nature a world of sparse pine forests, easily degenerating into heathland, broken only by the swamp woodland of the river valleys. It is somewhat surprising that in this distinctly unfavourable environment developed Franconia's greatest concentration of industry and population.

The south–north-flowing Rednitz sprang to importance from the 6th century onwards as a Frankish line of defence against the Slavs to the east and Bavarians to the southeast, and a major routeway between the Danube and Thuringia. It was secured by a series of royal fortresses (Königshöfe), such as Fürth, which acted as nuclei for later town development. All were, however, put in the shade by the royal castle which was founded on a sandstone rock above the Pegnitz, a tributary of the Rednitz, about 1040.

The growth of *Nürnberg* (472) was due initially to the favour of the German Kings, who preferred it as an administrative centre over towns under the control of the Church or the nobility, like the bishop's town of Bamberg. Above all, however, the rise of Nürnberg to be one of the greatest medieval towns in Europe was due to the industry of its inhabitants. In a situation almost completely lacking in natural resources, they developed advanced handicrafts of all kinds, the skilled working of metals from iron to gold, and above all the famous toy trade. In the late medieval flowering of German city life Nürnberg stood supreme, with artists like Dürer and Stoss, poets like Hans Sachs.

After the development of ocean trade began a period of decline, and the customs barriers of the rising princely states slowly throttled the overland trade of the free city. Then, after union with Bavaria, the Zollverein and the development of railways came a remarkable new rise, when the traditional skill of Nürnberg merchants and workers flowed into modern industries. Today, Nürnberg is one of the greatest West German centres of electrical manufacture, making transformers, household appliances, radio equipment, cables, lamps and many other items. Second in importance comes the making of machinery, from cranes and diesel engines to typewriters and precision instruments. It is still the capital of the West German toy industry, and is famous for its pencils and artists' colours.

The former rival town of *Fürth* (97) is now continuous with Nürnberg in a conurbation of over half a million people. The economic union between the two formerly rival centres may be dated to the building of the first railroad of Germany to link them together (1835). Established industries include glass working and furniture making, but since 1945 industrial expansion has been in the clothing, radio and television industries.

The Nürnberg agglomeration also includes the university town of *Erlangen* (78), which has a tradition of receiving refugees, beginning at the end of the 17th century with the Huguenots. The textile and glove industries that they brought with them are still represented in the town. A fresh wave of refugees arrived after the last war, and with them the offices and laboratories of the Siemens-Schuckert electrical group from Berlin, which now dominate the town physically and occupationally.

Nürnberg–Erlangen–Fürth forms Bavaria's second population agglomeration, but expansion has been less rapid than in the Munich region. The loss of ties with East Germany has left the region rather isolated from the rest of West German industry. The motorway link to Frankfurt was completed only in 1964, and extensions to Stuttgart and Regensburg scheduled only for the 1970s.

Immediately outside Nürnberg, Bamberg and other towns,

are intensive market gardens, using the light, easily-warmed sandy soils, enriched by centuries of town refuse, to produce early vegetables, spinach, asparagus, lettuce and other crops. Another intensive use of light land along the river is the irrigation of water meadows, originally by creaking wooden water wheels, now by electric pumps. South of Schwabach is a famous district of hop gardens. The numerous ponds, producing carp and other freshwater fish, which were also characteristic of the Rednitz Basin, are gradually disappearing, but there is still enough water and meadow land left to feed the storks which nest even on the rooftops of the busy city of Nürnberg itself.

The Franconian Jura. The Franconian scarplands are terminated eastwards by the Franconian Jura. The transition from the Swabian Jura is made through the *Ries*, a curious, almost circular depression of volcanic origin. The Ries is filled with loess-covered Tertiary rocks, and its large nucleated villages, with *-ingen* and *-heim* place-names, date from the earliest period of Germanic settlement.

Beyond the Ries, the Franconian Jura at first resembles the Swabian Jura, except that one important river, the Altmühl, rises in the Keuper country and meanders right across the escarpment in a spectacular limestone gorge to join the Danube. The lower valley of the Altmühl was actually carved by the Danube, which has been diverted southwards, leaving the Wellheim gap (Fig. 42). The Danube itself has a magnificent gorge section just above the Altmühl confluence.

After the Franconian Jura swings through a right angle into an approximately southeast–northwest course, it begins to change character. The west-facing scarp becomes lower, and is rendered less impressive by an intermediate bench formed by the ferruginous Dogger Sandstone, worked in the Pegnitz valley for ironstone. In this more continental location spruce replaces beech in the scarp-top woodlands.

Structurally, also, the Jura changes. In the Tertiary mountain building period, the rise of the Bohemian massif caused the whole of the eastern part of the Jura to be faulted and uptilted, so that there is a minor east-facing scarp as well. The plateau of the northern Franconian Jura, seamed with dry valleys, provides an extremely poor and thinly populated environment. The Jura is here a real barrier to communications, so that there are few routeways to bring life to the hamlets of this isolated plateau.

Upper Palatinate. Between the Franconian Jura and the Bohemian Forest is the Upper Palatinate Lowland, drained southwards by the river Naab. This is one of the few regions of Bavaria where some local raw materials are available as a basis for industry. Tertiary brown coals are used to generate electricity, and Cretaceous iron ore was the basis for the development of minor iron and steel centres at *Amberg* (42) and elsewhere. Although menaced by competition from larger EEC producers, most of these plants have managed to survive by specializing on products like sheet steel and tubes for the Bavarian market. There has been some beneficial diffusion of industry from the Nürnberg region, notably the manufacture of electrical equipment. On the other hand the pottery industry based on local kaolin and china clays is rather static.

The Northeastern Border Mountains. The Bavarian boundary runs through the mountainous fringe of the Bohemian massif. This is poor, forested country; the *Bavarian Forest* in particular is a classic problem area, where poor soils, small farms and remoteness have caused a hundred years of depopulation. There is a little mining and quarrying, notably of graphite north of Passau, but the existing wood and glass industries are not prosperous. In spite of the use of federal money to improve the road system it is difficult to attract industry into such a thinly populated area; indeed the new roads tend to be used by commuters to move out to better placed centres like Regensburg and Passau.

The *Fichtelgebirge* is perhaps slightly more prosperous, with pottery industries and a glass industry that received a new impetus after 1945 with the settlement of refugee workers from Czechoslovakia. However neither of these industries is an expanding one, and the region remains very much a problem. So too is the *Frankenwald*, which developed the same textile, glass and pottery industries as adjoining Saxony and Thuringia. The creation of the new boundary cut the region's former ties with Central Germany. Towns like *Hof* (55) were now at a dead end, and unfortunately the local industries, after a period of postwar prosperity, are now static or declining. Attempts are being made to build up alternative sources of employment in machine building and miscellaneous metal industries.

THE GERMAN ALPS

The narrow strip of German Alpine territory has three sections, all politically part of Bavaria. In the *Allgäu Alps*, in the west, the mountains consist principally of folded sandstones and shales of the early Tertiary Molasse and of Flysch. These rocks weather rapidly, forming somewhat rounded ridges rising to 1,200–2,000 m/4,000–7,000 ft.

As in all the outer band of the Alps, precipitation is extremely high, frequently exceeding 2,000 mm/80 in, and the productive land is under grass or forest. Settlement is in the form of loose hamlets and isolated farmhouses. The heavily manured land close to the farmhouses provides hay for stall feeding in the long winter months, either in the farmhouses themselves or in the many field barns scattered through the meadows. The milk is delivered to central dairies, mainly for cheese manufacture (Emmentaler). Pasture fields occupy the poorer and more distant slopes. Above the trees rise the high mountain pastures (*Almen*), but as elsewhere in the Alps the traditional transhumance is in decay. It is difficult to find labour willing to undertake the lonely life of cattle-herding and cheese-making in the mountain chalets. Some *Almen* have been equipped with milk pipelines to the valleys, but greater economic returns can be obtained by devoting the chalets to the tourist trade.

Even such a remote area as this has received its share of Bavaria's postwar industrialization. In the chance way in which refugee firms were located in the postwar chaos, *Immenstadt* gave shelter to a refugee Sudetan German stocking firm, which now has one of the largest plants in Germany. The region also has quite an important plant manufacturing agricultural equipment.

Further east, in the *Bavarian Alps*, the frontier once more swings south. The outer Flysch and limestone pre-Alp ranges are much cut up by valleys, giving easy access to the limestone High Alps to the south, culminating in Germany's highest mountain, the Zugspitze (2,963 m/9,735 ft). Here all the characteristic forms of a glaciated mountain range can be observed, deep U-shaped valleys, frost-shattered pyramidal peaks and arrêtes, cwms and eternal snows. The splendid mountain scenery, and the relatively easy access, have made *Garmisch-Partenkirchen* into Germany's best-known mountain resort. Many hydroelectric stations use the rapidly descending mountain streams. On the third occasion that the frontier swings south, it encloses the *Berchtesgaden Land*, where a circle of high limestone peaks overlook the basin which contains the Königs-See and the small resort town of Berchtesgaden.

Although income from foreign tourists is not very important for Germany as a whole, Bavaria benefits greatly from internal tourism, both in summer and for winter sport. There is also some incidental benefit from the summer and winter surges of the population of northern Europe and Germany to Austria, Italy and other southern countries. Most of the tourist resorts are in the Alps and the attractive lake-strewn country of the inner part of the Alpine Foreland. The greatest intensity is in the centre, between Garmisch and Munich, itself a major tourist attraction.

THE ALPINE FORELAND

The Land. As the Alps were raised, a great furrow was also created running round the outer side of the mountain arc. The furrow was filled by a sea, in which débris from the rising mountain chains was laid down to form Tertiary sandstones and clays, known as Molasse. The close of Tertiary times saw the Molasse gently uplifted to form the plain of the Alpine Foreland, sloping gently downwards from the Alps to where the Danube flows at its outer edge. The surface detail of the Foreland, however, depends primarily on the events of the Pleistocene Ice Age, when with each glaciation ice issued from the Alpine valleys to coalesce in a piedmont glacier on the plain.

Four or five major advances of the ice took place (see Table on p. 26). The most extensive was the one before last, the Riss, when the glaciers advanced roughly to the latitude of Munich. The last (Würm) advance, however, produced only a series of looped moraines opposite the mouths of the Alpine valleys. This varying effect of glaciation in the different parts of the Foreland provides the basis for regional subdivision.

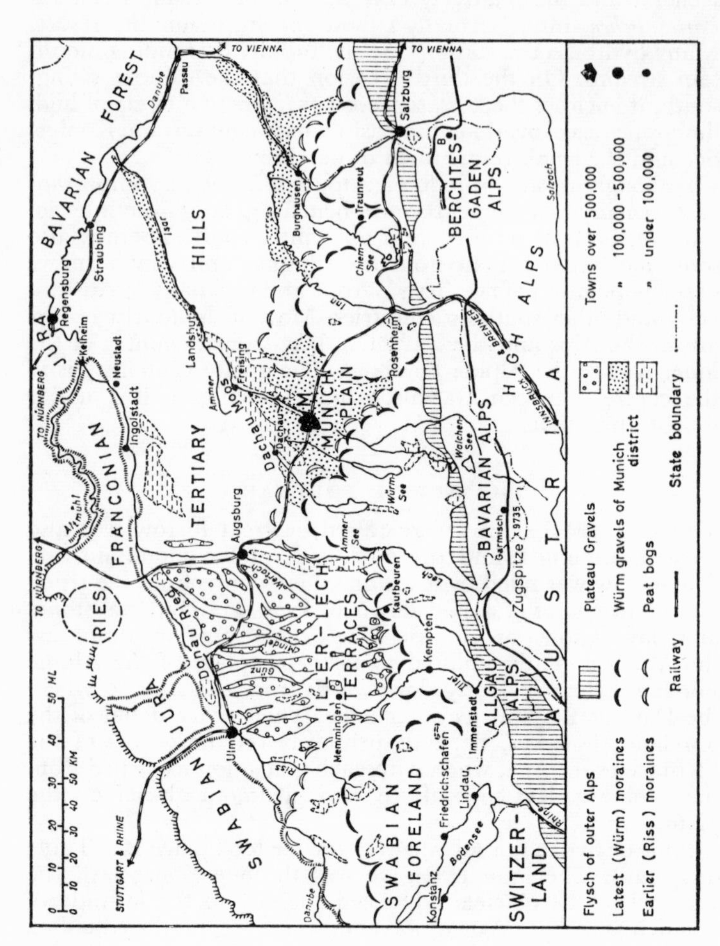

FIG 43. The Alpine Foreland.

The Swabian Foreland. The western end of the Foreland belongs mainly to Baden-Württemberg, but can most conveniently be described here. As the Foreland is at its narrowest, and the invading ice came from the powerful Rhine glacier, it is not surprising that the Würm moraines nearly reach the Danube. Within the circle of confused forested hills left by the glacier is a basin containing the greatest lake in Germany, the Bodensee (Lake Constance). From the lake the Rhine escapes westwards, breaking through the moraine wall to pass between the German and Swiss Juras to reach the head of the Rhine Rift Valley.

Between the moraine wall and the lake the surface is covered with boulder clay; drainage has been much interrupted, leaving many areas of marsh and bog. Such terrain and a rainfall of about 1,000 mm/40 in at an elevation of 400 m/1,300 ft and more have encouraged the development of dairy farming; settlement is rather scattered.

In contrast, the warmer slopes overlooking the lake itself carry vineyards, orchards, hop fields and market gardens. Settlement of this favoured area was early; Neolithic and Bronze Age men built their villages by the lake, and today nucleated villages line the shores. As a result of political fragmentation there is no single large town to dominate this natural focus. The lake shores are shared by Switzerland, Austria and by three of the former German states, each of which tried to develop its own port. Baden reached the lake through *Konstanz*, Württemberg through *Friedrichshafen*, where the Zeppelin airships were built, and Bavaria through *Lindau*. Industrially the lake region has a number of textile, engineering, vehicle and aircraft plants, linked to the Swabian industrial region further north. It is a favoured location for the great Swiss food and chocolate firms, producing for the German market.

The Iller–Lech Terraces. East of the country of the Rhine glacier the Foreland widens, while the ice streams were fed only from small catchment areas in the northern Alps. Consequently, in the sections between the Iller and Lech rivers, the glaciers advanced only some 30 km/20 miles from the foot of the Alps. Outside the terminal moraine, glacial melt water laid down sheets of gravel. Between each glaciation, there were periods of renewed slight uplift of the Foreland, which caused the south–

north flowing rivers to incise their valleys into the gravel sheet, and even into the underlying Molasse, leaving a terrace feature to either side. The process was repeated with each ice advance, so that the country presents a picture today of a succession of south–north strips of gravel of different heights. The general effect is of a repeating pattern of fertile terrace strips, lined with villages, poised between forested interfluves and marshy valley floors.

The principal town of the region is *Augsburg* (211), the Roman *Augusta Vindelicorum* on the Lech, which lived on as a Christian bishopric. Its merchants traded southwards over the Alpine passes, and northwards through the Ries to Frankfurt; the wealth so gained was used in late medieval times to found famous banking houses, especially that of the Fugger family. Like many other free cities, Augsburg lost its importance with the opening of ocean routes and the growth of rivals favoured by the Princely states, but has become in modern times the most important centre of the Foreland for textile manufacture, including wool textiles. Other products are printing presses, cash registers, diesel engines, sewing machines and aircraft.

In recent years Augsburg's growth has been very much overshadowed by that of Munich, and it is tending to extend in a southeasterly direction to link in a single city-region with the Munich agglomeration. Further south in the same region *Kaufbeuren* provides another example of the settlement of refugee industries. A wartime arms plant was used to house refugee Sudetan German manufacturers of the so-called Gablonz ware, artificial jewellery made from glass. Soon there were hundreds of small manufacturers, and the associated settlement of Neu Gablonz had over 10,000 inhabitants, 95% of them former inhabitants of Gablonz or their offspring.

The Eastern Foreland and Munich. The glaciers of the Isar, Inn and Salzach valleys advanced much further from the foot of the Alps than those of the Iller–Lech region. They have left behind the usual features of lake basins, partly or wholly silted up, confused boulder clay country with much interrupted drainage, and crescentic terminal moraines, covered with forest. Owing to altitude and high rainfall (1,000–1,500 mm/40–60 inches a year) the moraines are devoted to dairy farming, and the settlement mainly dispersed.

Outside the terminal moraines the outwash gravels form the large undissected fan of the Munich Plain. The gravels are very dry, and are covered with monotonous spruce forests. In the north the fan dips beneath the water table, held up by the underlying Tertiary Molasse, and great peat bogs like the Dachau Moos have developed. Generations of farmers have toiled to reclaim the bogs, draining, cutting the peat, and cultivating the land beneath.

Where the old road from Salzburg to Augsburg, keeping on the dry gravels between the forests to the south and the peat bogs to the north, crossed the Isar, Henry the Lion founded the town of *Munich* (München 1,211). Less important than Augsburg in medieval times, Munich grew rapidly, especially from the 19th century, with the development of the more easterly approach by the Inn valley to the Alpine passes, and as the capital of the independent kingdom of Bavaria. The little medieval town was transformed into a city of broad avenues and imposing buildings in the classical style of the early 19th century. In the inter-war years the city acquired a reputation for political extremism, culminating in Hitler's rise to power. Today one thinks rather of Munich's cosmopolitanism, its large student population, the large number of visitors, a third of them from abroad, and its possession of the largest foreign colony of any town in Germany.

Munich's position commanding the ascent towards the Brenner pass, and its function as a capital caused it to become the main rail centre of the Foreland. This aided the development of industry, including machine construction, light and precision engineering, and the manufacture of motor cars, lorries, locomotives, wagons, aircraft engines and electrical equipment. The most famous industry is, however, the brewing of beer, consumed by tourists from vast stoneware mugs in the numerous beer-cellars of the city to the sound of *Lederhosen*-clad brass bands.

The central parts of the city are increasingly given over to administration, commercial offices, banking and insurance, as is to be expected in the capital of the West German *Land* with the largest territory and the second largest population. The spread of offices and shops has led to a thinning out of the population in the centre. By contrast the city administration has acted vigorously to create a ring of new workers' housing schemes around the city. Private enterprise is at work too, converting the farm buildings of neighbouring village streets into the garages and shops of new local service centres, and covering their fields with flats and houses. Something like 25,000–30,000 people are added to the population of Munich every year. In the 1950s when like most large German towns it was recovering from wartime devastation it had the most rapid growth of them all, increasing its population by a third, becoming in 1957 the third German city to have more than a million inhabitants. If population growth in Munich itself was slightly less hectic in the early 1960s this was because expansion was transferred to the expanding fringes of an agglomeration approaching 2 million in total. To enable all these people to reach their places of work without finally jamming the centre with cars Munich has initiated an ambitious programme for linking the suburban rail network by tunnel beneath the centre of the city and for constructing a supplementary underground railway system.

The Munich agglomeration is surrounded by a ring of tributary towns and villages which are partly commuter settlements, partly industrial centres in their own right. *Dachau* (31), for example, has had a considerable industrial development since the war, notably in radio and electronics. *Rosenheim* (32) is a good example of the characteristic wide scattering of industry in Bavaria, being the organizing centre for scores of textile and clothing plants spread along the valleys of the Inn and its tributaries. Munich really forms part of a growing industrial triangle that also includes Augsburg and the expanding industrial centre around Ingolstadt.

The Chemical Triangle. At the eastern end of the Bavarian Alpine Foreland, in the triangle Inn–Salzach–Chiemsee is the only part of Bavaria where hitherto the chemical industry has been of any great significance. The basis of the industry is the Inn, which with its tributaries accounts for over a third of Bavaria's water-power potential. The industry derives from the application of electricity to Ruhr coal and limestone to produce carbide, which is used in turn to produce nitrogen fertilizer and a range of plastics, fibres, insecticides and other chemical products. Today most of this group of chemicals can be produced much more cheaply from oil without the need to expend vast quantities of electricity and to bring in coal and limestone. Fortunately for the future of the area a branch line from the TAL pipeline has been constructed to supply a refinery which will provide the raw material for reorganizing the chemical industry on the new basis.

Industry in the 'chemical triangle' is characteristically Bavarian in location in that the chemical plants are divided among a number of towns, none of any great importance; the largest is *Burghausen*. Here as elsewhere in Bavaria the arrival of refugee industries has helped to diversify the employment structure, especially for women. The development of *Traunreut* is characteristic. Before 1939 it was a forest, which became a plant for producing poison-gas weapons, its buildings understandably dispersed over a wide area. It was provided with road and rail connections, electricity and water supplies. In the period of postwar shortages these facilities combined with the availability of local and refugee labour were sufficient to attract a substantial plant manufacturing electrical components as well as a very varied group of other industries. A small town of about 10,000 inhabitants, predominantly refugees, has grown up beside the group of plants.

The Tertiary Hills. North of the Munich Plain the Tertiary Molasse comes to the surface to form a sharply undulating, low hill country. Because of the clay content of the Molasse, the valleys are ill-drained, and are left as meadow land. Fields occupy the slopes, and patches of uncleared woodland remain on the hilltops. The farms stand singly or grouped into hamlets. North of Munich the Tertiary hills contain Germany's largest hop-growing region, the Hallertal.

The Danube Valley. With over 1,600 km/1,000 miles to go before reaching the sea, the Danube has little cutting power. The great quantities of alluvium which have poured down from the Alps have choked the stream, causing the division of the channel into many branches and the creation of marshland. It is not surprising in these circumstances that the Danube in its upper reaches is an obstacle rather than a routeway. Towns like Ulm (p. 193) are crossing points rather than ports.

Water traffic on the German Danube is hampered by these characteristics of the river channel, and also by the irregular Alpine régime, with great floods when the snows melt in spring and early summer. The isolation of the river from the rest of the West German waterway system is a serious disadvantage, while the political situation lower down the Danube was for years after 1945 extremely unfavourable to the development of traffic with Germany, although these difficulties have largely disappeared. In recent years the navigable channel has been improved by barrages erected in connection with Austrian and German-Austrian power plants where the river cuts through the resistant rocks of the fringe of the Bohemian massif. Traffic is now considerably greater than before the war; Austrian steel, Hungarian and Roumanian seed maize, Jugoslav bauxite and pyrites and Roumanian oil and reeds are characteristic of the upstream traffic, while Ruhr and American coal is sent downstream for the Austrian steel industry. The Danube navigation will of course be transformed at the moment when the Rhine–Main–Danube canal reaches the head of navigation at *Kelheim*, and a waterway stands open from Rotterdam to the Black Sea.

At present the bridge-town of *Regensburg* (125), at the northernmost bend of the river, is the main port of the German Danube. On this site stood one of the key legionary fortresses of the Roman frontier, *Castra Regina*, near the point where the *Limes* began to make its way across country to the Rhine. The site was occupied by a bishopric and a Carolingian palace, around which the medieval town grew. Although Regensburg is somewhat removed from the main centres of West German economic activity it is at least relatively better served by land and water communications than the remote Bavarian Forest at its back, from which it is able to attract rural labour for its engineering and other industries. Much the same is true of the frontier town of *Passau* (31) downstream.

The most striking industrial developments in the Danube valley have been in the area of *Ingolstadt* (68). Until not long ago the main industries were making textile and other machinery, and a not very successful car plant. Ingolstadt and near-by Neustadt are now the main oil refinery complex for Bavaria, served by the trans-Alpine pipelines from Genoa and Trieste, as well as by a branch from the French pipeline at Karlsruhe. Ingolstadt was selected as a point midway between the two main markets in the Munich and Nürnberg agglomerations, with good motorway links to each. The subsidiary Augsburg market is equally close. The Danube offered process water and the future possibility of a water route for product distribution. Ingolstadt increased its population by 45% in the decade ending in 1965, and further expansion of this key area appears inevitable.

Industry and Population in Bavaria. Before the last war, the Bavarian economy was based firmly on agriculture, from which 28% of the people drew their living directly, and many others indirectly. The Bavarians were regarded as deeply attached to their land, and traditionally conservative in outlook. The postwar years have seen a remarkable economic development, so that the proportions of the active population employed in industry and the services are now not very different from those of West Germany as a whole. Bavarian economic progress has been secured in the face of postwar difficulties greater than in most other *Länder* in West Germany.

First of all, the breaking of former close links with East Germany and to a lesser extent with Czechoslovakia created a difficult employment situation all along the northeastern frontier of Bavaria. The situation was made worse by the fact that precisely this region had a heavy dependence on industries that have proved to be static or declining in postwar Germany, notably textiles, glass, pottery and the timber industries. Fortunately Federal Government assistance has been made available to improve the economic structure and attract industry, but there are still many problems, especially in the thinly-peopled Bavarian Forest and Upper Palatinate Forest regions bordering Czechoslovakia.

Bavaria was also one of the eastern rural areas that received the full flood of refugees at the end of the war, a heavy burden for what was then an economically weak part of Germany to bear. Together with later arrivals from East Germany the refugees and their descendants still make up about a fifth of the population, although many have moved on to other parts of Germany. Fortunately many of the refugees were highly skilled; those from Czechoslovakia in particular were frequently able to use abandoned military buildings to start up their traditional textile, glass and jewellery industries in their new homes. Similarly a number of large firms formerly situated in East Germany and Berlin set up afresh in Bavaria, especially in the smaller towns, where in the difficult postwar years they were able to find plentiful labour. This dispersion of industry to the smaller towns has been followed by much of the subsequent development. Although Bavaria contains two of Germany's larger agglomerations of population (Munich with nearly 2 million people and Nürnberg with over 1 million) the industrial regions have characteristically a loose spatial structure. Chief among them is obviously the growing Munich–Augsburg–Ingolstadt grouping, followed by Nürnberg–Erlangen–Fürth. Lesser industrial groupings are found in the Frankenwald and the 'chemical triangle'.

A further difficulty, accentuated by the formation of the European Economic Community, is remoteness from the main axis of German and indeed European economic development on the Rhine. The disadvantage has been accentuated by postwar impediments to trade with eastern Europe. The necessary reorientation has been assisted by the postwar electrification of the rail routes to the Rhinelands and the North German ports (Fig. 36) and by new motorway construction (Fig. 38). The arrival of oil pipelines has been of enormous benefit by reducing the dependence upon coal expensively hauled 550 km/350 miles from the Ruhr (Fig. 30). Northern Bavaria has also benefited from the canalization of the Main, and the continuation of the waterway through Nürnberg to the Danube is eagerly awaited. Improved political relations with the Danube states have also done something to break down isolation. Nevertheless Bavaria like Hamburg and Schleswig-Holstein remains somewhat marginal to the principal centres of European economic activity, and the considerable economic progress achieved since the war is therefore all the more remarkable.

Chapter 13
MIDDLE WEST GERMANY

South Germany terminates northwestwards in a transitional belt of country which runs from the Saar across the head of The Rhine Rift Valley to Hesse. This major region contains about 10 million people and has a clear focus in the cities of the Rhine–Main confluence. In it are some of the earliest centres of Frankish and German power, yet for centuries it has been politically divided. The division was perpetuated by the 1945 settlement, which still left *Land* frontiers running along the Rhine, breaking up the natural unity of the valley.

The fragmentation of the region centring on the Rhine–Main confluence merely mirrors, on a smaller scale, the disunity of Germany. Either Mainz or Frankfurt might have grown into a great regional capital (and probably the capital of Germany), but one was an Archbishop's seat, the other an independent Free City. Neither could be expected to forge a great territorial state. The only secular state that showed signs of rising to predominance, the Palatinate with its capital at Heidelberg, fell victim to the religious wars of the 17th century. This strategically vital region remained a power vacuum. Inevitably, surrounding states tried to expand into it, Prussia from the north, Bavaria from the east, Baden from the south, France from the west. Not one of the intruders was able to give political unity; indeed, it was in the interest of one of them, France, striving for the Rhine as a 'natural frontier', to perpetuate disunity if possible.

THE SAAR-NAHE LANDS

South of the Rhenish Uplands, while the Hercynian mountains were being built, there developed a depression in which sedimentary and volcanic deposits of Carboniferous and Permian age were accumulated. The effect of erosion on these diverse rocks has been to produce the very varied country of the Saar-Nahe Hills, between the Hunsrück and the sandstone Haardt (Fig. 40). In the extreme southwest of these hills, the northeast to southwest-trending Saar Saddle brings up productive coal measures to outcrop at surface.

The Saar Coalfield. The outcrop of the main productive coal measures is about 15 km/10 miles across and stretches for about

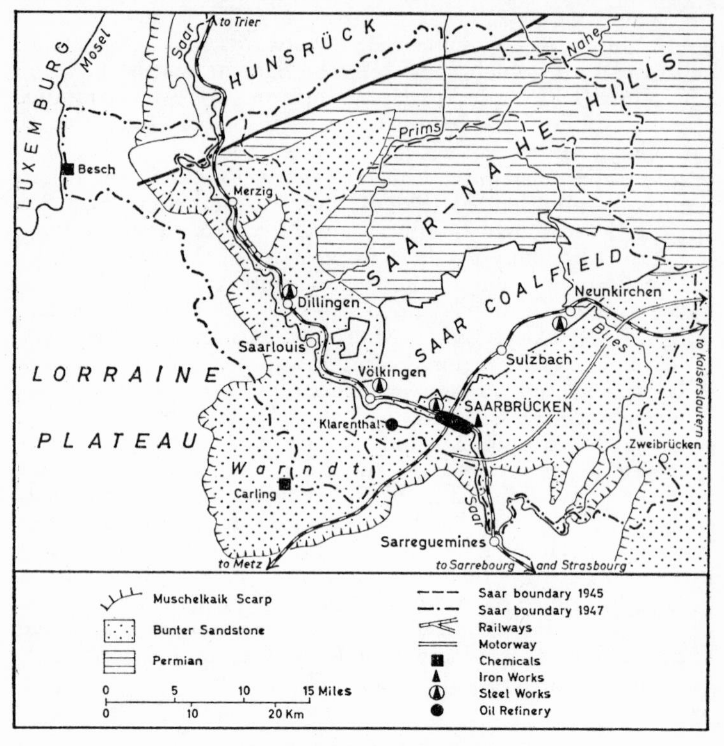

FIG. 44. The Saar region.

100 km/60 miles from the river Blies southwestwards to just beyond the Saar river near Völkingen (Fig. 44). At this point the coal measures disappear beneath the Bunter Sandstone, where they are mined in the concealed Warndt field by French mines beyond the frontier. Saar coal production is about 11% of the German total. Coke can be made from Saar coal only

with the admixture of about 20% of Ruhr coal, which increases the costs of the local steel industry. Gas from the coke ovens is fed into a grid which reaches Mannheim to the east and Lorraine to the west.

On the basis of its coke and of the low-grade Minette ore from Lorraine the Saar built up a steel capacity of about 3·7 million tons a year. Much of the steel went to local heavy industry, which in turn tended to concentrate on supplying the needs of the coal and steel industries. The lighter forms of engineering, and other modern growth industries, were conspicuously lacking.

The Saar Problem. Before the development of heavy industry what is now the Saar district was just a thinly populated border region between the much more important population centres of the Palatinate and Mainz to the east, Trier to the north and Lorraine to the west. Then in the middle of the 19th century the development of coal mining changed the geographical values in the Saar completely. It became the centre of a dense industrial population, and the subject of intense political and economic rivalry between France and Germany.

Twice in thirty years the Saar was detached from Germany. The Versailles settlement gave its mines to the French, and placed the territory under League of Nations' authority; it was returned to Germany after a plebiscite in 1935. After the Second World War an enlarged Saarland was administered by an independent government economically subordinate to France, but once again reunion with Germany followed, being completed by 1959. The price paid by the Germans included agreement to the canalization of the Mosel, which benefits Lorraine heavy industry rather than the Saar. The French also retained the right to mine coal from the Warndt field.

In the context of a united Western Europe it is doubtful if the Saar problem can be said to exist in any political sense. Today's Saar problem is an economic one, that of any region predominantly dependent on coal, steel and heavy industry. There is the usual story of mine closures and the dismissal of mining labour. The Saar iron and steel industry has increasingly replaced Minette ore with high-grade imported ores, but this tends to emphasize the region's disadvantage by comparison with the large new coastal plants. The coming of the

Coal and Steel Community made matters worse by opening the Saar's South German markets to competition. The industry has tried to meet the situation by diversifying into products that can less easily be produced in the mass, like castings and steel tubes. Saar heavy engineering has also found its outlets diminishing with the crisis in coal and steel.

After lengthy attempts to attract new forms of industry to the Saar plants have been set up to manufacture machinery, electrical equipment, clothing, wood products and foodstuffs, but it is difficult to change an industrial structure so closely geared to the needs of the coal and steel industries. A considerable step forward was the acquisition of the Ford Saarlouis press shop, which is capable of extension into an assembly plant. Although the canalization of the Mosel has brought very limited benefit, some of the region's isolation has been reduced by the building of the motorway and the electrification of the rail routes to the Rhine. Even more encouraging in view of the past history of the region are the attempts to meet the common problems of the Saar, Lorraine and Luxemburg by developments stretching across frontiers. A new Franco-Saar oil refinery at Klarenthal will enable the French coal-chemical plant at Carling to turn over to a petroleum base, while another unit making intermediate products for the plastics industry is being developed at Besch on the navigable Mosel, where the French, Saar and Luxemburg frontiers meet.

Population and Settlement in the Saar. The Saar's 1·1 million inhabitants live mainly in two intersecting belts of population. The first axis follows the valley of the Saar upstream from the Merzig area, where it is still quite rural, apart from some pottery industries. The characteristic heavy industry of the Saar valley begins with *Dillingen.* The largest steel centre is *Völkingen* (42), but foundries and heavy engineering works are found all along the valley to Saarbrücken. Continuing over the Bunter Sandstone plateau towards *Zweibrücken* (34) is an area of lighter and more varied industries. The second axis begins at *Neunkirchen* (46), the only iron and steel centre of importance outside the Saar valley, and follows the coal outcrop southwestwards. It is a huddle of coal mines, coke ovens, glass works and workers' settlements. Where the two population axes meet is *Saarbrücken* (134), which is both an industrial town with iron, steel and engineering industries, and also the commercial and administrative capital of the Saarland.

THE PALATINATE

The Palatinate Forest and Rhine Plain. The Permian rocks of the Saar-Nahe hills disappear southwards beneath the Bunter Sandstone plateau of the Palatinate Forest, the uptilted eastern edge of which forms the Haardt, rising to 600 m/2,000 ft. The Forest is typical Bunter Sandstone country and bears one of the largest areas of woodland in Germany, predominantly pine, with some beech.

Naturally, this is extremely thinly populated country, and towns are almost entirely restricted to the eastern and western fringes. *Kaiserslautern* (86) commands a west–east depression that gives a routeway between the Palatinate Forest to the south and the Saar-Nahe hills to the north. To its existing engineering activities it has added a large vehicle components plant. The one important town in the Forest is *Pirmasens* (52), which has conquered its remoteness from main lines of communication to become Germany's foremost centre of boot and shoe manufacture.

In the east, the Haardt drops extremely steeply for 400–500 m/1,300–1,600 ft to the Upper Rhine Plain. Lining the foot of the Haardt, beneath the chestnut trees of the slopes, are the vineyards of the Palatinate, the largest area of vines in Germany. This rich belt of vineyards and orchards, with its string of large vine growers' villages and small towns, forms the *Weinstrasse*, corresponding with the *Bergstrasse* across the river, or with the foothill towns of the Vosges to the south.[1]

The Upper Rhine Plain is wider in the Palatinate than east of the river. Expanses of loess-covered terrace and the warm, dry climate of the Rhinelands permit the cultivation of numerous specialized crops, including tobacco, sugar beet, malting barley, hops and early vegetables. On the terrace edge, overlooking the Rhine, are two of the most important cathedral towns of medieval Germany. Both have been overshadowed by the recent growth of the Rhine–Neckar agglomeration. Both have been drawn into the developing chemical industry of this part of the Rhine, *Speyer* (41) with a new oil refinery supplied

[1] See E. Estyn Evans, *France* (Frederick A. Praeger), p. 116.

from the French pipeline, *Worms* (64) with a large detergent plant.

The Rhine–Hesse Plateau. Only at the extreme northern end do the Tertiary rocks which fill the Rift Valley come to the surface for a considerable extent, forming the limestone Rhine–Hesse Plateau. Where the limestone is cut by the Rhine, prominent quarries supply some of Germany's largest cement plants. The even loess-covered surface is almost exclusively devoted to arable fields, with never a hedge and hardly a tree to break the view. The villages are in the deep valleys, where alone a little meadow land is found. The valley sides and the outer slopes overlooking the Rhine are covered by famous vineyards.

This warm, dry corner of the Rhine Rift Valley has been settled by farmers since Neolithic times, and the predominance of *-heim* place-names points to the early Germanic occupants. The Romans established the capital of *Germania Superior* here, and its ruins became the seat of a Christian bishop. The town of *Mainz* (143) which grew around this nucleus was one of the most important in medieval Germany, reaching its height in the 12th–14th centuries. Today it is the westernmost town of the Rhine–Main industrial region, with cement, engineering, optical glass and food-processing works (Fig. 45).

Mainz was selected in 1945 as the capital of *Land* Rhineland-Palatinate, which was assembled from the Palatinate, Rhine–Hesse and a large part of the southern Rhenish Uplands, mainly with the object of providing a zone of occupation for the French. With a population of 3·6 millions Rhineland-Palatinate is economically one of the weaker *Länder*. From the day of its creation its division between surrounding *Länder* or merger with one of them was confidently predicted. Like many political arrangements of the kind, however, it has proved remarkably durable.

THE RHINE–MAIN REGION

At its northern end, the Upper Rhine Plain broadens eastwards to form the Rhine–Main Basin. The Basin is filled with the same Tertiary rocks that outcrop in Rhine–Hesse, much disturbed by faulting, but hidden by a relatively thin skin of terrace gravels and other superficial deposits. The terrace gravels north of the Main are generally covered by loess, but south of the river fields of blown sand and sand dunes predominate. Consequently, there are here large stretches of coniferous forest, little cleared until the growth of housing estates in the present century.

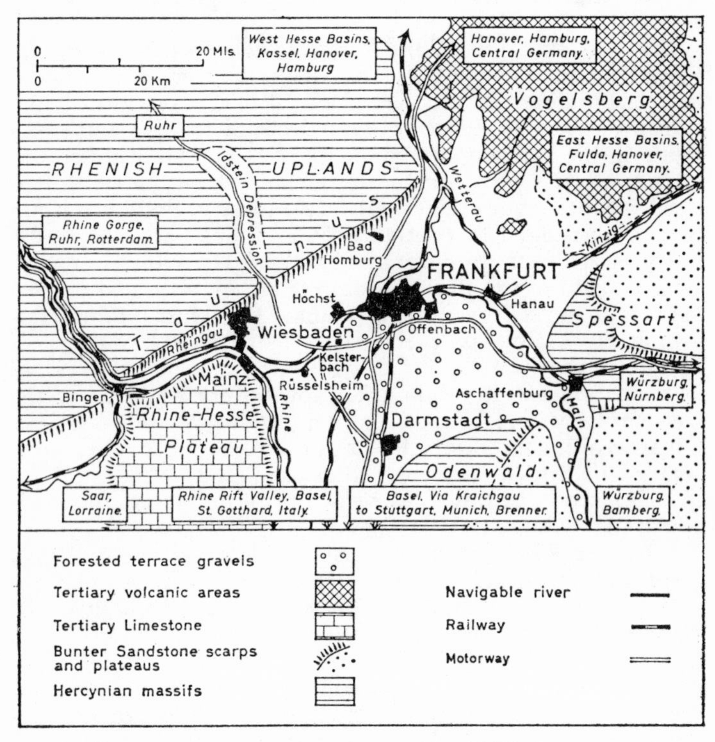

FIG. 45. The Rhine–Main Region.

The Rhine–Main Lowland forms a most clearly defined unit, surrounded as it is by the uplands of the Taunus, Vogelsberg, Spessart, Odenwald and the Palatinate (Fig. 45). Through gaps in the upland the routeways converge: by the Rhine Gorge from the Ruhr, by the Rhine Rift Valley from southern

Germany and Switzerland, by the Hessian Basins from the Northern Lowland and Central Germany, by the Nahe from the Saar and Lorraine, and by the lower Main from Nürnberg and Bavaria. The routes focus like the spokes of a wheel on the Rhine–Main region, especially on Frankfurt. Yet Frankfurt is not alone; it is but the largest of a complex of towns which form one of Germany's most important industrial regions.

Like Swabia, the Rhine–Main region specializes in the lighter manufacturing industries, especially engineering and vehicle building. It, too, draws much of its labour in widespread daily movements from hundreds of villages and small towns in the surrounding rural districts. The main difference from Swabia is provided by the Rhine, which has permitted the development of a heavy chemical industry. Frankfurt is not in a cul-de-sac, like Stuttgart; it is a link, a great traffic junction, between southern and northern Germany.

The towns of the Rhine–Main region are arranged on two axes, a main east–west axis Hanau–Frankfurt–Mainz, following the Main, and a subsidiary axis running southwards parallel to the Rhine as far as Darmstadt. *Frankfurt* (691) is, as its name suggests, in origin a ford town of the Main. Here the German Emperors were elected, and from 1562 crowned also. Great wealth came from the cloth trade, and from the twice-yearly fairs, which drew merchants from all over the German-speaking world to this free city at one of the great crossroads of Europe.

After the Reformation, the money changers essential in a great trade fair developed into private banking houses of international reputation, among them the firm of Rothschilds. The 19th century brought great changes; in 1848–9, the town was the seat of the Frankfurt Parliament, Germany's ill-fated experiment in liberalism. The middle years of the century saw the building of the railways, incorporation into Prussia, and the beginning of industrial development in what had been previously an almost exclusively commercial and financial centre.

However revolutionary the new developments were, they still reflected the unchanging geographical advantages of Frankfurt's situation. The town became a major junction in Germany's rail and, subsequently, motorway net. A satisfactory connection to the Rhine routeway was provided by the improvement of the Main from the 1880s onwards, so that today heavy goods like coal, gravel, petroleum, chemicals and ores are received by water.

A superb geographical position and excellent modern communications compensate for the lack of local raw materials, power, or cheap labour. The principal industry, measured by the workers employed, is engineering, with numerous works located in the western and northwestern suburbs and at the Main harbours. The chemical industries, second in terms of labour employed but first in terms of the value of their product, are located where they can use the Main for process water and for the transport of heavy raw materials: *Hoechst* just west of Frankfurt is the principal centre. The change from coal to a petroleum base has been facilitated by the extension of the Rotterdam oil pipeline southwards to a new refinery built at Kelsterback just west of Hoechst expressly to serve the chemical industry of the region.

Following the Main axis eastwards, industrial development is practically continuous to *Offenbach* (117), which has important leather and engineering industries, and *Hanau* (51), where rubber and non-ferrous metals industries are now more important than the traditional jewellery trade. Across the Bavarian boundary the Aschaffenburg region with its rayon and synthetic fibres plants has been increasingly drawn into the Rhine–Main orbit (p. 195).

West of Frankfurt lie the principal chemical plants of the Hoechst complex. *Rüsselsheim* (50) is almost a one-industry town, dominated by the Opel car plant (pp. 146–8). Of a very different nature is *Wiesbaden* (261), the capital of Hesse, at the foot of the Taunus. The twenty-seven warm mineral springs of *Aquae Mattiacae*, welling up on the line of the Taunus fault, were already appreciated in Roman times. Today they are the basis of a spa with all the usual characteristics of pump room, baths, clinics, hotels, parks and pompous villas of the Kaiser's day. The darker side of elegant Wiesbaden is provided by the southern industrial suburbs, where chemical and cement plants, paper mills and engineering works cluster along the Rhine. Wiesbaden is linked with Mainz by the Rhine bridge into a single conurbation of over 400,000 inhabitants.

On the north–south axis the pleasant wooded slopes of the Taunus are a favoured middle-class residential area. There is a scatter of light engineering plants, as at the spa town of *Bad Homburg*. South of the Main axis *Darmstadt* (140) was formerly capital of the state of Hesse–Darmstadt. As is typical in the Rhine–Main region, the town has a well-balanced assortment of chemical, engineering, plastic, electrical and paper industries. South of Darmstadt are wells from which natural gas is piped to the Ludwigshafen chemical plant.

HESSE

Physically Hesse consists of the country between the Rhenish Uplands in the west and the Thuringian Forest in the east. Politically it also includes much territory in the eastern Rhenish Uplands, and stretches southwards through the Rhine–Main region nearly as far as Mannheim. The present *Land* Hesse, created in 1945, had a population in 1965 of 5 millions, of whom 23% were refugees.

Hesse in the physical sense is a barrier, but a barrier pierced by faulted Tertiary basins, which prolong the Rhine Rift Valley northwards. These depressions give Hesse a pronounced division into four belts of terrain, the West Hesse Depression, the Hessian Central Uplands, the East Hesse Depression and the Rhön.

The basins are the vital element in the human geography of Hesse. Their Tertiary sands and clays do not always provide good soils themselves, but fortunately they are almost always covered by loess. The climate is warm, with continental tendencies in the south, and because of the shelter of the Rhenish Uplands, precipitation is low, varying from 500 mm/20 in in the south to 680 mm/27 in in the north. These are the grain lands of Hesse, settled since Neolithic times. In addition, the basins provide major routeways, connecting southern Germany with the Northern Lowland and the North German Ports.

West Hesse Depression. The southernmost basin, the fertile Wetterau, which is drained southwards to the Main, is separated by only a low sill from the Giessen Basin to the north. *Giessen* (72) developed rapidly in the 19th century as a rail junction, but is not itself very industrialized, living as a central place and university town. In the immediate neighbourhood however is a variety of plants producing light machinery, electrical equipment, cameras and cigars. The basin and its fringes is typical *Haufendorf* country, with very small and fragmented farms. All around Giessen the villages are swollen into settlements for workers, many of whom must travel long distances daily. So great is West German labour shortage that the great Rhine–Main electrical firms have established branch plants in the villages where women can work part-time at component assembly. Iron ores from the Palaeozoic rocks of the Lahn and Dill valleys are smelted near by at *Wetzlar*, a town best known for its optical and camera works.

North of Giessen the lavas of the Vogelsberg stretch far to the west, completely blocking the natural routeway of the Tertiary basins. Fortunately the valley of the Lahn provides a narrow way northwards to the university town of *Marburg* (49), beyond which the railway is able to swing round north of the volcanic massif to enter the large Kassel Basin.

The Tertiary rocks of this basin contain brown-coal deposits, worked mainly for electricity generation. *Kassel* (214) lies at the northern end, and is another major meeting place of routes. From here, the railway is able to follow the valleys of the Fulda and Werra tributaries of the Weser and cross the low Eichenberg gap into the Leine Rift Valley and so reach Hanover and the Northern Lowland. Other routes run westwards to the Ruhr, and eastwards to Thuringia, while Kassel is also the head of the Weser navigation. These good communications have enabled the town to develop as quite an important centre of industry, producing railway engines, rolling stock, heavy commercial vehicles, textile fibres, electrical goods and machinery. The 18th-century Landgraves of Hesse transformed the town with their baroque palaces, and colossal cascades and fountains on the surrounding hills. So great was the expense of creating all this magnificence that the Landgraves were reduced to selling their unfortunate subjects as mercenary soldiers, particularly to England for use in the American War of Independence.

The Hessian Central Uplands. The volcanic areas of Hesse range in size from the 2,500 sq km/950 sq miles of the *Vogelsberg*, the largest continuous basalt area in Europe, to the thousands of eroded volcanic necks which all over Hesse form abrupt forested hills, rising above the surrounding countryside. The Vogelsberg itself is an almost circular mass, with drainage radiating from the Taufstein (774 m/2,539 ft). In the 19th century arable cultivation still penetrated up the valleys to the

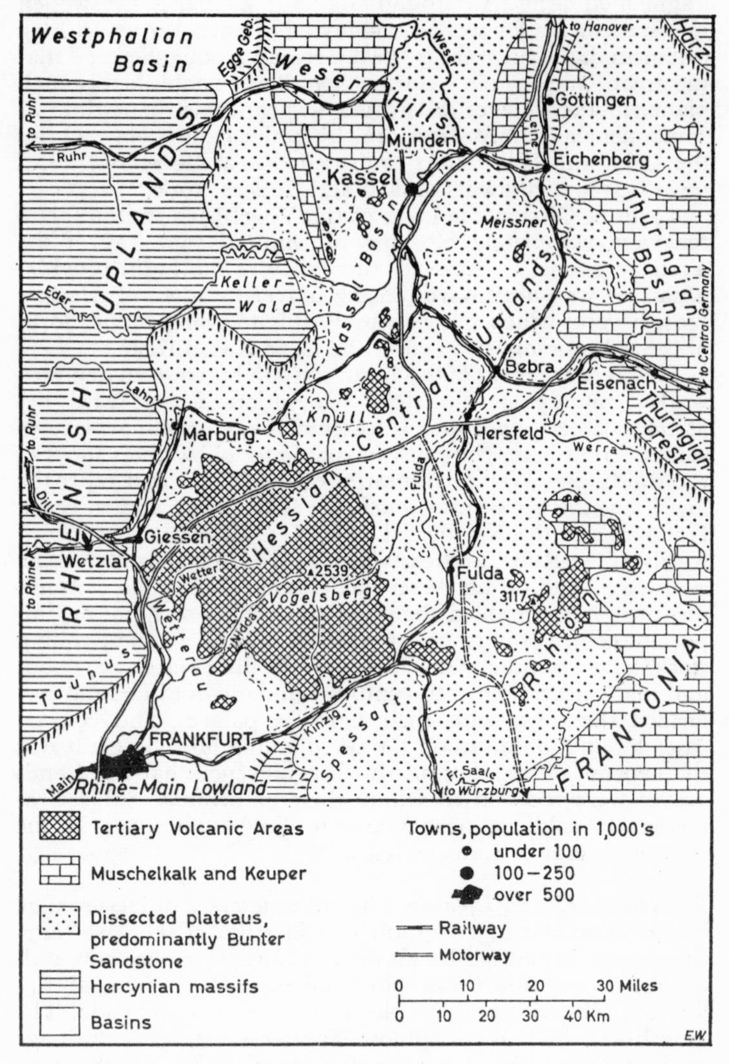

Westphalian Basin
Egge Geb.
Weser Hills
Weser
to Hanover
Harz
to Ruhr
Ruhr
RHENISH UPLANDS
Göttingen
Leine
Münden
Eichenberg
Kassel
Kassel Basin
Meissner
Thuringian Basin
Keller Wald
Eder
to Central Germany
Central Uplands
Bebra
Eisenach
Thuringian Forest
Lahn
Knüll
Marburg
Hersfeld
Werra
Hessian
Fulda
Dill
Giessen
Wetzlar
to Rhine
Wetter
2539
Vogelsberg
3117
Rhön
Wetterau
Nidda
Taunus
Kinzig
Spessart
FRANCONIA
FRANKFURT
Main
Rhine-Main Lowland
Fr. Saale
to Würzburg
Tertiary Volcanic Areas
Muschelkalk and Keuper
Dissected plateaus, predominantly Bunter Sandstone
Hercynian massifs
Basins
Towns, population in 1,000's
under 100
100–250
over 500
Railway
Motorway
0 10 20 30 Miles
0 10 20 30 40 Km
E.W.

FIG. 46. Hesse.

remarkable height of over 600 m/2,000 ft, while the block-strewn lava flows were used as rough grazing. The close of the 19th century saw a first period of retreat from such excessively marginal land. State and communal forests were planted on the higher areas, with spruce replacing the original beech. The Vogelsberg is today one of the characteristic problem areas of the German Central Uplands. Everywhere there are signs of abandonment and retreat of arable; the parallel strip fields of the slopes, with the characteristic straggle of hedges along the lynchets between them, are increasingly grassed over or even afforested. The Federal Government has put large sums of money into the drainage of meadows and the clearing of the former rough pastures in order to make possible a sound grass-based livestock industry. New roads to benefit agriculture, forestry and the commuting worker also stimulate the growing tourist traffic. The highland axis is continued by the Knüll, a thinly peopled region of basalt-capped Bunter Sandstone hills rising to 634 m/2,080 ft, and terminates in the Meissner massif, overlooking the Werra valley.

East Hesse Depression and Rhön. The Tertiary basins of the East Hesse Depression are smaller, but are linked by river valleys to form a second south–north corridor. Ancient routeways from Frankfurt up the Kinzig valley and from Würzburg converge on *Fulda* (45), a town which grew around the great abbey founded by Boniface in 744. The routeway passes northwards through Hersfeld, site of another of Boniface's abbeys, and uses sections of the Fulda and Werra valleys to reach the Eichenberg gap.

West of Hersfeld is the Werra potash field, the largest in Germany, which is worked on both sides of the boundary between Hesse and Thuringia. Hesse is finally closed in the east by the Rhön, a more dissected volcanic massif than the Vogelsberg, but rising even higher, to 950 m/3,117 ft. This is another economic problem area, its position made worse by the cutting of the East German boundary across its northern end. The region may benefit from the projected motorway through the basins of western Hesse.

Chapter 14

THE RHENISH UPLANDS

THE BUILDING OF THE MASSIF

The faulted basins of Hesse set the eastern limit to the Hercynian massif of the Rhenish Uplands, which divides northern from southern Germany and disrupts the continuity of the Rhine Basin. The sharpest boundary of the massif is in the south, where it is broken off along the Hunsrück and Taunus ridges. Westwards it merges with the similar Belgian Ardenne, and northwards it declines under younger rocks. The regular outline of the block is broken by two great zones of subsidence; in the north, the Tertiary-filled Lower Rhinelands almost bites the massif in half, while in the Trier Lowland in the southwest it disappears beneath Permian and Triassic beds extending from the scarplands of Lorraine. The massif consists mainly of Devonian clay-slates, intensively folded in the Hercynian earth movements, but peneplained at the end of Hercynian times. The geological monotony is only occasionally relieved by bands of quartzite and limestone, or by the Tertiary volcanic outpourings of the Eifel and Westerwald.

The broad lines of relief in the Rhenish Uplands are determined by southwest to northeast-trending flexures, which are cut at right angles by the course of the Rhine flowing into the Lower Rhineland. As a result, there is a remarkable symmetry in the disposition of the various hill masses. In the south, the Rhine divides the Hunsrück in the west from the very similar Taunus in the east. These fall northwards to a depression, in which the river Mosel is matched by the Lahn. North of this, the complex Eifel block west of the Lower Rhinelands is balanced by the complex Westerwald–Sauerland block to the east.

In detail, however, relief is due to the effect of erosion. Gradual uplift of the massif since early Tertiary times has caused the cutting of a series of erosion surfaces, forming a giant staircase reaching from the highest parts down to the main river valleys. The principal surfaces are at about 500 m/1,650 ft and 600 m/2,000 ft, and are overlooked by residual hill masses, often on quartzite bands, rising still higher to 850 m/

2,800 ft. Into the surfaces the rivers have cut deep valleys, their slopes broken by Pliocene and Pleistocene river terraces. The later stages of valley cutting were very rapid; frequently on the Rhine and its major tributaries there is a precipitous fall from the mid-Pleistocene High Terrace at about 200 m/650 ft to the stream 150 m/500 ft below. The lesser tributaries, in their

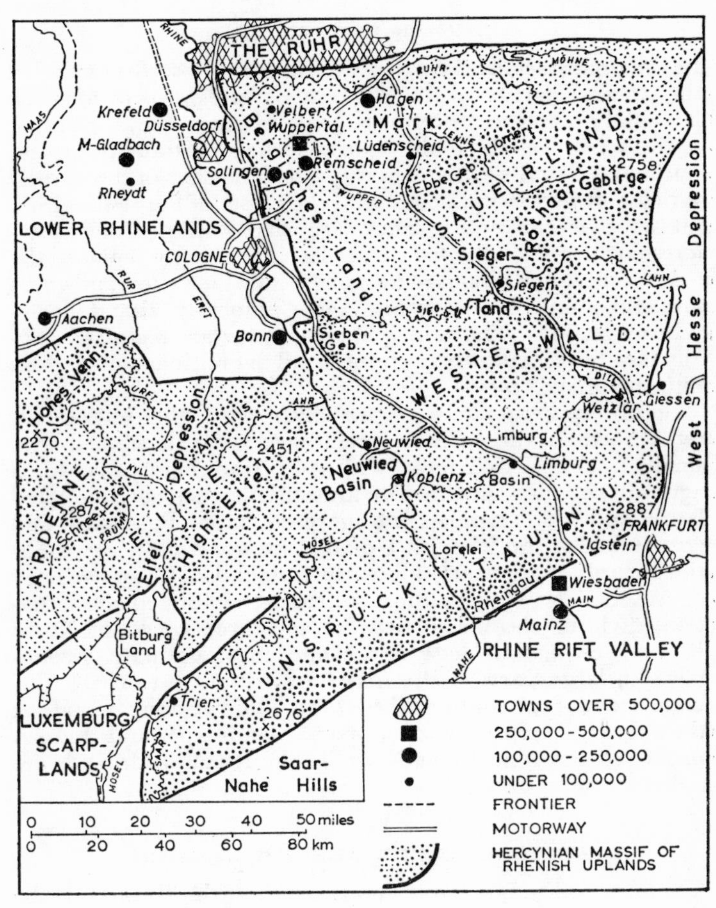

FIG. 47. The Rhenish Uplands.

efforts to keep pace with the main streams, have cut steep, V-shaped valleys into the surrounding plateaus. As a result of this erosional history, there are in the Rhenish Uplands two clearly contrasting types of relief, the gently undulating plateau surfaces, or upland plains, and the deep valleys cut into them.

HUMAN GEOGRAPHY

In the prehistoric and early medieval periods, settlers avoided the wooded barrier of the Rhenish Uplands, except for such favoured areas as river terraces. Only in the medieval clearing of the waste was the main plateau surface partially occupied, but to this day the settlement is sparse. The sides of the narrow valleys cut into the plateaus, and the slopes of the residual hill masses that rise above them, are alike still predominantly forested, although planted spruce has increasingly replaced the oak and beech. Ribbons of meadow follow the valleys, in which are also found the mills and the—frequently abandoned—railway stations. The principal settlements are characteristically far above, typically in spring-head depressions sunk lightly into the upland plains.

South approximately of the river Sieg the settlements established in the medieval clearance have developed into small nucleated villages, with the traditional open-field agriculture much modified by altitude. Further north isolated farms and small hamlets are more common. Politically and economically, the Rhenish Uplands are not a unit; the traditional capitals are nearly all on the fringes, like Cologne, Trier or Mainz. The 1945 political settlement continued this situation, dividing the massif between the three *Länder* of North Rhine-Westphalia, Hesse and Rhineland-Palatinate. Economically, large parts of the north are tributary to the Ruhr, large areas of the south to the Rhine–Main region. In spite of their great uniformity of physical landscape and human response, economically and socially the Rhenish Uplands are a divide, not a unity.

REGIONS OF THE RHENISH UPLANDS

The Rhine Valley. The most familiar part of the Uplands is the deeply cut valley of the Rhine, in which Germany's greatest waterway is accompanied by intensively used rail and road routes (Chap. 10). To the passing traveller, the valley is a world of its own, bounded by cliff-like slopes, with only an occasional hint of the plateau that lies above.

The Rhine at the northern end of the Rift Valley flows for a space at the foot of the Taunus before swinging north at Bingen to traverse the massif. Immediately there is a dramatic narrowing to the main gorge section, between Hunsrück and Taunus. Where the river cuts resistant quartzite bands, the valley is spectacularly narrow and steep, as at the great Lorelei cliff, and the waters slide dangerously over rocks in the stream bed. Where the gorge opens slightly, man has cultivated every shred of land, in order to take advantage of the warmth and shelter of the valley. Above all, on every slope turned towards the sun are vineyards, held in place by stone terrace walls. Where a tributary valley or a fragment of river terrace offers foothold there are villages and towns, wealthy from the vine, Rhine shipping and, today, tourism. On the slopes above are ruined castles, reminders of the centuries when there was no strong power in Germany to prevent every petty ruler from levying toll on the traffic passing on the great river beneath.

At Koblenz the valley broadens out into the Neuwied Basin (p. 231). Then it narrows again to a further gorge section between the Eifel and Westerwald until near Bonn, with the vineyards and villas of the volcanic Siebengebirge on the right hand, the Rhine enters the Cologne Lowland.

The Eifel. The northeastern section of the massif is one of the most complex. It is traversed by the *Eifel Depression*, linking the Cologne and Trier Lowlands. The depression is filled at either end with Triassic rocks which in the north contain formerly important lead deposits. With its favourable limestone areas it was a zone of early settlement, and still provides a relatively easy routeway between Cologne and Trier.

West of the depression, on the Belgian frontier, lie the *Schnee Eifel* and the *Hohes Venn*. The latter has a remarkably even plateau surface at 600–700 m/2,000–2,300 ft on which poor drainage and a rainfall of 1,000–1,250 mm/40–50 in a year have encouraged the accumulation of peat bog. The surrounding slopes and the lower 500 m/1,650 ft Eifel plateau surface are the scene of a dairying industry providing liquid milk for industrial populations to the north. The farmhouses, standing isolated or loosely grouped in villages, are protected from the rain-bearing winds by tall beech hedges and vast overhanging roofs. Around them are small irregular pasture fields, surrounded by beech hedges. The more open field land further out has much rotation grass, with some oats and provides hay, although the water meadows on the floors of the deeply incised streams are tending to revert to forest use. The dairying region has lately been expanding south and south-eastwards as the fragmented arable fields of the Eifel have given place to consolidated pastures.

East of the depression, the ridge of the *High Eifel*, dominated by the ruins of Tertiary volcanoes like Hohe Acht (747 m/2,451 ft), looks southwards over a plateau which stretches to the Mosel. The plateau surface was cleared in the Middle Ages to heights approaching 600 m/2,000 ft, and still retains a pattern of arable strips in open fields, which today mainly produce fodder crops for feeding to cattle. The small nucleated villages lie in sheltered hollows just below the surface of the plateau, yet avoid the deep forested gashes cut by tributaries of the Mosel or Rhine.

The Eifel is one of the poorest parts of western Germany, a region in which traditionally high birth rates were matched by high emigration. Of recent years the development of commuting has helped population to remain in place on the northern and western fringes. Tourism is developing, especially short-period visits by the altitude-seeking Dutch.

The Mosel. The Eifel declines southwards to the Mosel, which is superimposed into the slates of the plateau in a fantastic series of giant incised meanders. Nowhere is the importance of aspect in vine growing more clearly demonstrated. A slope facing the sun will be covered from top to bottom with the finest vineyards in Germany, but as the river meanders round, the vines will give place to worthless scrub on a north-facing slope. It is scarcely surprising that routeways mainly avoid this narrow, winding valley in favour of the more open country just to the north. The narrowness of the valley prevents industry from taking much advantage of the canalization of the river, which mainly benefits Lorraine.

The principal town of the Mosel is *Trier* (86), sited to the west of the difficult meander section. The medieval town grew round a bishop's seat, crouching in the ruins of the Roman *Augusta Treveorum*, once capital of Gaul, Britain and Spain. This is an area where industrial development may follow the completion of the canal.

The Neuwied Basin.[1] The Mosel joins the Rhine in a Tertiary-filled basin, where the work of erosion has hollowed out a lowland overlooked by the older rocks of the plateau. The individuality of the region comes from the effects of the last phases of volcanic activity of the near-by Eifel. Some 10,000 years ago, a number of volcanic explosions spread a layer of pumice fragments and dust, known to the Germans as *Bims*, over the land. This warm, sheltered basin, covered with pumice and loess, is very dry and fertile, with a marked lack of surface drainage. It is like an outlier of South Germany, with open arable fields, fruit trees and large villages.

The Rhine in the Neuwied Basin is lined with industrial plants. Steel works concentrate on sheet steel and tinplate, some of which is used for canning the local fruit. There are engineering, paper, cement and pottery works. But the characteristic industry of the region today is the working of pumice in shallow pits, which are subsequently restored to agriculture. The pumice fragments are mixed with cement and moulded into widely used light building blocks. Because the basin is small, and has often been politically divided, no single regional centre has grown in it. The largest town is *Koblenz* (102), successor to the Roman *Confluentes* and a former capital of the ecclesiastical state of Trier.

Hunsrück and Taunus. These two regions provide some of the highest and wildest country in the whole of the Rhenish Uplands. In both, there is a northern section in which plateaus cut across the Devonian slates rise southwards in stages to 600 m/2,000 ft. The plateaus were cleared of forest in the Middle Ages, and bear a pattern of strip fields and small villages. From time to time quartzite bands form forested ridges rising from the plateaus; southwards these become more frequent, and reach the greatest heights of the massif, culminating in the Feldberg (880 m/2,887 ft). From this southernmost

[1] Some German geographers prefer to call this the 'Middle Rhine Basin', restricting the term 'Neuwied Basin' to the lowest part of the region, near the Rhine.

ridge, the ground plunges spectacularly southwards along the remarkably straight faultline escarpment that bounds the massif.

These are backward, isolated regions in which too many people are struggling to wring a living from the poor upland soil by outdated methods of arable cultivation. The Hunsrück in particular is a problem region, but the Taunus is a little more varied. In the southeast its foothills, falling to the Rhine, form one of Germany's greatest wine-producing regions, the Rheingau, with tier upon tier of vines held in place on the steep hillsides by stone terraces. The general air of warmth, together with the mineral springs that break out along the Taunus faults, have stimulated the growth of spas like Wiesbaden (p. 221). The Taunus also benefits from proximity to Frankfurt and to the routes which run northwards from the city, passing through the Taunus ridges by means of the Idstein depression, on the way to Limburg (Fig. 45).

The Lahn Valley and the Westerwald. To the west of the Tertiary basin of Limburg, the Lahn cuts a deep gorge, with incised meanders repeating on a less spectacular scale those of the Mosel, but mainly lacking in the variety brought by the vine. North of the river, the familiar slate plateaus rise to over 600 m/ 2,000 ft again, but are this time given originality by extensive lava flows. The basalt weathers to a heavy, impervious soil which, however, is rich in plant foods owing to the basic parent rock. In the higher parts of the Westerwald the wide, mature valleys are still boggy and ill-drained, but the slopes bear basic pastures and scattered arable strips. Villages avoid both the marshy valley floors and the windswept plateau level, and are protected by clumps of conifers and long shelter belts. Overpopulated and relying on outdated agricultural techniques, the Westerwald is another of the problem regions of western Germany.

The Siegerland. North of the little-dissected Westerwald, there is a contrasting region where the Sieg and its tributaries have carved the plateau into a maze of steep, wooded ridges and narrow valleys. This is the Siegerland, the centre until the mid-19th century of an iron industry based on vein ores in the Devonian rocks, the charcoal of the oak coppices that covered the hillsides, and the power of the swiftly-flowing streams.

The iron mines are now approaching 1,200 m/4,000 ft in depth and are scarcely economic. The ore goes partly to the Ruhr, partly to local furnaces. Today, the industrial importance of the district rests on the production of special quality iron and steel, the re-rolling of Ruhr steel to produce fine sheet metal work and the building of machine tools. The chief town is *Siegen* (50).

The Sauerland. The Siegerland is buttressed to the northeast by the upwarped Rothaar massif, a heavily forested hill mass rising to 841 m/2,758 ft. From the Rothaar the plateau slopes generally northwards and northwestwards, and is increasingly dissected by streams draining to the Ruhr and Rhine. The drainage has picked out the weaker bands of the planed-off Upper Devonian and Lower Carboniferous rocks, so that an almost 'Appalachian' structure results. Limestone bands form depressions, one of them providing a convenient routeway through the hills on the line Düsseldorf–Wuppertal–Ennepetal–Hagen. The limestones are worked in a series of large quarries to supply the Rhine–Ruhr iron and chemical plants. Small villages and hamlets of half-timbered houses, often hung with slates against the rain-bearing westerly winds, take advantage of dissected remnants of plateau surfaces or the limestone depressions for their arable fields. The valley bottoms bear meadows, and their steep sides provide timber and pit props for the Ruhr coalfield. Many valleys have been dammed to provide great reservoirs, again for the benefit of the conurbation to the north.

In the water-power stage of the iron industry the valleys of the northern Sauerland, in what was formerly the County of Mark, were lined with mill dams driving a succession of iron hammers, slitting mills for the nail trade and wire mills. The smiths used bar iron from the Siegerland, and coal brought by horses from seams outcropping in the valley of the Ruhr river. After the middle of the 19th century Mark, like the Siegerland, was unable to compete with the large-scale industry developing on the Ruhr coalfield. The iron and steel industry was reduced to plants for the hot and cold re-rolling of Ruhr steel, together with foundries and hammer works. To survive Mark concentrated on the making of an enormous range of small metal products, including wire goods, screws, vehicle springs, metal pressings and stampings of all kinds, and machine parts for assembly in the engineering and vehicle industries elsewhere. The fabrication of aluminium and other non-ferrous metals is also important, especially at *Lüdenscheid* (59). Various types of machinery and electrical equipment are also produced.

This is Germany's industrial equivalent of the English Black Country, and although in an upland massif has a higher density of population than the average for the industrial *Land* of North Rhine–Westphalia. There is a scatter of medium and small manufacturing towns, but with the growth of the Ruhr all have been overtaken by *Hagen* (203). Here two major routes enter the highlands. One runs southwestwards through the limestone depressions to the Rhine, and is now doubled by the motorway to Cologne. The second is the electrified freight route across the Rhenish Uplands through Siegen to southern Germany. It too is doubled by the motorway to Giessen. Hagen is almost a Ruhr town, with steel and chemicals, as well as the lighter metal industries and machine building typical of the Mark.

Bergisches Land. West of the Sauerland, between Sieg, Rhine and Ruhr, is the lower country known as Bergisches Land, named after the former County of Berg. The plateau is here cut by the higher terraces of the Rhine, which are frequently covered by loess and loam deposits. The country has been cut into a series of east–west ridges, separated by the deep valleys of tributaries of the Rhine. The ridges carry the cultivated land, the high roads and the market towns. Typically the large isolated farms lie in spring heads, just below plateau level. The steep valley sides are either wooded or divided into enclosed pastures, grazed by dairy cows supplying the industrial towns of Ruhr and Rhine.

Industrially Bergisches Land like Mark concentrates on the lighter forms of iron and steel processing, but its products are more highly finished. Typical in this respect is the ridge-top town of *Solingen* (174), traditional capital of the German cutlery industry. The town also makes razor blades, precision and measuring instruments and a variety of metal parts for assembly elsewhere. Across the deeply-cut Wupper valley *Remscheid* (133) is the principal German centre for the making of hand tools of all kinds. It also makes power tools, small machine tools and household equipment. Another typical

Berg specialization is the manufacture of about half Germany's locks and keys, especially at *Velbert* (55).

Standing out from the other Berg towns in its type of industry, its size and its valley situation is *Wuppertal* (423). The fundamental industry is textiles, the traditional specialization being in ribbons, tapes and braid, with the larger weaving concerns concentrating on linings, upholstery fabrics and other specialized goods. Out of ribbon manufacture grew successively the manufacture of elastic tapes, corsetry, elastic bands, rubber soles, motor tyres, insulated cables and electrical equipment. Out of the demands of the dyeing industry grew a chemical industry. Most of it subsequently moved away to Leverkusen on the Rhine, leaving some remnants such as pharmaceuticals and paints. Rayon and synthetic fibres manufacture link both with the textile and the chemical industries. The clothing industry is another outgrowth, and the demand for buckles and buttons stimulated the manufacture of small metal articles generally. From this developed the manufacture of various kinds of machinery and precision instruments, often with an application in textiles, but not always so. The manufacture of zip fasteners is the modern representative of the traditional button making. Finally the demand for packing materials has stimulated the development of the paper industry. Wuppertal thus provides an excellent example of the way in which industrial diversification and linkage can build a powerful and expanding economic base for an area, able to seize new opportunities for growth or weather depression that may occur in any particular branch of industry. The town was created in 1929 by an amalgamation of the three valley settlements of Elberfeld, Barman and Vohwinkel. The problems of communication in such an elongated valley site led to the construction of the well-known overhead railway, running for the most part above the Wupper.

Siegerland, Mark and Bergisches Land, although physically part of the Rhenish Uplands, belong economically and politically to the great industrial *Land* North Rhine–Westphalia. In these hills were developed many of the skills in iron and steel production that were applied in the development of heavy industry on the Ruhr coalfield to the north. Specialization on the highly skilled production of a wide and constantly varying range of small metal articles has maintained and increased prosperity and population, resulting in a density of population in this hill country that is exceeded in North Rhine–Westphalia only by the Ruhr itself.

SUGGESTIONS FOR FURTHER READING

T. H. ELKINS, 'An English traveller in the Siegerland', *Geographical Journal*, 122, 1956, pp. 306–16.

T H. ELKINS and E. M. YATES, 'Lower Berg', *Geography*, 43, 1958, pp. 104–14.

T. H. ELKINS and E. M. YATES, 'The Neuwied Basin', *Geography*, 45, 1960, pp. 39-51.

E. M. YATES, 'The development of the Rhine', *Trans. Inst. Br. Geographers*, 32. 1963, pp. 410–25.

Chapter 15

NORTH RHINE–WESTPHALIA

Germany's two great axes of population, aligned along the Hercynian Foreland and the Rhine, intersect in the *Land* of North Rhine–Westphalia, where 16 million people form the greatest population concentration of the country. Here is Europe's leading industrial region, with just over a quarter of West German population and 40% of its industry. North Rhine–Westphalia not only dominates in basic and heavy industry, but has a third of consumers' goods production as well. This predominance the North Rhine–Westphalian or Rhine–Ruhr region owes to the presence at its heart of the industrial Ruhr, where 5 million people produce 80% of German coal (half the output of the European Economic Community) and 66% of German steel (one-third of Community output).

THE RUHR COALFIELD

The Land. The northern fringe of the Rhenish Uplands consists of Carboniferous rocks, forming a low hill country. Into these Carboniferous rocks, still within the Uplands, is superimposed the winding valley of the Ruhr, which is separated by a last low ridge from the lowland to the north, where today the Ruhr conurbation stands. The outcrop of the actual coal-bearing rocks is limited to a narrow belt on either side of the Ruhr river, stretching from Mülheim to Unna (Fig. 50). Northwards the coal seams dip gently beneath the Cretaceous rocks of the Westphalian Basin, and by Münster they are over 1,200 m/4,000 ft down. The southern edge of the Cretaceous outcrop takes the form of an even, loess-covered platform, running from east to west. This is part of the Hercynian Foreland loess belt, a zone of rich agriculture and early settlement, followed by the historic routeway known as the Hellweg.

The loess of the Hellweg gives way northwards to sand as the ground declines to the swampy valley of the river Emscher. Beyond the Emscher is a forested rise, again through sandy country, to the more open Recklinghausen Ridge, where the loamy soil has encouraged denser agricultural settlement. North of this again, there is a final slope down to the Lippe valley, which marks the approximate limit of the coalfield today.

The Ruhr coalfield is thus divided into a number of contrasting east–west belts of terrain. In the west, however, these are cut at right angles by the Rhine, with its accompanying gravel terraces. This intersection of east–west terrain belts by

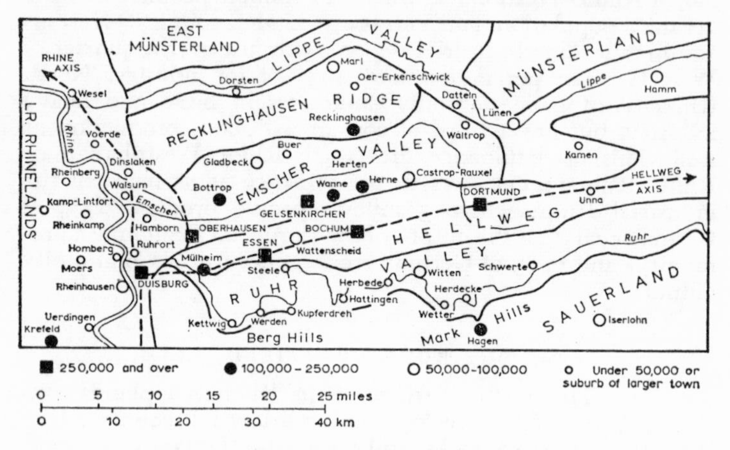

FIG. 48. The Ruhr: sub-regions and towns.

the south–north valley of the Rhine is reflected in the pattern of communications. At the mouth of the Ruhr river, the Hercynian Foreland and Rhine routeways intersect: there could not possibly be a more favourable situation for the development of a coalfield and the growth of an industrial region than at this great crossroads of Europe.

The Development of the Coalfield. Coals have been worked from the exposed coalfield in the valley of the Ruhr since medieval times. In the first half of the 19th century most of the mines were still adits, driven into the valley sides and draining naturally into the river. But from the first sinking of a shaft into the coal beneath the Cretaceous cover in 1839 the importance of the exposed field along the Ruhr declined, as larger and larger mines were opened up at ever greater depths to the north.

Many of the fifty to seventy workable coal seams are over 2 m/6 ft thick, and the average is 1·2 m/4 ft. The seams vary in their nature from the base upwards (Fig. 49). The lowest seams are semi-anthracitic coals (providing about 10% of production) and steam coals (5%). Higher in the sequence come seams of coking coal (60–70%), and then gas and long-flame coals at the top (15–20%). The seams, dipping off the hills to the south, were planed off by erosion prior to the deposition of the Cretaceous cover in such a manner that only the lowest, non-coking, coals outcrop to any extent in the exposed coalfield. The coking coals appear on the line of the Hellweg, the gas

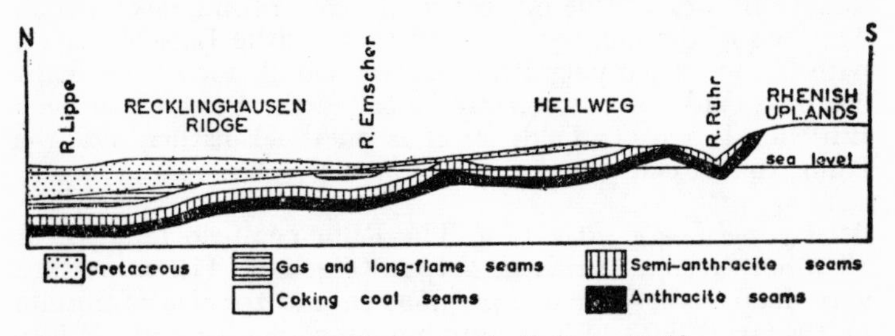

FIG. 49. Section across the Ruhr coalfield.

coals on the Emscher, and the long-flame coals beneath the Recklinghausen ridge.

The advance of mining into the concealed field was mainly determined by the search for coking coal for the growing iron and steel industry. In the second half of the 19th century the frontier of mining stormed forward across the Hellweg, and across the Emscher valley, to come to rest on the Recklinghausen ridge, where, with the exception of a few mines on the Lippe, it remains to this day. Mining has not, as might have been expected, subsequently extended still further down the dip, because north of the Recklinghausen ridge the highest seams are of the less desirable gas and long-flame type, and the coking coals are below the economic depth of working. Instead, mining has expanded laterally, following the coking coals preserved in long WSW–ENE troughs beneath the Cretaceous cover. Accordingly expansion in the first half of the 20th century was by sinking large, modern mines in two regions: the northeast, beyond Hamm, and the west, across the Rhine, where early expansion was prevented by the difficulty of sinking shafts in the waterlogged Rhine terrace gravels (Fig. 50). Since 1945 physical expansion of the mined area has virtually ceased.

The Ruhr mines are thus arranged in a flattened ellipse, some 130 by 50 km/80 by 30 miles, with the two extremities of its WSW–ENE axis at Hamm and just west of the Rhine, and the bulk of the mines between the Hellweg in the south and the Recklinghausen ridge in the north. With the exception of a few small mines in the south producing semi-anthracitic coal and a few large mines in the north producing gas and long-flame varieties, all the pits concentrate on raising coking coal. The axis of the ellipse is marked by the little Emscher river, with its accompanying Rhine–Herne canal; today the Ruhr coalfield could more correctly be called the Emscher or even Emscher–Lippe coalfield, for it is on the Emscher, not the Ruhr, that it centres.

Mining and Use of Ruhr Coal. The Ruhr coalfield far exceeds all other German fields in output (Fig. 29). The mines are very deep, some over 900 m/3,000 ft, and the size of mining unit is large. 60% of Ruhr production comes from about fifty large mines, each employing 3,000–6,000 men to produce more than a million tons of coal a year. The unit of management is also large. Postwar decartelization has been followed by a regrouping of mines into combines, a movement tending towards a unified organization for the whole field. All the Ruhr blast-furnace plants have re-established their links with coal. Some mining companies are now owned or partly owned by steel firms in neighbouring European countries, which in the period of postwar fuel shortage attempted to ensure their supplies of coking coal in this way.

Ruhr coal is rather soft, and owing to the high degree of mechanization comes to the surface in a much broken condition. In the southern zone of non-coking coals, briquette plants and power stations are often found built at the pit head, in order to use this fine coal. From the coking-coal mines on either side of the Emscher axis the fines go to the pit-head coking plants, which take about half of Ruhr coal production.

The by-product gas from the coke ovens is piped to steel works and industrial plants throughout the Ruhr and is fed into a gas grid reaching as far afield as Hanover and Mannheim. Owing to the progressive closure of coke ovens the continually increasing demands for 'Ruhr' gas are being met by drawing on the natural gas fields of N. Germany and the Netherlands. The mining firms have also developed power stations as a means of utilizing their high-ash coal. About 70% of Ruhr

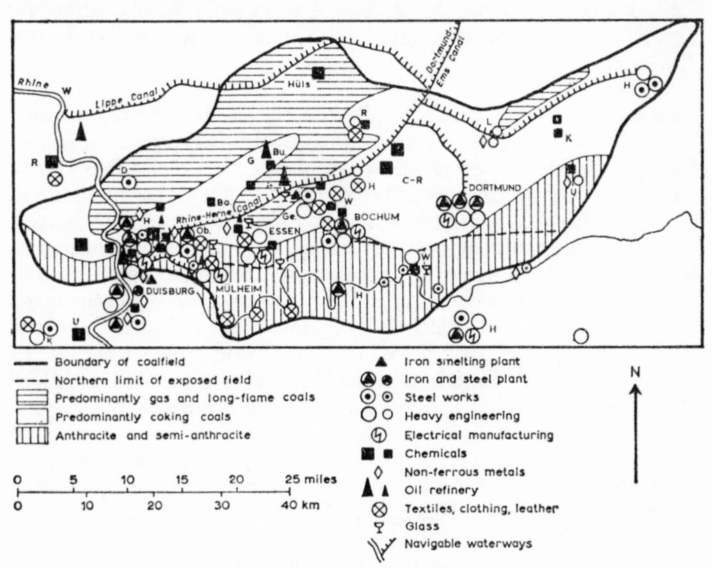

FIG. 50. The Ruhr coalfield.

power output is provided by the mining industry, and as other outlets for coal decline, many firms are extending their power-station interests. On balance the Ruhr both produces and consumes about a quarter of West German electric power, but at any one moment may be importing or exporting power over a system linking with the Rhenish brown-coal field and the Alps.

Ruhr mining reached a postwar peak output of 125 million tons in 1958, then suffered increasing competition from oil and natural gas. The less economic mines had to be closed, affecting particularly the older southern half of the field. The labour force was slashed, falling from nearly 500,000 in 1957 to below 300,000 in the mid-1960s. Output per man-shift underground rose steadily, exceeding three tons at the close of 1965, overtaking the prewar maximum, and this marked increase of productivity coupled with strong state support prevented any catastrophic fall in total output until the mid-1960s (107 million tons in 1965). The accumulation of unsold stocks then forced a second wave of pit closures and dismissals, affecting this time some of the greatest mines of the Hellweg and Emscher.

Chemicals from Coal. Traditionally the chemical industry is based on coal. Tar from the coking plants of the Emscher axis moves for first processing to distillation plants on the Rhine–Herne canal, which in turn supply derivatives for Rhine chemical plants to turn into anything from dyestuffs to aspirins. Coke-oven by-products also include benzol and sulphate of ammonia, which is also produced by a number of independent nitrogen plants using coke-oven gas. Until the end of the war large hydrogenation and Fischer-Tropsch plants located on the Emscher axis also produced motor fuel and various chemicals direct from coal. Pipelines from these plants in turn supplied the Buna synthetic rubber plant at Huls, south of the Lippe.

The New Age of Oil. In a postwar Germany starved of capital equipment the uneconomic plants for producing oil from coal were pressed into service as oil refineries. With the return of prosperity experience showed that refinery locations such as these, in the middle of the great Rhine–Ruhr market, had considerable economic advantages. The Emscher refineries were greatly extended, pipelines built to bring crude supplies from Wilhelmshaven and Rotterdam, and new refineries founded on the Rhine. The great concentration of Ruhr industry and population, built up because of the existence of coal resources, turned increasingly to fuel supplies from far distant lands.

With the arrival of oil Ruhr chemical industry progressively turned from a coal to petroleum base. A key to this development is the Huls plant, now one of the greatest chemical complexes of Germany. Operating mainly on a petroleum base, the plant produces synthetic rubber, plastics, solvents, insecticides and many other chemical products. A network of pipelines links Huls with the Ems gasfields, the Rhine–Ruhr refineries, with the Emscher coke ovens, and with chemical plants as far afield as Düsseldorf and Leverkusen. The acquisition of such postwar growth industries as oil refining and petrochemicals has gone far to revivify the Ruhr economy and to counteract the decline of older industries, such as coal. The arrival of natural gas from the Netherlands field seems likely to accelerate this move of Ruhr industry away from its own coal as a fuel and power base.

The Iron and Steel Industry. Until the middle of the 19th century iron was produced in charcoal furnaces dispersed in the hills of the Rhenish Uplands, and output from the coalfield was negligible. The first smelting of iron with Ruhr coal in 1849 was followed by the rapid rise of the coalfield industry, using coking coal provided by the development of the concealed field. Renewed expansion followed the introduction of the new processes for the mass-production of basic steel in the late 1870s.

After the check provided by damage and dismantling resulting from the Second World War, production rose by the mid-1960s to a peak of 18 million tons of iron (nearly 70% of West German production) and 23 million tons of steel (65%). Ruhr production alone, without the rest of Germany, approximately equalled that of the United Kingdom and exceeded that of France. Since the war Ruhr industry has resumed its tendency to concentrate into ever larger combines, uniting coal and ore supplies, steelworks and engineering plants. Even so, the mid-1960s saw this great steel industry in serious economic difficulty as a result of competition from the modern coastal plants of Common Market neighbours, able to receive rich foreign ore and cheap American coal without the need for transhipment. To meet the situation Ruhr firms formed even larger sales groupings to restrict competition, and the Federal Government tried to reduce their cost disadvantage by subsidizing Ruhr coke. With both coal and steel in difficulties, the whole basis of Ruhr prosperity was threatened.

Distribution of Steel Plants. In the early stages of Ruhr development, the coalfield iron plants were scattered over the Ruhr valley and Hellweg zones. After 1860 the change from Coal

Measure ore to imported ores led to increasing concentration in the neighbourhood of Duisberg, where the Rhine intercepts the Hellweg, and economical water transport is available. Today half of Ruhr iron production is in the west. From these blast furnaces on the banks of the Rhine the iron is able to pass in molten form directly to the steel plants, which mass-produce heavy rolled products like rails, beams, plates, sheet steel and tubes on a vast scale.

The completion of the Dortmund–Ems canal in 1899 aided Dortmund, at the other end of the Hellweg, to survive as a second centre producing between a third and a quarter of Ruhr iron and steel. Producers in this area, marginally less well placed than those on the Rhine, have begun to transfer the earlier, mass stages of iron and steel production to the Netherlands coastal plant at Ijmuiden, concentrating instead on re-rolling and further processing. Between the two extremities the smaller plants of the interior Ruhr concentrate on the production of high-quality steel, drawing on supplies of local scrap and using the open-hearth and electric processes. The production of heavy steel castings and forging tends to be concentrated in the steel plants of the central and eastern Ruhr. Special quality steels are also made off the coalfield, notably at Krefeld in the Lower Rhinelands and at various points in the hills to the south.

Industrial Diversification. The steel which is produced in such abundance is the basis of the traditional heavy and constructional engineering industry, producing bridges, cranes, locomotives, rolling mills and similar massive equipment, as well as heavy machine tools. Even before the war, engineering (including vehicles) made up the Ruhr's third most important branch of industry. Postwar progress has been substantial, and the branch now challenges steel for second place to the sickly giant of coal in the employment structure. Up to 1962 only heavy motor vehicles were made in the Ruhr (Essen), but in that year the industrial structure was enriched by the opening of the Opel car assembly plants at Bochum. Another branch poorly represented before the war was the manufacture of electrical equipment, which was mainly represented by the manufacture of generating equipment at Mülheim. This branch has been greatly enriched by the transfer of plants from Berlin and the establishment of refugee firms, notably at

Mülheim and Essen. Finally the postwar period has seen the marked rise of consumers' goods industries, especially clothing. The attraction here is the pool of female labour available in a district which previously provided mainly employment for men in heavy and basic industry. In all, the Ruhr today is industrially far more advanced, more complex and more varied than in 1939. The coal and steel industries that then accounted for over half of Ruhr employment have lost importance relatively and, in part, absolutely, providing now only something like a third of employment. Coupled with the growth and modernization of the chemical industry this degree of diversification gives ground for hope that the Ruhr, situated as it is at the crossroads of Europe amid Germany's greatest concentration of population, will conquer its difficulties and find a new economic role in the years ahead.

REGIONS WITHIN THE RUHR

The Ruhr Valley. The valley from which the coalfield draws its name has now regained much of its former peace, as the focus of industry and mining has moved away to the north. Only occasionally is there a small colliery, feeding its semi-anthracitic coal to a briquette works or power station. The surviving representatives of a former coal-based industry, such as the quality steel, engineering, glass and chemicals of *Witten*, tend to be small and specialized. The principal economic importance of the Ruhr valley today is as a source of water for the industrial conurbation to the north and as a recreational area. Such is the relative attractiveness of the valley that the mobile Ruhr population of today is tending to move back there to live, in preference to the crowded central parts of the conurbation.

The Hellweg. Where routes emerging from the Rhenish Uplands intersect the historic Hellweg, there grew up a series of walled medieval market towns, stretching from Duisburg on the Rhine to Dortmund in the east. After the middle of the 19th century, iron, steel and heavy engineering industries were set up on the outskirts of these towns, and mines were sunk into the concealed coalfield to supply them with coking coal. By now the Hellweg mines are small by Ruhr standards, producing less than a million tons a year each, and very many have been closed in recent years. Although the frontier of mining moved away northwards it was not followed by heavy industry, which remains in its original sites in the Hellweg towns from the Rhine to Dortmund.

The little towns provided the growing points for the great urban development that accompanied the rise of industry. While a monotonous grid-iron pattern of tenement streets spread around them, the nuclei were transformed into shopping, banking and entertainment centres, far more varied and pleasant than might be expected in the midst of an industrial conurbation. In fact the Ruhr, or at least the Hellweg, is by no means as gloomy as might be imagined. Between the towns there are mines, of course, with attendant housing estates, but few spoil banks and little derelict land; instead, there are stretches of farmland, growing wheat and sugar beet on the fertile loess soils.

The greatest of the Ruhr cities is *Essen* (727). The boundaries of the city have been progressively expanded from the nucleus on the Hellweg, so that the southern middle-class suburbs stretch to the attractive country of the Ruhr valley, while the northern industrial suburbs extend to the Emscher. This pattern is repeated more or less faithfully by all the Hellweg towns.

Industrially Essen means Krupp, a firm which developed after the middle of the 19th century from a small works producing steel castings to one of the great industrial empires of the world, linking coal and iron mines, iron and steel works, chemical, engineering and shipbuilding plants. The war brought greater industrial changes to Essen than to any other Ruhr town. The iron and steel works, shattered by bombing and postwar dismantling, were not rebuilt, although the remaining Krupp plants continue to build locomotives, lorries, diesel engines, electrical equipment and a variety of other engineering products. The town has many other engineering works and foundries, as well as chemical and plastics plants. Diversification since the war has brought in electrical manufacturing, light engineering and consumers' goods industries. The former steel town has thus acquired a very varied industrial structure, and dominates Ruhr engineering. Many of the new plants are actually situated on the vast area of the former Krupp steelworks, replanned as an industrial estate west of the town.

Further east *Bochum* (357) repeats the Essen pattern on a smaller scale, except that the quality iron and steel plants escaped dismantling. As at Essen, the postwar period saw much diversification through the introduction of many light industries, including radio, television and clothing. The closure of many mines in this southern part of the coalfield led in 1962 to the opening of the Opel car plants as a source of alternative employment. *Dortmund* (656) is the dominant centre of the eastern Ruhr. The availability of the Dortmund–Ems canal for ore transport has enabled the town to retain a share in the mass iron and steel industry, and it is the biggest Ruhr manufacturer of heavy machine tools. Among the Ruhr population Dortmund is probably best known for its enormous breweries. In spite of the improvement of the river Ruhr in 1927 to take 2,000-ton barges to *Mülheim* (192) the town has lost its iron smelting, while retaining steelworks, foundries, heavy engineering works and, in particular, the manufacture of generating sets and other heavy electrical equipment. There is a traditional leather industry.

The Rhine Front. The westernmost Hellweg city is *Duisburg* (490), which is also a Rhine city; indeed, it now sprawls for about 20 km/12 miles along the river, uniting practically all of the industrialized right bank that falls within the Ruhr region. Medieval Duisburg stood on a patch of gravel terrace at the confluence of the rivers Ruhr and Rhine. Both rivers have long migrated from the walls of the old town, so that Ruhrort developed from the 16th century as the confluence port. Today Duisburg–Ruhrort, where the Rhine–Herne canal joins the Rhine, is the greatest inland port of Europe, unloading ores, timber, grain and other bulk commodities for the industrial Ruhr, and loading coal, coke, steel, petroleum products and chemicals.

The banks of the Rhine provide an ideal location for plants which use Ruhr coal to process heavy raw materials transported on this superb waterway. On the east bank there are three main complexes of iron and steel plants, mines and coking plants, linked by railways and pipelines. The Phoenix complex, forming the greatest iron and steel works of Germany, stretches northwards from Ruhrort to Dinslaken. At Huckingen, south of Duisburg, a second group of plants concentrates especially on tube manufacture. A third group lies just to the east, at

Oberhausen (see below, p. 249). Associated with the steel works are some of the greatest constructional and heavy engineering plants of the Ruhr. Copper, tin and zinc are also smelted on the banks of the Rhine, providing by-products for the near-by chemical works. Large oil refineries at Duisburg are a more recent addition to the industrial scene.

On the opposite bank of the Rhine is the large Rheinhausen steel works and associated constructional engineering plant. The large modern mines of the recently developed part of the coalfield west of the Rhine supply the steelworks and also chemical works, now as everywhere turning over to a petroleum base. The Permian salt beds beneath the Lower Rhinelands are worked for alkali production at *Rheinberg*, which also participates in the Lower Rhinelands textile industry.

The Emscher Valley. The valley of the little river Emscher has in the last 100 years been transformed into the main axis of mining. The river is now no more than a concrete drain, and the greatest contributor to the pollution of the Lower Rhine, 'Europe's greatest sewer'. Fortunately energetic measures are being taken to remedy this situation. The valley is followed by the Rhine–Herne canal, which takes European-standard barges through to the Dortmund–Ems canal. This is one of the busiest waterways of Germany, its banks lined with coal-loading ports, coke-ovens, glass works, chemical plants and power stations. Here also were the wartime plants for producing oil from coal, now transformed into oil refineries.

The towns which grew up in the latter part of the 19th century on either side of the Emscher axis lacked the attractive old nuclei of the Hellweg; they grew with the speed of American cities, and on a similar grid-iron plan. Both industrially and socially, the Emscher towns are less varied than those of the Hellweg. Coal mining and coal processing have tended to dominate the industrial structure, and although the postwar years have brought some diversification, pit closures have hit the region hard. Some of the Emscher towns have actually lost population in recent years.

The largest Emscher town, *Gelsenkirchen* (374) also has the most varied industrial structure. The great coal firms that dominate the town themselves developed iron and steel plants, foundries, glass works and chemical plants as outlets for their coal. Two wartime plants for producing oil from coal subsequently became oil refineries. The available female labour in this region where most employment opportunities have hitherto been in basic and heavy industry has since the war attracted much light industry, especially clothing. Parallel with this industrial diversification Gelsenkirchen has deliberately set out to become a more balanced community by the development of shopping, cultural and recreational facilities. *Oberhausen* (260) in the west benefits from the proximity of the Rhine, and has iron, steel, engineering and chemical plants. In the east, *Wanne-Eickel* (108), *Herne* (108) and *Castrop-Rauxel* (87) are almost entirely devoted to coal and chemicals, still predominantly derived from coal, and employment has suffered accordingly. In these towns also there has been much expansion of clothing and similar light industries employing women.

The towns north of the Emscher are smaller but growth is rapid on this expanding frontier of the conurbation. *Recklinghausen* (129) is a small medieval walled town that has become the principal centre of the coalfield between Emscher and Lippe. Here the continuously built-up area ends; beyond, as far as the Lippe, the few large, modern mines stand isolated among fields and woods, each with its own housing estate. There is one industrial giant, the Huls chemical plant (p. 243). This site south of the Lippe was selected for the wartime Buna plant because it offered ample industrial land, a sufficient water supply and coal for electricity generation, while the coal hydrogenation plants of the Emscher that provided the gas on which the process was based were not far distant. In its postwar resurrection Huls has become an enormous chemical complex employing many thousands of people; its growth is reflected in the population expansion of *Marl* (75).

The most important Lippe towns are towards the east, where the river coincides with the axis of the coalfield. *Lünen* (72) has an important aluminium plant based on electricity from the Ruhr and from the Rhenish brown-coal field. *Hamm* (70) manufactures wire and wire goods, but is best known for its enormous marshalling yards, through which passes most of the traffic from the Ruhr to northern Germany and Berlin. This eastern fringe of the Ruhr, from Hamm and Lünen southwards to Unna, is a favoured area for the establishment of new industrial plants. At the confluence of the Lippe with the Rhine *Wesel* (33) appears to be another expanding industrial centre, with a new refinery and engineering works.

The Changing Ruhr. While the Ruhr remains the greatest industrial centre of Europe, and a steadily expanding one, it is nevertheless true that the rate of expansion after the Second World War was below that of Germany as a whole. Reasons for this relative lagging include the decline of the coal industry, the prevalence in the Ruhr of branches of heavy and basic industry that are no longer expanding rapidly, the shortage of labour and lack of attractive industrial sites. Yet the mere existence of such an immense concentration of population and industry has been sufficient to attract new branches of industry, and to draw in alternative sources of power in the form of oil and gas with which to nourish the new developments. Accordingly the Ruhr is not without its share of such growth industries as oil refining, chemicals, engineering and vehicles, although many of the new plants chose locations peripheral to the main mass of the conurbation. There is a similar story with population, which has grown less rapidly than that of West Germany as a whole in the period since 1939, and has had to be strengthened by the importation of foreign workers. Even more than with industry, growth tends to be most rapid on the fringes of the crowded conurbation. The prosperous and mobile Ruhr workers of today are tending to avoid the densely built-up expanses of the Hellweg and Emscher valley in favour of the wider spaces towards the Lippe and Rhine, or even in the abandoned coalfield of the Ruhr valley to the south.

REGIONS OF NORTH RHINE–WESTPHALIA

The Ruhr, the industrial heart of North Rhine–Westphalia, is surrounded by a circle of tributary regions, from which it draws food and consumers' goods for its 5 million people and raw materials for its industries, while providing in return fuel and heavy industrial products for further processing. Something of this relationship has been seen in the three regions of this *Land* which lie within the Rhenish Uplands, the Siegerland (pp. 232–3), Berg (pp. 234–5) and Mark (pp. 233–4), but on all sides a similar situation is found.

The Westphalian Basin. The Cretaceous rocks which cover all but the extreme south of the Ruhr coalfield are physically part of a much larger region, the Westphalian Basin. Like the London or Paris basins, this has a rim of older rocks, with progressively younger rocks preserved towards the centre. The rim consists of Upper Cretaceous limestones; in the south they form a dry, frequently loess-covered platform, narrow in the Hellweg and broadening eastwards in the Paderborn Plateau,

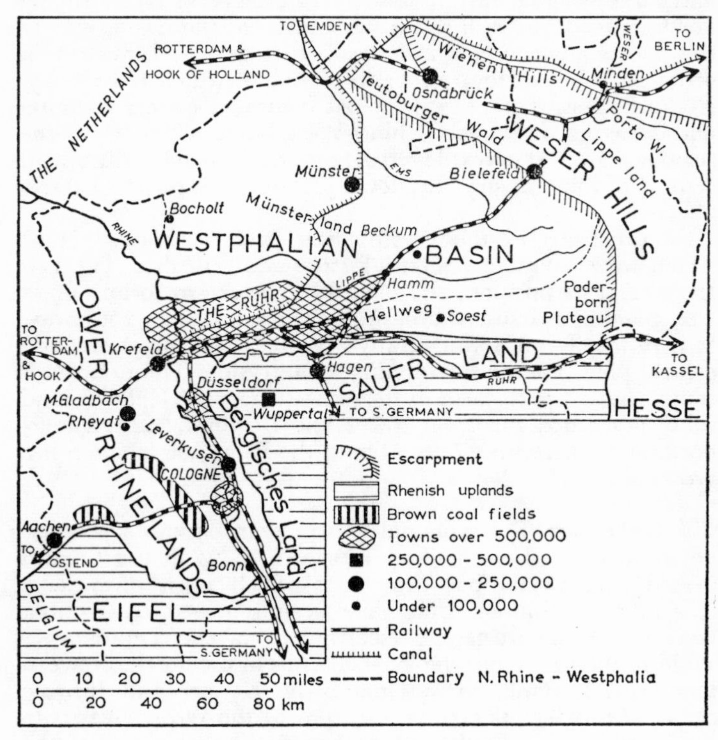

FIG. 51. North Rhine–Westphalia.

but in the north they are sharply folded in the Teutoburger Wald escarpment. The heart of the basin is occupied by the overlying clays of the Upper Cretaceous, which form the damp lowland of the Münsterland, broken only by occasional low ridges of sandstone or limestone. The proximity of limestone, clay and Ruhr coal has enabled *Beckum* to become a major centre of the German cement industry.

With its westerly outlook and high rainfall, the Westphalian Basin makes ideal grazing country; it is the Ruhr's biggest supplier of milk, fresh meat and bacon. The countryside has a very 'English' appearance, with cows grazing in hedged fields, and large isolated farmhouses set in clumps of trees. In the north, glacial outwash sands have invaded the basin, and in this poorer environment man has had to develop industries in order to live. A group of small towns, of which *Bocholt* (25) is the largest, form the principal centre of cotton spinning and weaving in North Rhine–Westphalia. After 1960 the region shared the textile crisis common to most European centres of the industry; the local jute mills were particularly affected.

At the heart of the Westphalian Basin is *Münster* (129) which grew around a Frankish fortress and cathedral (Fig. 12). In spite of its position, the town has not grown to any great size, perhaps because the basin lacks a main river routeway. It is primarily an administrative centre, university town and central place for the surrounding countryside. The important centres have always been in the south, where the Hellweg land route nourished medieval towns like Dortmund and Paderborn, and where, in modern times, the Ruhr conurbation has grown up.

The Weser Hills. The synclinal Westphalian Basin is succeeded northwards by the anticlinal Weser Hills. As in the English Weald, the Cretaceous limestones which must once have formed a continuous arch have been removed by erosion, leaving the inward-facing escarpments of the Teutoburger Wald in the south and the Wiehen Hills in the north. Between them is a lowland floored mainly by Keuper and Jurassic clays. Through the northern escarpment the Weser escapes to the Northern Lowland in the magnificent water gap of the *Porta Westfalica*, near Minden.

The Weser Hills are politically divided between North Rhine–Westphalia and Lower Saxony. The main Westphalian portion is the Lippe region, which is traditionally subject to rural overpopulation. Cheap labour is, or was, the attraction for shoe, cigar and food industries, while the beech forests of the hills are the basis of the lumber, plywood and furniture industries. A particularly interesting history of industrial development is shown by *Bielefeld* (170). Out of a local linen industry developed the making of men's shirts and underwear, and from this the making of sewing machines. Looking for a way to diversify their production, some sewing machine firms took up the assembly of the newly-invented bicycle. Many of the parts come from the small metalworking establishments of the Mark, but some are made locally, which has led to the development of light and precision engineering.

The Lower Rhinelands. The Westphalian Basin forms one of the 'bays' which in Germany penetrate into the northern edge of the Central Uplands. Adjoining it to the west is another 'bay', the Lower Rhinelands, which penetrates even further south, and is very different geographically. The rocks of the Lower Rhinelands are not gently folded, as in Westphalia, but sharply downfaulted, allowing the accumulation of thousands of feet of Tertiary sands and clays, topped by immense gravel spreads deposited by the glacially swollen Rhine and Maas. In contrast with Westphalia, south–north lines dominate, especially the Rhine itself, clinging to the extreme eastern edge of the lowland, and providing the great waterway that the Westphalian Basin so notably lacks.

The Lower Rhinelands can be divided into southern and northern portions by the all-important northern boundary of loess, roughly on the latitude of Düsseldorf. South of this line the lowland consists mainly of loess-covered High Terrace gravels. The even, open plains are almost entirely arable, growing fine wheat and sugar beet. Villages are large, and bear early German or even Celtic place-names. The country towns have developed overspill industry from the great centres of the Rhine. *Düren* (54) makes vehicle components and agricultural machinery. *Neuss* (110), opposite Düsseldorf, reflects both Rhine communications and its agricultural hinterland in its oil and grain mills, and its plants producing machinery for agriculture and for the food industries.

To the west of Cologne one discordant element mars the rural scene. The Tertiary rocks contain a seam of brown coal, which in places reaches 100 m/300 ft in thickness. Generally the seam is below workable depth, but beneath the wooded Ville ridge it is upfaulted, and is worked in a series of immense open pits by giant excavators. One excavator alone is capable of delivering 110,000 tons of coal per day onto the continuously moving belts that lead to the pit head. Roads, railways and rivers are diverted, villages obliterated and built anew as the miles-long working faces sweep across the country. This low-grade and waterlogged fuel must be processed in some way before leaving the pit head. The usual method used to be compression into household briquettes, but today the greater part of production is fed directly to a group of large power stations. Because of the efficiency of the mining operations, brown coal is a cheaper source of electricity than Ruhr coal, and accounts for a basic 30% of the West German public supply. Much power is also consumed in electrochemical and aluminium plants on the brown-coal field itself.

North of the loess boundary, swampy valleys divide the terraces into isolated blocks, which also carry wooded moraines left by the ice sheet at its greatest extent. Settlement is dispersed, and there is much dairying for near-by industrial towns. Local agriculture and imports by the Rhine are the basis for food industries, often Netherlands-owned, including oil and grain milling, the manufacture of margarine and chocolate and the canning of fruit and vegetables. Agricultural raw materials also served as an initial basis for the characteristic consumers' goods industries of the region, boot and shoe manufacture and textiles. From the original linen production the textile industry has evolved two areas of specialization.

Mönchengladbach (154), *Rheydt* (98) and *Viersen* (42) are predominantly cotton spinning and weaving towns, with a little wool. They have also developed textile machinery and clothing industries, but since 1955 they have been severely affected by the textile crisis. The second textile specialization is the traditional silk working of *Krefeld* (221) now mainly dependent on synthetic fibres. Here too textile finishing, the clothing industry and textile engineering have developed. The demands of the textile industry for chemicals, dyestuffs and synthetic fibres have also stimulated the development of chemical industries in Krefeld's Rhine suburb of Uerdingen. Krefeld has important special steel, machine building and electrical equipment plants, and this degree of industrial diversity allowed the town to continue to develop after 1955 when the more purely textile centres were static or declining.

The Düsseldorf Region. The main axis of industry in the Lower Rhinelands is provided by the Rhine, which is lined by heavy

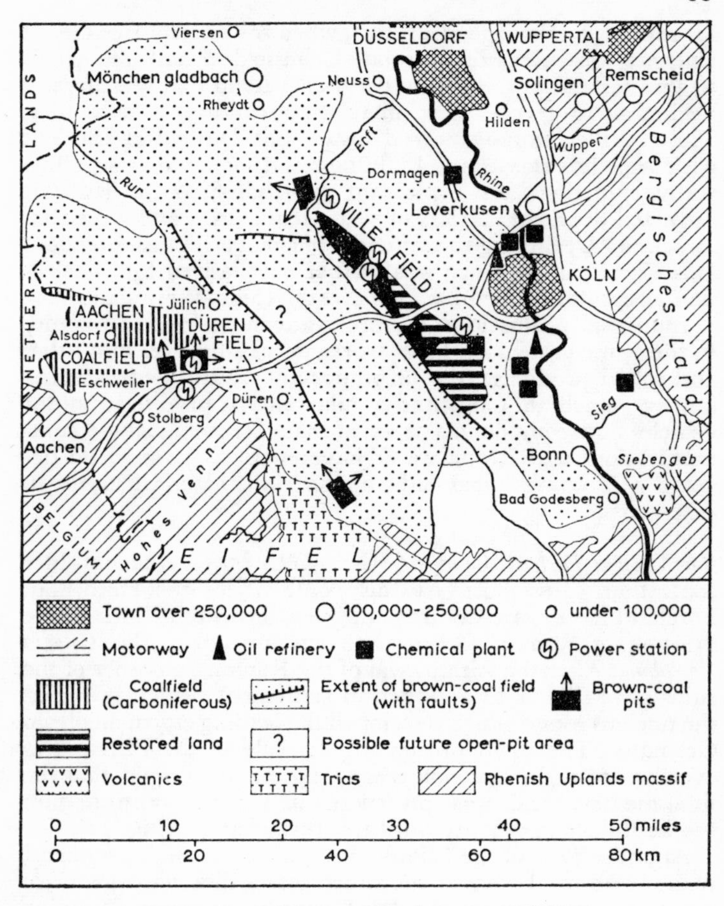

FIG. 52. Cologne and the brown-coal field.

industrial plants, especially oil refineries and chemical works, from the Ruhr southwards to Bonn. Two cities are rivals for predominance here, Düsseldorf and Cologne. *Düsseldorf* (700) was a mere village when Cologne was one of the greatest cities of medieval Europe. In 1288 the Duke of Berg raised it to town status as his outlet to the Rhine, and in 1248 he made it his capital. In the Age of Princes, when the ancient free city of Cologne was increasingly isolated, Düsseldorf had free access to a hinterland in the hills of Bergisches Land that was already beginning to specialize in metal manufactures and textiles. The court eventually moved away, but Düsseldorf was left with some fine streets and buildings, and some minor administrative functions. As a pleasant town close to the Ruhr it attracted the headquarters of many Ruhr firms and industrial associations, eclipsing the influence of Cologne in this direction. Düsseldorf's importance was further emphasized by its selection as capital of the new *Land* North Rhine–Westphalia.

Industrially Düsseldorf has taken advantage of its proximity to the Ruhr to develop large works processing steel into tubes and rolled products. It is an important centre for producing boilers, machine tools and similar heavy products; motor vehicles and components are also manufactured. Rhine communications and Rhine water have enabled the town to develop a large chemical industry, specializing particularly in detergents.

The Cologne District. Cologne (Ger. Köln 855) has much older roots than Düsseldorf. At this point where the Hercynian Foreland land routeway from the west meets the Rhine, there grew up a Roman fortress and trading town, the *Colonia Agrippina.* After the withdrawal of the Romans, a corner of the ruins gave shelter to a cathedral settlement, which provided the nucleus round which developed the leading city of medieval Germany. The town prospered, the rule of the Bishop was overthrown and expansion was so early and so rapid that the final medieval wall was constructed in 1180; it was to remain the boundary of the city until the 19th century (Fig. 11).

After the close of the Middle Ages, Cologne's independence, maintained until Napoleonic times, was a disadvantage, since it cut the city off from the developing life of the surrounding princely states. Administratively Cologne has never been of any particular significance; it owes its modern growth to the advantages of its geographical situation and the energies of its people. Cologne is primarily a trading and commercial city, and it was the 19th-century unification of Germany, the abolition of internal barriers to trade and the building of the railways that gave the opportunity for new development. Although Düsseldorf has gained the stock exchange and *Land* central bank, Cologne is still a great centre of banking and commerce, and the leading German insurance centre.

Unlike Düsseldorf where commerce tended to follow industrial development, in Cologne industry developed initially from commerce and the Rhine trade. Cologne traditionally specializes in the processing and distribution of sugar, tobacco, cocoa and other 'colonial' products. The railways and proximity to the Ruhr also brought engineering industry, especially in the suburbs of Mülheim and Deutz across the Rhine (Fig. 11). There are most important plants producing motor cars, diesel engines, tractors, heavy road vehicles, machinery of many kinds, wire rope, cables and electrical equipment. There is a long-established chemical industry, with both fine products like 'Eau de Cologne' and mass products like fertilizer, alkalis and synthetic fibres. A major postwar development has been the erection of oil refineries and petrochemical works on the Rhine in the Cologne region. South of Cologne a wartime plant to produce motor fuel from brown coal was developed after the war as a refinery linked to the Rotterdam pipeline, with associated petrochemical plants. A second complex was created immediately north of the city. On the right bank is the immense *Leverkusen* (104) chemical plant, initiated when the dyestuffs industry moved from Wuppertal to a point where coking by-products could be received by Rhine barge. Inevitably the plant has turned over to petroleum as a base and owing to shortage of space further expansion is taking place across the river next to the existing *Dormagen* fibres plant.

Cologne has been hampered in its physical expansion because, being on the west bank of the Rhine, it was fortified against French attack until after the First World War. The field of fire outside the Prussian fortifications of the 1880s remains open to this day, occupied by railway yards, parks, landscaped mountains of rubble from the bombing and the university. Only beyond this belt do the suburbs of the 19th and 20th centuries begin (Fig. 11). The city suffered appallingly from bombing; its rebuilding included a highly successful pioneer scheme for the removal of vehicles from the main shopping streets. New Rhine bridges have been built to deal with the constantly increasing road traffic, and an underground tramway system for the city centre is being created.

The Aachen District. On the northern fringe of the Eifel is another famous medieval town. *Aachen* (177) is first of all a spa, with the hottest spring in Europe (76° C/169° F), frequented since Roman times. Selected by Charles the Great as his capital, the town has progressively lost its central position as the German frontier has been driven eastwards. After the cession of Eupen and Malmédy to Belgium by the Treaty of Versailles, the Netherlands and Belgian frontier formed a half-circle around the town at only 5 km/3 miles distance.

Aachen has a small and declining coalfield, which since the creation of the Coal and Steel community has been able to benefit from proximity to coal and coke markets in Belgium and Luxemburg. Brown coal from the large open pits west of Düren is mostly fed directly to electric power stations (Fig. 52). The lead and zinc ores of the Eifel are now unimportant, but were the original basis of the non-ferrous metals and cables industry of *Stolberg* and district. Another traditional industry is the manufacture of high-quality woollen and worsted cloth. The iron and steel industry proved unable to survive in this frontier location, far from waterways, but engineering plants and the traditional needle manufacture remain. More recently a frontier location has proved a positive attraction to Belgian and Dutch firms wishing to produce electric bulbs, television tubes and rubber tyres within the German customs area. The town was severely damaged in the battles of 1944, which reduced its population to 6,000, but the prewar population had been reached again by 1961.

The Federal Capital. Where the Rhine leaves the Rhenish Uplands is Bonn (142). Before the war it was a sleepy residential town known, if at all, for the university installed in the 18th-century palace of the Archbishop of Cologne. The reasons for its selection in 1949 as the Federal capital are obscure. Clearly the great regional capitals that were also *Land* capitals, such as Hanover, Stuttgart and Munich, had to be excluded. This still left Cologne and Frankfurt, but both were in ruins. The place selected had in any event not to be so big that the government would be tempted not to return to Berlin at the hoped-for reunification. Possibly decisive was the personality of Adenauer, whose house lay in the volcanic Siebengebirge across the river. The Federal Parliament was installed in a former teachers' training college on the Rhine, the little town sprouted ministries, embassies and party headquarters; together with *Bad Godesberg* (70) to the south it entered into a period of unprecedented growth. Not surprisingly most of the employed population is in administration and the services. On the opposite bank of the Rhine the forested gravels have been much taken up by such space-demanding activities as chemicals, plastics and glass plants, as well as new engineering plants. This has become one of the industrial growth areas of North Rhine–Westphalia.

Population. There have been enormous population changes in this highly industrialized *Land* since 1939. During the later stages of the war hundreds of thousands of people fled from the ruined cities and the menaced western frontier. Few of the incoming refugees settled in this devastated region where the towns could offer neither shelter nor work.

With economic recovery, the position was revolutionized. Especially during the 1950s people flocked from all over Germany to the rebuilt towns and industries, and population of the *Land* rose to over 16 millions. By the 1960s there were signs that the process was complete. Ruhr population was static, even declining in part. Population growth was faltering in the other 'older' industrial regions east of the Rhine (Bergisches Land, Düsseldorf, Mark, Lippe). Such expansion as remained was essentially peripheral to the Ruhr, especially in the Cologne–Bonn region. There were even signs of a 'drift to the south' by migration to Baden-Württemberg and Bavaria, hidden in the total population figures by the inward movement of foreign workers, especially Turks, to replace Germans in the less enviable forms of employment.

SUGGESTIONS FOR FURTHER READING

T. H. ELKINS, 'The Cologne brown-coal field', *Transactions Inst. Br. Geographers*, 19, 1953, pp. 131–43.

P. HALL, *The World Cities*, ch. 5 (World University Library), 1966.

N. J. G. POUNDS, *The Ruhr: a study in historical and economic geography* (Faber and Faber), 1952.

Chapter 16

LOWER SAXONY

THE LAND

Lower Saxony (Ger. Niedersachsen) is divided into two contrasting parts, the hills of the Central Uplands in the south, and the sandy lowland to the north, stretching as far as the coastal marshes. Between the two parts runs the narrow, fertile loess belt of the Hercynian Foreland. Lower Saxony derives its name from the Saxons, who at the time of the great migrations occupied northern Germany from the Rhine to the Elbe. The adjective 'Lower' came into use in the 16th century, to avoid confusion with the territory in the Elbe basin that is known as Saxony today.

THE HARZ

The southeastern corner of Lower Saxony is buttressed by the Harz Mountains, a roughly oval Hercynian massif stretching for some 100 km/60 miles from southeast to northwest. Its intensively folded Palaeozoic slates and intruded granites are cut by various erosion levels, the highest now forming a rolling surface at 500–600 m/1,600–2,000 ft. This is overlooked by a few residual masses, such as the granite Brocken (1,142 m/3,747 ft), just east of the Lower Saxon boundary.

Streams radiating from the Harz massif have been forced to cut narrow and steep-sided valleys in order to reach the surrounding lowlands. Such slopes, and a rainfall of over 1,000 mm/40 in a year, have encouraged the preservation of forest, which consists of mixed beech and oak below 400 m/1,300 ft and then spruce reaching above as far as the bare, windswept rocks of the Brocken.

The historic Harz mining industry has been in decline since the 18th century, although the district still supplies about a third of the small West German output of lead, zinc and copper. Thrust forward as the most northerly of Germany's Hercynian mountains, the Harz once frightened the plainsmen as an abode of witches. Now it attracts them to its fresh woods in summer and to its snows in winter. It also makes an excellent water tower; from the reservoirs constructed in its deep valleys pipelines run far into the Northern Lowland.

The Harz is surrounded by a series of small towns and castles,

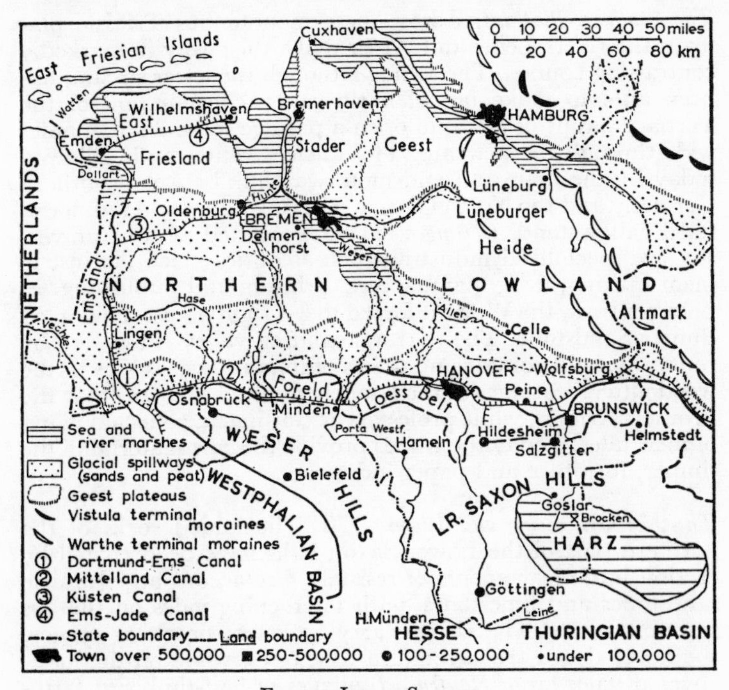

FIG. 53 Lower Saxony

each at the mouth of a valley leading into the mountains. The most famous is *Goslar* (41), one of the most important towns of medieval Germany, adjacent to the silver mines which financed the Salian kings. The town now shelters a very large refugee clothing firm from Stettin.

THE LOWER SAXON HILLS

The Harz is surrounded by outcrops of Secondary rocks, which on the north, west and southwest form the Lower Saxon Hills.

Towards the south the rocks are horizontal or gently domed, but in the north they are folded into a series of southwest to northwest-trending anticlines and synclines.

The Southern Plateaus. Across these monotonous Triassic plateaus the rivers Leine and Weser make their way in markedly contrasting courses. The Leine, although the lesser stream, has been able to make use of a rift-valley continuation of the Tertiary basins of Hesse to open a passage some 8 km/5 miles wide through the plateaus. This ancient routeway is followed today by the main rail and motorway link between southern Germany and the North German ports. In the sheltered, loess-filled valley stands *Göttingen* (111). Associated with its university are specialized industries such as optics, scientific instrument making, drug manufacture, printing and publishing.

In contrast, the Weser is forced to cut right across the domed Bunter Sandstone. The narrow, winding valley is avoided by routeways and contains no towns of importance. It was in the woodcutters' cottages of these lonely forested plateaus that the Brothers Grimm, while professors at Göttingen, collected many of their tales. Today the woods provide the raw material of the timber, furniture and paper industries.

The Northern Leine and Weser Hills. The folded rocks of the northern part of the Lower Saxon Hills have been etched by erosion into escarpments of resistant Cretaceous and Jurassic sandstones and limestones, with intervening vales on the less resistant strata. The ridges carry forests of beech or spruce, the lower slopes are covered in fruit trees, while on the loess-covered vales large *Haufendorf* villages of half-timbered farmhouses are set among their open arable fields. This rural scene is rarely broken by industry. The glass making originally based on the sands and forests of the Cretaceous ridges still survives, together with wood and paper industries, quarrying and cement making.

The Lower Saxon Hills are prolonged westwards into the Wester Hills, which have been described above (pp. 252–3). The Lower Saxon section of these hills surrounds *Osnabrück* (142), a cathedral city and historic centre of linen production. To iron and steel making, based initially on local ore, have been added non-ferrous metal, wire, engineering, textile and paper industries. Already a major rail junction, the city has greatly benefited from its connection with the Mittelland canal.

FORELAND LOESS BELT

The escarpments of the Leine Hills are continued north of the Harz, but are more widely spaced, standing as wooded islands in wide stretches of loess-covered plain. Towards the north the loess plains become ever more even, more monotonous and more devoid of trees and hedges, except round the large nucleated villages. Wheat is the main cereal, and this is one of the principal German areas of beet-sugar production. The tops and pulp from the beet help to support a large stall-fed cattle population. Another speciality is vegetable growing, especially near Brunswick.

The dry loess terrain was used by the great medieval highway following the Hercynian Foreland to the Elbe and beyond. Where routes emerge from the hills to intersect the highway, towns like Hanover and Brunswick grew up. Much the same route is today taken by the railway, motorway and Mittelland canal from the Ruhr to East Germany and Berlin.

The agricultural riches of the surface are repeated by the mineral wealth of the Secondary rocks which underlie the Foreland and stretch out beneath the sands of the Northern Lowland. Salt-dome structures are numerous, caused by the tendency of salt from the Permian beds to collect together and to migrate upwards along lines of weakness. They provide potash and practically unlimited supplies of common salt, and on their flanks small oilfields are trapped. A narrow Tertiary basin that stretches over from East Germany near Helmstedt also contains an extension of the Central German brown-coal field. The Helmstedt field provides about 7% of West German output; most is used on the spot for power generation or making briquettes.

The main mineral resource of the district is iron ore of Cretaceous and Jurassic age. Germany's most important single source of ore is at Salzgitter, where the Lower Cretaceous deposits reach 90 m/300 ft in thickness. The ores, which are mostly worked underground, have a 25–32% iron content, but the disadvantage of a high silica content. Such lean ores are most economically smelted on the orefield itself, so that, after the technical problems of using this difficult ore had been solved, a new iron and steel plant was erected here on a green-field site in 1937. A branch of the Mittelland canal was built to enable coal to be brought from the Ruhr, with concentrated ore as a return freight.

Following extensive postwar dismantling, the plant was re-constructed to provide work for the German refugees who settled in the huts abandoned by the wartime slave labourers. These have now been replaced by the sprawling 'new town' of *Salzgitter* (116); nearly half the population consists of refugees or their children. Associated with the steelworks are engineer-ing and heavy vehicle plants.

Germany's second orefield is provided by the calcareous 22–32% Upper Cretaceous ore of the *Peine* (31) district, which supports a small iron and steel plant. Should the German steel industry ever change from its present preference for rich imported ores there would appear to be ample reserves of lean ore in Lower Saxony. A thick seam of 32% Jurassic (Malm) ore is known to extend in a trough northwards from Salzgitter to-wards the East German boundary. More recently oil borings have discovered moderately rich (32–42%) ores of Jurassic (Dogger) age deep beneath the North German Lowland in the area south of Bremen.

Another completely new industrial centre is *Wolfsburg*, east of Brunswick, where Volkswagen cars are made in the largest motor works in Germany. Once again a predominantly refugee labour force has replaced wartime slave workers in a rapidly growing 'new town' (81).

Older and more varied industries are found in the cities of Hanover and Brunswick. Both grew as medieval trading points between hill and plain, as river crossings on the Hercynian Foreland routeway, and as heads of river navigation. *Hanover* (Ger. Hannover 559) developed as a flourishing medieval market town on the right bank of the Leine. From 1635 to 1866 it was a state capital, and between 1714 and 1837 its rulers were also kings of England. Today it is the capital and largest town of *Land* Lower Saxony, and the scene of West Germany's principal annual industrial fair. The modern town is still a major route centre, where the railway and motorway from southern Germany through the Leine Rift Valley to the North German ports intersect the Hercynian Foreland rail, canal and motorway routes. Communications, rather than local raw materials, have enabled Hanover to grow into a major industrial city. Typical is the largest industry, rubber processing and tyre manufacture. Other industries are machinery construction, chemical manufacture and the building of tractors, heavy lorries and Volkswagen commercial vehicles. The loss of East German supplies has led to the growth of electrical, radio and gramophone industries.

Brunswick (Ger. Braunschweig 236), at the crossing of the Oker, was until 1945 capital of *Land* Brunswick, now merged in Lower Saxony. Industries include the canning of the locally grown vegetables, the manufacture of tinplate and cans, and also of machinery for the canning, beet sugar and flour-milling industries. Other branches are optics, pianos, drug manufacture, the building of commercial vehicles and publishing. The town is served by the Mittelland canal and the Ruhr–Berlin motorway. *Hildesheim* (100) was, like Goslar, a centre of the medieval Saxon and Salian kings. Now it is drawn into the industrial pattern of the Foreland, with canning, sugar, agricultural engineering, vehicle accessory and clothing industries.

THE NORTHERN LOWLAND

The fundamental physical and human dividing line of Lower Saxony runs just north of Brunswick, Hanover and Osnabrück. It marks the change from loess to sand, from wheat to rye growing, from dense agricultural populations and industrial towns to lonely heaths. North of the dividing line begins the glaciated country of the Lower Saxon part of the Northern Lowland. Since Lower Saxony lies entirely outside the limits of the latest (Vistula) glaciation, the drifts are much leached, and the few remnants of terminal moraines are greatly eroded. Great sheets of sand and gravel predominate, and these have been divided into a number of separate blocks by wide channels cut by glacial meltwater. The sandy blocks are called *Geest* (from a Friesian word meaning infertile). This light land was favoured by prehistoric man, who began the process of burning and grazing which turned the initial vegetation of oak and birch woodland into open heathland, with leached and impoverished soils. The oceanic climate of this part of Germany has also favoured the growth of vast peat bogs, especially in the ill-drained depressions. In contrast, fertile marshes line the coast and the great estuaries.

The Lüneburg Heath (Ger. Lüneburger Heide). This, the largest of the *Geest* blocks, has a hilly spine formed by remnants of the Warthe terminal moraine, rising to over 150 m/500 ft (p. 26). Until the 19th century the sandy *Heide* consisted, as its name suggests, mainly of heathland, useful only for sheep and bees. Only occasionally did large *Esch* fields, with their accompanying small *Drubbel* villages, form islands of cultivation in the waste (Fig. 8).

In the 19th century the appearance of the Heide was greatly changed through the division of large areas of heathland among individual owners. The poorer land was planted with spruce, and on the better land the introduction of artificial fertilizers enabled cultivation to expand rapidly. The sandy soil grows rye and potatoes, which nourish great numbers of pigs, and advantage is taken of all the valleys and swampy depressions to provide pasture for cattle.

Fortunately a few places remain where it is still possible to see the land in autumn purple with heather for miles, broken only by the dark green juniper bushes or by the silver and gold of the scattered birch trees. Piles of rounded boulders originally brought down by the ice from Scandinavia form 'giants' graves', in reality Stone Age tumuli. Occasionally groups of tall oaks hide the typical Lower Saxon farms, great long buildings which unite under one roof barn, byre and house. They are entered by a central arched doorway beneath the gable, which is usually decorated with the crossed horses' heads emblem of Lower Saxony.

The small towns of the Heath cling to its edge, like ports to a coast. *Celle* (59) marks the crossing of the Aller, while in the north the attractive brick-built town of *Lüneburg* (61) had a considerable medieval prosperity due to its salt springs and its function as a port on the small river Ilmenau.

The Western Geest. To the west of the Aller and Weser the *Geest* is lower and more level than the Lüneburg Heath, and is split by ill-drained depressions into many separate blocks. The river marshes and some of the peat bogs have been drained to make good cattle pasture. The whole region is lacking in industry, and the towns are small. The main exception is *Oldenburg* (128), situated at a crossing of the river Hunte, which has a prosperous group of food-processing and light industries. *Delmenhorst* (61), an industrial outlier of Bremen, has a linoleum industry, initially developed to use the waste resulting from bottle-cork making for the Bremen wine trade. The demand for jute cloth for linoleum called into being a jute-spinning and weaving industry. Delmenhorst's woollen and worsted industry is also closely linked with Bremen wool merchants.

The Emsland. Of great geographical and human interest is the long and bitter struggle to settle the peat bogs (*Moore*) found in the northwestern part of Lower Saxony, especially on either side of the river Ems. The first serious advance into the peat lands came with the introduction from the Netherlands of the *Fehnkolonie* (p. 84 and Fig. 17). More recent methods involve the drainage of the bogs, followed by the use of giant ploughs to bring up sand from beneath 1·5 m/5 ft of peat. The mixture of sand and peat, with the addition of artificial fertilizers, makes a reasonable arable soil; if the peat is thicker than 1·5 m/5 ft, it may be worked for industry, or left under pasture. By this process, new farms are being created, and new life brought to this lonely frontier district.

The cutting of the Dortmund–Ems canal in 1875–99 made little difference to the economy of the region, but the discovery of oil near Lingen in 1942 was more of a revolution. The main oilfields of Lower Saxony are found beneath the sands of the Northern Lowland in a belt stretching from east to west, parallel with the front of the Central Uplands. Production at first came from small oilfields trapped on the fringe of salt domes in the Harz Foreland and the Aller valley, near Celle. This is still the main field, although the oil now comes from much deeper structures. The Emsland discoveries provided a second field of approximately equal importance. A refinery and other industrial works have been built on the Dortmund–Ems canal at Lingen, and a pipeline carries natural gas to the Ruhr chemical industry (p. 243). A more recently discovered field lies between the Ems and the Weser, and there are smaller oilfields near Hamburg. The Emsland oil discoveries have not been followed by the development of industries other than refining, probably because of the general isolation of the area, and the existing textile industries are not a dependable source of employment. Under the special *Emsland Plan* an attempt is being made at a co-ordinated improvement of the whole structure of this difficult area.

The Coast. Much richer than the sandy *Geest* is its fringe of sea and river marshes. The marshland is all won from the waters, but the battle has not always gone smoothly. Drowning of the coast in the first centuries A.D. forced the inhabitants to build themselves artificial mounds (*Würten*) to live on, which still provide sites for many farms and tightly clustered villages. Gradually over the last 800 years dykes have pressed the sea and river waters back from the fertile land, although with many disasters. Settlement often took the form of *Marschhufendörfer*, strings of farms built along an interior dyke, with their farmland going off in long, narrow strips at right angles into the marsh (Fig. 8). In the modern polders, protected by powerful pumps, settlement is dispersed. The marsh land is fertile when first drained but heavy, so that most is in grass, the basis of the important coastal meat and dairying industry.

The coast was the homeland of the Frisians, a separate German people from the Saxons, great seafarers, with a distinctive speech. The immense Frisian farmhouses are even larger than those of the Saxons, and also contain barn, byre and house under one huge roof.

Outside the sea dyke lie the mud flats of the Watten sea, beyond which the sandy East Frisian Islands continue the line of the dune coast of the Netherlands. The beaches fringing the dunes are the basis of a prosperous holiday industry.

Population. The present united *Land* Lower Saxony dates only from 1945. This was one of the parts of Germany most affected by the arrival of refugees; from a total of 4·5 millions in 1939 population rose to 6·8 millions in 1950. With the recovery of the West German economy population began to move out of this rather poor, rural *Land* to employment opportunities in the Rhinelands. The losses have been balanced by natural increase, but the resultant static total population contrasts markedly with the expansion of more fortunate *Länder*. Refugees and their children still make up the high figure of 30% of the total population.

SUGGESTIONS FOR FURTHER READING

E. SCHRADER, *Die Landschaften. Niedersachsens: ein topographischer Atlas*, Hanover (Niedersächsisches Landesvermessungsamt), 1957.

Chapter 17

SCHLESWIG-HOLSTEIN AND THE NORTH SEA PORTS

SCHLESWIG-HOLSTEIN

The Land. Schleswig-Holstein occupies the base of the peninsula of Jutland, and so forms a barrier between the North Sea and the Baltic, and also a land bridge from Germany towards the Scandinavian lands. Routeways, and conflicts for the control of routeways, have dominated the history of the region. As a barrier, Schleswig-Holstein had to be crossed by prehistoric and medieval traders from the Baltic who wished to avoid the stormy sea route around the north of Jutland. It was control of this route across the base of the peninsula that brought immense prosperity to Lübeck and the Hanseatic League (p. 74). A much later route was the Kiel (Nord–Ostsee) canal, constructed in 1887–95 to allow freedom of passage for the German navy between the North Sea and the Baltic.

A witness to the importance of Schleswig-Holstein as a land bridge is the *Dänewerk*, an impressive earthwork across the peninsula, which dates from the struggles between German and Dane in the 9th–12th centuries. Conflict was renewed in the 19th century, when the two duchies of Schleswig in the north and Holstein in the south were claimed by both Danes and Germans, and were seized by Prussia in the war of 1864. Following a plebiscite in 1920 North Schleswig, with a population of about 160,000, was returned to Denmark.

Physically Schleswig-Holstein is transitional between the western and eastern sections of the Northern Lowland. The western side of the peninsula resembles Lower Saxony, with sandy *Geest* plateaus and a fringe of coastal marshes, mud flats and islands. In the east, the sands are buried beneath the piled-up moraines of the last (Vistula) glaciation, which splay out southwards to form the looped moraine walls of the Eastern Lowland. This gives the basis for a three-fold division of the country, with a spine of poor, sandy heathland dividing the rich marshlands of the west from the rich moraine belt fringing the Baltic (Fig. 54). The climate is naturally influenced by the sea, giving mild winters, cool summers, prolonged autumns and plentiful rain throughout the year. In the circumstances, grass grows well and farming is based mainly on livestock. Mineral resources are few, apart from a little salt and oil from

FIG. 54. Schleswig-Holstein.

buried salt domes, and this coupled with remoteness limited the growth of industry. With such a long coast, the tourist and holiday industries are well developed.

The West Coast. Overlapping the edge of the *Geest* is a fringe of coastal marshland, which has been progressively invaded by the sea since the end of prehistoric times, and partially reclaimed in recent centuries. Remnants of sand dunes form outer islands which shelter wide tidal mud flats, known as *Watten*, above which rise occasional low, muddy islands known as *Halligen*. Many of the islands have been joined to the mainland by embankments, such as the Hindenburg Dam and railway to Sylt, constructed in 1925. These have the double purpose of improving communications and of encouraging the deposition of silt, which can then be embanked and drained. Following the 1953 Netherlands flood disaster and the German flood disaster of 1962 a major programme of dyke strengthening and shortening was initiated.

The new land is so fertile that it provides record crops of wheat, roots and vegetables. In this region of heavy rainfall, however, the best long-term use is for grass. Young beef cattle are bought in spring, fattened on the rich grass, and marketed in autumn. Dairying, the rearing of horses and the fattening of pigs are also important. Downstream from Hamburg, the Elbe marshes are used for fruit and vegetable growing. Settlement forms of the marsh resemble those of coastal Lower Saxony (p. 269).

The Geest. The Schleswig-Holstein *Geest* consists, as usual, of gently-undulating plateaus of sandy material left from the Warthe glaciation. Into the plateaus, meltwater escaping from the later Vistula ice front to the east cut broad depressions which, towards the west, are often filled with peat. Because of the heavy rainfall and the many stretches of peat, about half of the *Geest* today is under grass, the basis of an important dairying industry. Modern methods and fertilizers also allow the sandy land to produce reasonable crops of animal feeding stuffs, such as rye, oats and potatoes.

Rural settlement on the *Geest* takes the form of small villages, with many scattered farms between. A road with an almost continuous line of settlement follows the western edge of this well-drained land, just above the marshes. Where the road dips to cross a river, a crossing town and port is usually found; such are *Husum*, *Itzehoe* (37) and Hamburg itself. The eastern edge of the *Geest* is followed by the central route of the peninsula northwards through *Neumünster* (75), which has leather, textile and engineering industries. The main road northwards (E3) tunnels beneath the Kiel canal at *Rendsburg* (36) before carrying its busy tourist traffic onwards to the Danish border.

The Eastern Moraine Belt. The comparatively recent Vistula drift deposits in the east of the peninsula have been little attacked by erosion. The numerous terminal moraines form the highest country of Schleswig-Holstein, rising to over 150 m/500 ft. Between the hills are boulder clay plains and numerous lakes. Long inlets from the Baltic, known as *Förden*, occupy channels cut by water under the ice sheet.

The boulder clay of the Eastern Moraine Belt has not had time to be badly leached, so that it forms a heavy but fertile brown-earth soil, initially covered by beech woods. About 80% of the land is arable; wheat can be grown, but most of the crops are fed to livestock, especially to dairy cattle, in a type of farming resembling that of Denmark (p. 127). The fields are small, and bounded by hedges, giving a very English appearance. Enclosure has encouraged the dispersion of farms, blurring the initial pattern of settlement in villages.

The oldest and most important towns of Schleswig-Holstein are situated at the head of the long *Förde* inlets from the Baltic. *Flensburg* (96) has suffered the curtailment of its hinterland by the Danish boundary. It is a military and naval centre, produces most of Germany's rum, and has a shipyard. For a few days in May 1945, this town, at the northernmost extremity of western Germany, was the seat of the short-lived government of Admiral Dönitz, who was nominated by Hitler as his successor. *Kiel* (270) resembles Wilhelmshaven in the way that its fortunes have fluctuated with those of the German navy. There was great distress after 1945, partly countered by the building up of new light industries. Fortunately Kiel has never depended entirely on its dockyard; its *Howaldt* shipyard is one of the largest in Germany, there are associated engineering and electrical industries, it is the *Land* capital and has a university.

Lübeck (240) lies 15 km/10 miles inland on the Trave estuary. From its foundation in the middle of the 12th century this trading town grew rapidly; it became the leading member of the Hanseatic League, dominated the Baltic trade and in the 13th and 14th centuries was one of Europe's largest cities. When the great maritime discoveries turned the Baltic into a backwater, the League, and Lübeck with it, declined. The town has never regained its former importance, although there are shipbuilding yards, smelting plants and engineering works. In the postwar years, maritime trade with Scandinavia developed vigorously, since East German ports were no longer used. A bridge now links the island of Fehmarn to the mainland as part of a new road and rail ferry link from Puttgarden to Rödby in Denmark, replacing the earlier route through Warnemünde in East Germany.

Population. Schleswig-Holstein was the refugee *Land* of West Germany. Germans from the East poured into this predominantly rural area at the end of the war, raising the population by 70%, in places by over 100%. Although many refugees were farmers, land reclamation schemes and the division of large Holstein estates could provide land for only a fraction. Others have had to move to find work in Hamburg or the industrial Rhinelands. Population dropped more than 10% in the first decade of economic recovery, then stabilized and even began to increase slightly at the end of the 1950s. Nevertheless refugees and their children still make up nearly a third of the population, the highest proportion of all the West German *Länder*.

Heligoland (Ger. Helgoland). This island was administratively attached to Schleswig-Holstein after its cession by Britain in 1890 in exchange for Zanzibar. Its steep Triassic cliffs are in constant danger from the sea, and need costly protection. Bombing and demolitions during and after the war have further shattered the cliffs of this fortress island, which is now being used once more as a resort, bird sanctuary and emergency harbour.

NORTH SEA PORTS

A glance at the population map (Fig. 22) shows that the German North Sea ports are isolated from the nearest centres of dense population and industry by the poor sandy stretches of the Northern Lowland. The great industrial centres of West Germany more easily trade by the Rhine with Rotterdam or Antwerp than with Hamburg or Bremen. This isolation of the German ports, which has greatly hampered their development in recent times, was accentuated by the 'iron curtain' and the creation of the European Economic Community which left them in something of an economic backwater.

Hamburg (1,857), the largest port, the largest city and the largest single industrial town of West Germany, is situated at the head of the Elbe estuary, about 115 km/70 miles from the open sea. The Elbe here flows on the floor of one of the great

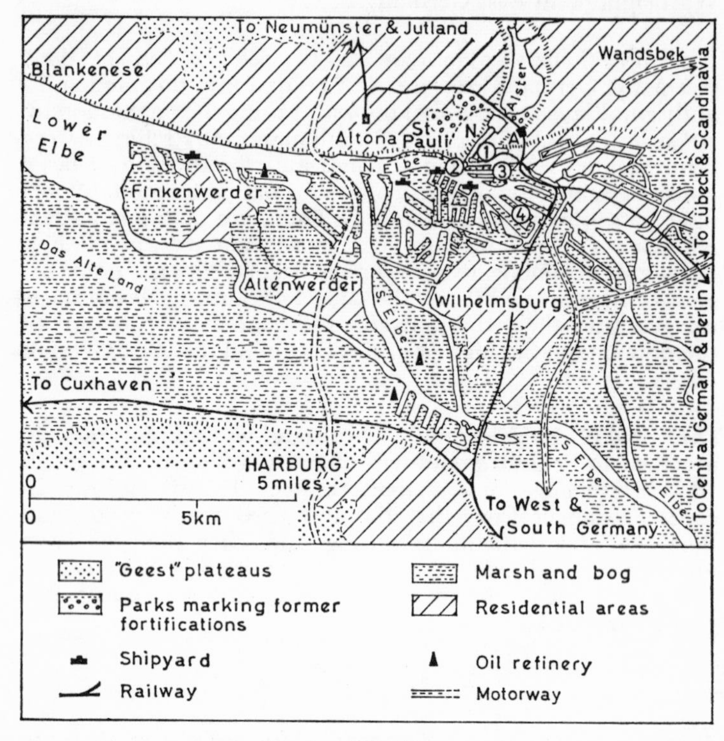

FIG. 55. Hamburg.

ice-margin trenches or *Urströmtäler*, which are typical of the eastern part of the Northern Lowland. The river meanders on a marshy floor between steep *Geest* slopes, and divides into a number of branches at the head of the estuary. A glacial overflow channel, by which water escaped from the Vistula ice front to the northeast, is now occupied by a right-bank tributary of the Elbe, the Alster.

On a dry spur of *Geest* between the Alster and the Elbe marshes grew up one of the chain of crossing settlements and minor river ports that follows the edge of the Schleswig-Holstein *Geest* (p. 273). Here, on the left bank of the Alster was established, about A.D. 820, a Carolingian fortress, the Hammaburg, and in its shelter, among the creeks below, grew a small settlement of sailors and merchants. Hamburg rose above the other little Elbe ports through its selection by the Hanse port of Lübeck as the North Sea terminus of the overland trade route from the Baltic. The little port in the Alster mouth, sheltered from the storms of the estuary, grew busy, and the merchants of the adjoining town prospered.

Unlike Lübeck, Hamburg did not decline with the decline of the Hanseatic League. Its access to the North Sea enabled it to profit from the new trade in colonial products which followed the development of ocean routes to America and Asia. When the Alster harbour became too small and congested, the port was able to expand by becoming an Elbe harbour for the first time. Ships were moored in the *Niederhafen*, sheltered by a boom, and their goods taken in lighters to the tall, narrow warehouses lining the creeks and canals of the city. Unlike so many German towns, Hamburg thus continued to expand after the close of medieval times. Its area was doubled by building the *Neustadt*, across the Alster, and the whole city surrounded in 1615–25 by the elaborate fortifications which enabled it to preserve its independence through the troubles of the Thirty Years War.

The 19th century brought the age of steam ships, and also the rise of Germany to be a unified industrial power. Unloading in the stream was no longer swift or safe enough, but once more Hamburg's physical environment was capable of meeting the demands made on it. Dock basins could easily be constructed in the marshy land between the city and the northern branch of the Elbe, and owing to the low tidal range, no lock gates were necessary. When more basins were required after 1888, they were constructed in the marshy islands on the other side of the Northern Elbe. Successive programmes for deepening the Elbe channel (currently to 12 m/40 ft) have taken place with the growth in the size of ships, but sandbanks at the mouth are troublesome, and the port is not accessible to the very largest bulk carriers. Accordingly in 1961 Hamburg gave up all rights to its former outport of Cuxhaven, receiving in return the right to construct a deep-water port on the mud-flats of the Watten Sea, near the island of Neuwerk. The small Schleswig-Holstein port of Brunsbuttelkoog at the entrance of the Kiel canal has also taken advantage of the deepening of the Elbe channel to build a quay for the bulk carriers that cannot reach Hamburg (Fig. 54).

Hamburg's relations with the main centres of German industry on the Rhine have always been hampered by distance and the lack of a good waterway, although an indirect connection was provided in 1938 by the continuation of the Mittelland canal as far as the Elbe. Not surprisingly, Hamburg's traditional trade links were by the Elbe and its connecting canals to Berlin, Saxony, Silesia and Czechoslovakia rather than with West Germany.

Postwar recovery was slower than at Rotterdam, Antwerp or even Bremen, and only in 1955 did traffic pass the immediate prewar figure, to run at about 30 million tons in the mid-1960s. Today the 'iron curtain' lies only 40 km/25 miles away, and trade from the East German portion of Hamburg's former hinterland has been diverted away from the Elbe route to the new ocean port of Rostock. Similarly, Silesian trade now goes to the Polish Baltic ports. Czechoslovakia and Hungary have remained rather more faithful, but in general the eastern transit trade is less than a third of its prewar total.

To make matters worse, the Mittelland canal route from the Rhinelands and industrial Lower Saxony has to pass into East German territory in order to descend the Elbe to Hamburg, and this has discouraged the growth of water traffic with an alternative West German hinterland. In the creation of alternative land routes the city has suffered from its isolation north of the sandy lands of Lower Saxony. Most of the new traffic went to the roads, which were most inadequate before the completion of the link to the West German motorway system at Hanover. Electrification has progressively strengthened the north–south rail links with the Rhine and southern Germany. A more recent project is for a 1,350-ton canal from the Elbe above Hamburg across the Lüneburg heath to the Mittelland canal near Brunswick.

The slackening of Hamburg's transit trade has led to an emphasis on industrial development as a source of employment and of port traffic. As a major harbour, Hamburg inevitably attracted a group of characteristic port industries.

It is Germany's largest shipbuilding centre, with yards situated on the south bank of the Northern Elbe. Shipbuilding used to be Hamburg's biggest employer of industrial labour, but as in many European countries the industry has tended to decline in importance in recent years. A second group of port industries is devoted to the processing of imported commodities. Crude oil is the port's largest single import, and after 1945 Hamburg developed into Germany's largest centre of oil refining. In terms of turnover, although not of labour employed, this is Hamburg's most important industry, but with the development of new market-orientated refineries on the Rhine and in southern Germany the industry has ceased to expand. The smelting of non-ferrous metals, notably copper, and the chemical industry were similarly based on imported materials, although the latter is now greatly diversified. Other typical port industries are rubber and asbestos processing, oil milling with its related margarine and soap manufacture, flour milling and the processing of coffee, tea and tobacco. In Germany as a whole these port industries do not form a rapidly expanding group, and Hamburg as a location for them is now at some disadvantage compared with sites on the Rhine, near to the main German markets.

The demand from shipping and shipbuilding called into being a variety of subsidiary industries such as iron founding, mechanical and electrical engineering, and the manufacture of a range of supplies from paint to nautical instruments. A feature of postwar Hamburg has been the way in which, with transit trade and the port industries rather static, these subsidiary industries have enormously expanded and diversified. The arrival of refugees from East Germany and Berlin helped the process, especially in the important electrical manufacturing branch. Hamburg has also replaced Berlin as West Germany's principal press centre. The making of machinery of one sort or another is now Hamburg's biggest single occupation. Similar expansion and diversification has occurred with the chemical and pharmaceutical industries, precision instruments, printing and publishing, clothing and a range of other trades. The development of consumers' goods manufacture has been stimulated by the size of the market offered by Hamburg and neighbouring towns. As communications to the south improve, Hamburg is increasingly developing as the apex of an industrial triangle of 10 million people, with its western limb running through Bremen to Osnabrück, its southern limb following the Hercynian Foreland eastwards through Hanover and Brunswick.

The growth of port and industry have been paralleled by the growth of the city. In 1815 the fortifications were removed, and their place taken by a belt of parks in the west, and by the main railway station in the east. Beyond stretch the suburbs, in a half circle broken by the lake formed by the damming of the river Alster, a unique feature of the Hamburg landscape. Standing on the *Lombardsbrücke*, where the old fortifications divide the lake into two, the visitor can look northwards over the large Outer Alster, dotted with sailing boats, and surrounded by villas set in green banks. Turning from this almost rural scene to look southwards, he sees the Inner Alster, busy with ferry boats, and surrounded by elegant promenades with hotels, restaurants and shops. Above rise the tall brick spires which mark the old inner town, now the commercial and financial district. Nearer the port are great office blocks which house the shipping and importing firms, then come the warehouses and the busy harbour. Hamburg, almost alone among West German cities, is not provincial. Sailors, business men and visitors from all nations can be seen everywhere, patronizing the well-developed entertainment facilities. Hamburg, in fact, nearing the 2 million mark in population, is a world city.

Bremen (592), Germany's second port, stands like Hamburg at an estuary-head position. Because the Weser is smaller than the Elbe, Bremen differs from Hamburg in at least three ways: it commands an historic crossing of the main river (not of a tributary), it has been forced to develop a number of outports downstream, and it is not primarily served by inland water transport.

Bremen stands in the middle of a depression filled with marshes and peat bogs (Fig. 53). Fortunately, a long sand dune runs parallel with the right bank of the river, providing a dry natural causeway by which routes following the southwestern edge of the Lüneburg Heath can step over the Bremen depression to the Stader *Geest* in the north. Where the Weser approaches the dune, there developed also an estuary-head crossing of the river, used by routes from the Lower Rhinelands to the Baltic. On the dune was erected in 788 a bishop's church, to help in the conversion of the northern lands. West of the cathedral grew up a settlement of traders profiting from the interchange of goods at this crossing of land and water routes. As at Hamburg, growth continued after the end of medieval times. The *Neustadt* was founded on the opposite bank in 1625, and the whole city surrounded by the customary elaborate bastions and ditches.

From the beginning of the 17th century, the silting of the Weser and the growth in the size of ships forced the creation of outports, Vegesack in 1619 and Bremerhaven in 1827. Only

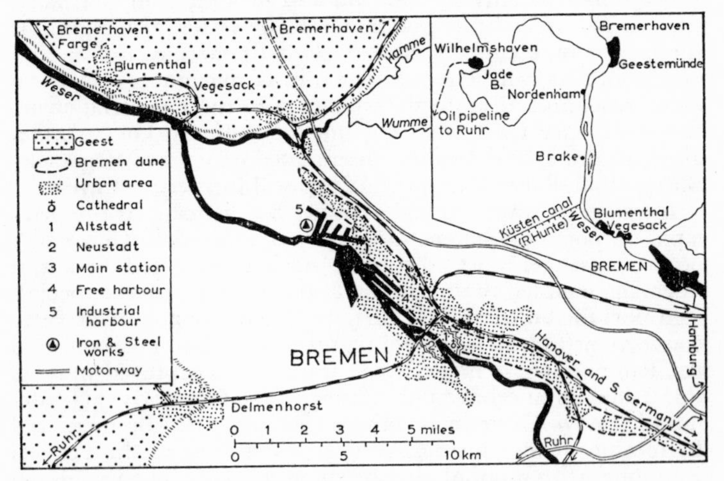

FIG. 56. Bremen.

in 1887 was the trend of traffic away from Bremen reversed by the dredging of the Weser. In 1888 Bremen joined the German Customs Union, and began the construction of docks in the alluvium immediately downstream from the city centre.

Bremen's imports consist less of bulk products than do Hamburg's, and more of such valuable commodities as cotton, wool, tobacco, coffee, wine and textile yarns. Bremen has specialized markets for many commodities, particularly cotton and wool, which are sent to manufacturers all over Germany. The port has always had particular connections with North and South

America. It gained a flying start over Hamburg in postwar recovery, and by 1956 was handling, with its outports, more than double the prewar volume of traffic, mainly owing to a steep rise in imports. Traditionally Bremen is a rail port, with a hinterland in West and South Germany, so that its trade has been less disturbed than that of Hamburg.

The industries of Bremen are typical of a large port, including shipbuilding and raw material processing, such as oil refining and wool combing (Blumenthal), jute spinning, grain milling, chocolate manufacture and tobacco industries. Bremen has the only coastal iron and steel plant in Germany, sited so as to receive its raw materials by water, although now the largest bulk carriers must dock at Bremerhaven and send on the ore by rail. The manufacture of machinery, electrical equipment and aircraft gives balance to the industrial structure. The city itself is strung out for some 20 km/12 miles along its dune, and also has the isolated quarter of Vegesack–Blumenthal–Farge lining the Weser still further northwest.

Bremerhaven (145), 70 km/45 miles downstream, is the principal outport of Bremen. Originally developed as Germany's ocean passenger port, the large dock constructed to admit liners has enabled Bremerhaven to be redeveloped as a specialized port for bulk iron-ore carriers. There are good waterway connections to iron and steel plants in the Harz Foreland and the Ruhr, but fast modern ore trains have captured most of this traffic. Bremerhaven has absorbed the former rival Geestemünde, now Germany's largest fishing port. Bremen and Bremerhaven together form the smallest *Land* in the Federal Republic, with a population of about 740,000. The remaining Weser ports mainly deal with bulk commodities, which may be processed in the non-ferrous metals, cable and fertilizer industries of *Nordenham* or the rubber, vegetable-oil and margarine works of *Brake*.

Emden (46) is the third of the North Sea ports, and rather a poor relation. Although important in medieval times, unfavourable political developments and the silting of the Ems estuary led to its decline. The present port is an artificial creation, consisting of dock basins cut into the marshland in the years 1899–1914, as part of an attempt to divert the valuable Rhine traffic from Rotterdam to a German port. The project has never been a success: Emden handles mostly bulk commodities like coal, oil, iron ore, scrap and grain. Even this trade is now threatened, as the port cannot take the large modern bulk carriers. It has failed to attract the processing industries that help to make Hamburg and Bremen prosperous; there is some fish preparation, an oil refinery, shipbuilding and, to bring some diversification, a branch plant of one of the German car firms.

The port of *Wilhelmshaven* (101) was carved out of the mud flats of the Jade Bight to provide the principal base of the German navy. Its fortunes in the past have fluctuated with those of the fleet. After 1945 there was a determined attempt at diversification, when office machinery manufacture and other light industries were set up. Wilhelmshaven can be reached by large modern tankers, and so was selected as the terminal of the oil pipeline to the Ruhr. *Cuxhaven* (46) was intended to be the outport for Hamburg, which has in fact preferred to improve the Elbe channel for larger vessels. In 1961 Hamburg ceded all rights in Cuxhaven to Lower Saxony, so that the existing fishing specialization can be further developed. Hamburg received in return the right to build an outport on the mudflats of the Watten Sea at Neuwark.

Finally it must not be forgotten that the busiest port handling German traffic is not in Germany at all. In most years Rotterdam, favoured by its position at the end of the Rhine waterway, handles more goods passing to or from Germany than any German port, even Hamburg.

SUGGESTIONS FOR FURTHER READING

C. Degn and U. Muuss, *Topographischer Atlas Schleswig-Holstein,* Neumünster (Karl Wachholtz Verlag), 3rd ed., 1966.

C. Degn and U Muuss, *Luftbildatlas Schleswig-Holstein,* Neumünster (Karl Wachholtz Verlag), 1965.

J. Bird, 'Seaports and the European Economic Community', *Geographical Journal*, 133, 1967, pp. 302–27.

PART FIVE
EAST GERMANY AND BERLIN

Chapter 18
INDUSTRY AND PLANNING IN THE DDR

After 1945 East Germany was faced with a more difficult task of adjustment than was the west. Having a much smaller area, it was understandably less diverse industrially, but above all its almost complete lack of heavy industry made the replacement of lost equipment extremely difficult. The Soviet zone of military occupation was also subjected to much more radical dismantling than anything known in the western zones. Of the plants that were allowed to remain, over 200 were placed under Soviet ownership and produced for Soviet account. It was 1953 before the last batch was returned to East German control. One concern only was retained, the large but mysterious 'Wismut AG', engaged in uranium mining in the Ore Mountains and adjoining Thuringia. Thus at a time when West Germany was already receiving Marshall Aid towards rebuilding the economy, East Germany was contributing in massive fashion towards reconstruction and development in the U.S.S.R.

Industrial recovery in East Germany was also affected by a great contrast in objectives from those accepted in the west. Concurrently with rebuilding, East Germany was also engaged in the expropriation by the state of the means of production, distribution and exchange, and was carrying through a political revolution to bring new men to positions of power. It is not necessary to take up a position either for or against these developments to see that they were liable to involve considerable confusion in the direction of economic activity, at least in the short run. Further difficulties were caused by the drift of population to West Germany, draining the work force of some of its most youthful and active elements. Comparisons between living standards in West and East Germany are not very meaningful, but at least it can be said that the repeatedly announced East German aim of surpassing the living standards of 'capitalist' West Germany is yet to be achieved. Even taking gross national product which, because it includes investment, gives a fairer picture of East Germany, it appears that the country was in 1950 still about a fifth below the 1936 level, whereas West Germany had already surpassed it. Both economies expanded at similar rates throughout the 1950s, leaving the relative position unchanged. The world economic recession of the 1960s then gave the planned East German economy the opportunity to close the gap a little.

Spatial effects of economic planning. A continuing aim of East German industrial planning has been to build up balanced industrial complexes in all parts of the country, in contrast to the excessive concentrations of industry in a very few places, which is regarded as an undesirable feature resulting from monopoly capitalism. Accordingly we find continuous attempts to direct new industrial development into the more remote east and north of the country, where the workers and intellectuals can diversify a previously rural and probably reactionary population. This trend has been a continuous one since 1950, but the general direction of industrial planning has undergone some curious changes.

After the immediate postwar period of emergency reconstruction, the five-year plan inaugurated in 1950 reflected the full rigour of the Stalinist position, that all priority must be given to heavy industry and the investment goods industries. Without a well-developed heavy industry, a socialist state would be obliged to turn to capitalist suppliers, and so inevitably fall under their neo-colonialist domination. The dogma was applied irrespective of the existence of a raw-material base for heavy industry, and has left East Central Europe littered with industrial white elephants. East Germany's contribution was the then Stalin iron and steel project, appropriately sited in the forests of the remote eastern frontier on the Oder. As East Germany has no significant production of either coking coal or iron ore, and the plant was not even conveniently situated with regard to markets, it is not entirely surprising that greater economic realism after Stalin's death stopped its development at blast-furnace stage.

A modification rather than a change of policy came in

with the second five-year plan 1956–60. With greater realism this put rather more emphasis on East Germany's existing specialties like chemicals and machine building, although consumers' goods were still out of favour. A great feature of this plan was the development of home raw materials to save exports; effectively in East German conditions this meant the maximum possible exploitation of brown coal. The principle was announced that brown coal, which under capitalism had been thoughtlessly burnt, would now be milked by the scientists of every possible chemical. Only the residue, in the form of coke, gas or electricity, would reach the consumer as a fuel. The monument to this period was the Schwarze Pumpe *Kombinat*, a giant assemblage of power stations, briquette plants and above all coking plants, which by a miracle of industrial chemistry would produce metallurgical coke and by-products from the unlikely material of brown coal. This key project was located in the 'underdeveloped' east, on the Lower Lusatian brown-coal field.

The second five-year plan did not last its term, being overtaken in 1959 by the changed conditions of the Soviet economy. Kruschev's U.S.S.R. was discovered to be rich in coal, iron, steel, oil and other products of the basic and heavy industry that had been created with so much sacrifice since the Revolution. On the other hand it had an almost insatiable need for all the complex industrial equipment needed by an advanced economy, while the individual Soviet citizens were beginning to demand some return from their efforts in the form of consumers goods. In these conditions it made no sense at all for East Germany to be pouring skilled technologists and scarce capital into the making of indifferent coke for the high-cost production of iron and steel. The building of the coking plants was postponed, apparently for good, and instead of carefully preserving brown coal as a raw material, giant power stations were built to burn it in the production of electricity for a growing economy. Even the existing production of motor fuel and chemicals from brown coal was to be supplanted by oil delivered by pipeline from the U.S.S.R. In return for these basic materials East Germany would concentrate on providing the communist world with just those products of an advanced industrial economy in which specialization had been developed under capitalism. Further development was to be on similar lines, taking advantage of the high level of East German technology in industries like electronics, the building of automated machine tools, petrochemicals, plastics and synthetic fibres.

In spite of this new, or revived, line of industrial development, the policy of favouring the 'underdeveloped' north and east has still been followed. This is shown in the location of one of the key plants, the Schwedt oil refinery, on the Oder to the northeast of Berlin. Yet because the 'old' industries are back in favour, much industrial expansion must inevitably take place at existing locations. The new petroleum-based chemical industry is centred on the existing chemical giant at Leuna, complex machine tools and textile machinery in the Karl-Marx-Stadt (Chemnitz) area of industrial Saxony, electrical and electronic equipment in East Berlin. Even the Berlin wall comes into the picture, for East Germany's performance as the chief supplier of machinery to the COMECON countries was menaced by the flight to the west of many of her most youthful and active citizens. The wall can thus be regarded as an economic necessity as well as a political act. (For parallel developments in neighbouring COMECON countries see R. H. Osborne, *East-Central Europe* [Frederick A. Praeger].)

Chapter 19

CENTRAL GERMANY

For the purpose of this account, Central Germany is the basin of the middle Elbe, between Magdeburg in the north and Dresden in the south. It is bounded on the west by the Harz and Thuringian Forest, on the south by the Ore Mountains and on the northeast by the sandy glacial heathlands of Lower Lusatia and the Fläming (Fig. 57). In many ways Central Germany repeats the geographical features of North Rhine–Westphalia. Here, too, a coalfield provides a nucleus, a power house for the whole region, but this time the coals are of Tertiary, not Carboniferous, age. Central Germany also possesses an older industrial region to the south, in the Hercynian massif of the Ore Mountains, corresponding with the Rhenish Uplands. Finally Central Germany is also drained by a single major river, but unlike the Rhine it runs not through the heart of the region, but along its northeastern edge, and this fact, together with its smaller size and more erratic régime, has made it of much less importance for transport purposes.

Politically, the divisions of Central Germany have always been complex, but three main units can be distinguished. Centred on the basin of the same name is Thuringia, an original German tribal area, which in 1945, was unified as *Land* Thuringia. East of Thuringia runs the Elbe–Saale line, along which Charles the Great stabilized the boundary between Germany and Slav (Chap. 5). Beyond this line, in what is thus German colonized territory, lie the other two units. The kingdom of Saxony had its nucleus in the Ore Mountains and the loess land immediately to the north; with the end of the monarchy in 1918 it became *Land* Saxony. The third unit consists of the Prussian province of Saxony, centred on the loess land of the Harz Foreland and Saxon Lowland; this became *Land* Saxony-Anhalt in 1945. As noted above (p. 57), this *Land* structure was broken up in 1952 by the creation of smaller Administrative Districts (*Bezirke*) based upon the central places of the region.

THURINGIA

The Thuringian Forest. Stretching northwestwards from the Bohemian massif, the long spur of the Thuringian Forest divides the basin of Thuringia from Franconia and Hesse,

FIG. 57. Central Germany.

although politically Thuringia stretches over into the headwaters of the Werra. The Thuringian Forest is a typical Hercynian massif, composed of Palaeozoic rocks, mainly slates, with granite and other intrusive rocks. The forested massif is uplifted to over 900 m/3,000 ft, but deeply cut by numerous valleys draining to either side.

The occupation of the valleys of the forest was late, mainly after A.D. 1000, and from the first inhabitants depended on industry for their existence in this bleak upland. Iron and copper ores, charcoal and water power were the basis of the smelting and working of metals. With the exhaustion of mining in the 17th century, the smelting works closed, but small metal-processing industries have remained, using the skill of the inhabitants in the little valley towns on both sides of the massif. Hardware, hand tools and nails are traditional products; from this industry has developed the making of watches, sewing machines, small machine tools and measuring instruments. Glass making, based initially on local sand and wood, and porcelain manufacture are also traditional. As in many poor upland regions there is a well-developed tradition of domestic industry, producing textiles, clothing and shoes. These small producers have now been grouped into state combines, and there is a tendency to develop factory production. The southern side of the Thuringian Forest is in particular the home of the well-known toy and Christmas-decorations industry, to which reference has been made in connection with West Germany (p. 198). Here is also found the *Bezirk* capital, *Suhl*.

Southeastwards the Thuringian Forest broadens into the lower and less forested Thuringian Hills. Here timber is the basis of furniture industries and of large rayon works on the Elster and Saale. Near the Saale is the small Maxhütte iron and steel works, important as having the only iron furnaces included within East German territory in 1945. Some of East Germany's most important uranium mines are also located near the *Bezirk* capital *Gera* (108) on the Elster.

The Thuringian Basin. Between the uplifted Thuringian Forest massif in the south and the Harz in the north is the Thuringian Basin. Surrounding it, the Bunter Sandstone forms forested plateaus, which in the northwest divide Thuringia from Hesse and Lower Saxony. Further in, the Muschelkalk Limestone appears, forming a rough saucer overlying the Bunter, with an outward-facing escarpment, generally wooded, and a dip slope plateau with much arable. The centre of the basin is occupied by Keuper Clay, forming a lowland covered with loess, on which an extremely fertile semi black-earth soil has developed.

This inner part of the Thuringian Basin has large villages standing among arable strip fields; meadow is limited to the vicinity of streams. Wheat, barley, sugar beet, vegetables and seeds are important crops, and cattle are fattened in the stall.

There are numerous medium-sized towns, due to the fact that until the 20th century Thuringia was a mosaic of petty states, each of which tried to develop its own capital. In spite of Thuringia's lack of raw materials, these towns possess a number of medium and light industries, including textiles, boot and shoe manufacture, light engineering and glass making. This industrial structure has been strengthened and extended in recent years. The area around *Müllhausen*, for example, has received new plants for cotton spinning, knitted textiles, clothing and the manufacture of light electrical and radio equipment.

The most important of the towns are on the routeway which, leaving the loess lands of Central Germany, crosses the Thuringian Basin to pass north of the Thuringian Forest. *Jena* (85) is a university town at the crossing of the Saale; it is the site of a typical Thuringian industry, the Zeiss works, which uses extremely skilled labour to produce optical instruments and cameras. The special optical glass is also produced locally. Of recent years the Zeiss establishment has increasingly evolved from optics to electronics, the production of precision measuring instruments for incorporation into automatic machine tools. *Weimar* (64) is the best known of the small Thuringian capitals, with its memories of Goethe and Schiller and of the brilliant intellectual life of its small court. The undoubted economic and communications centre of Thuringia is *Erfurt* (191), formerly the *Land* and now the *Bezirke* capital. To the older clothing and shoe industries Erfurt had before the war added light engineering, especially office machinery manufacture. On this basis, the Communist government developed heavy engineering, a radical change for Thuringia. Finally *Eisenach* (50) commands the gateway north of the Thuringian Forest. The town is overlooked by the Wartburg castle, in which Luther, while being sheltered by the Elector of Saxony, translated the Bible into German (p. 77). Eisenach is the centre of the important Werra potash field, and has motor industries.

The Harz. Thuringia is closed off on the north by the Harz (pp. 261–2). On the flanks of the massif, Upper Permian (Zechstein) rocks outcrop in a narrow band; they contain copper ores, on which is based the centuries-old Mansfeld copper mining industry. The ore is smelted locally, and there are non-ferrous rolling mills. The Zechstein also contains potash salt beds, which are mined in deep shafts sunk through the overlying younger rocks in a broad belt surrounding the Harz. Mining began in the east, at Stassfurt, but has spread south of the Harz as far west as the Werra. A major east–west routeway runs immediately south of the Harz, passing through the fertile, loess-covered lowland known as the *Goldene Aue*. The main route centre is *Nordhausen*, with engineering, agricultural machinery and clothing industries.

THE SAXON UPLAND

The Ore Mountains. The southeastern border of Central Germany is formed by the Ore Mountains (Erz Gebirge), a Hercynian block tilted so as to present a steep scarp face towards Bohemia, and a gentle slope on the German side. Up this slope German settlers advanced in the period of eastern colonization to clear the forested highlands. They settled in the characteristic *Waldhufendorf* villages, strings of farms following a valley, sometimes for miles, with the lands of each farmer going off at right angles in a single strip up the slope (Fig. 9). Not agriculture but mining, however, attracted people to settle in the highest towns of Germany, like *Annaberg-Buchholz* at 600 m/2,000 ft. Mining brought land clearance in its train, with oats, rye and potatoes grown at heights of 700 m/ 2,300 ft and above.

The mining of silver, copper, iron and tin was in decline as early as the end of the 15th century. The population that had been gathered for mining certainly could not live by agriculture at these altitudes, so turned to industry. The Ore Mountains accordingly developed a small-scale and domestic industry producing wood products, toys, small metal goods, machine parts, clocks, cut glass, gloves and, above all, textiles. Before the war, the Saxon Upland was the most important region of Germany for woollen and worsted spinning and weaving, and for the manufacture of hosiery, knitted goods and fine stockings.

Mining in the Ore Mountains, almost extinct at the beginning of this century, experienced an immense revival when in 1949 a Soviet-owned organization began the working of uranium at a number of points. Some towns high in the ore mountains increased their population two or three times between 1946 and 1955, but thereafter there was some decline as interest shifted to the Thuringian field (p. 29). After preliminary processing, mainly at Freital, the ore is shipped to the Soviet Union. Intensive prospecting for uranium led to the discovery or rediscovery of a number of other ores. The principal lead and zinc deposits are in the neighbourhood of *Freiberg*, the largest town actually within the Ore Mountains. Tin and various alloying metals such as Wolfram are worked. Nickel deposits occur in the western Ore Mountains; since 1945 important nickel deposits have also been worked and smelted in the adjoining Saxon Hill country north of Zwickau.

The Saxon Hills. The communications of the Ore Mountains follow the valleys downhill and are collected by a main routeway that follows a furrow excavated in Permian and Carboniferous rocks at their northern foot. The Zwickau field here contains most of East Germany's very minor reserves of coal of Carboniferous age, some of which is made locally into foundry coke. In the furrow are the regional centres for both the Ore Mountains and the Saxon Hills to the north. *Zwickau* (129) is the centre for many surrounding textile plants, and manufactures cars and machinery. *Karl-Marx-Stadt* (formerly Chemnitz, 295) is the *Bezirk* capital and principal organizing centre for the Saxon textile industry; it manufactures hosiery and knitted textiles. It is also one of the greatest engineering centres of East Germany, producing advanced textile machinery and heavy machine tools. With the development of automated production Karl-Marx-Stadt is becoming increasingly drawn into the manufacture of electrical equipment and electronics. Car manufacture is also important. Textile, engineering and vehicle industries spill out over all the smaller towns of the neighbourhood. The Karl-Marx-Stadt *Bezirk*, which includes most of the Ore Mountains and Saxon Hills, contains over 2 million people at an average density of about 350 per sq km/900 per sq mile, far higher than on the loess lands to the north. There could hardly be a better example of the way man can triumph over an initially unfavourable environment.

The Vogtland. The Ore Mountains are a marked barrier to movement, forcing the main south–north routes to pass at either end. In the southwest, routes from Nürnberg and Pilsen converge on the Vogtland, a knot of hills filling the angle between the Ore Mountains and the Thuringian Forest. Good communications have helped the growth of wood, pulp, paper and rayon industries, the latter supplying the old-established and varied upland textile industry. Another typical upland speciality is the manufacture of musical instruments. The route centre is *Plauen* (82) which has recently developed machine tool industries in addition to its traditional lace making.

The Dresden Region. At their other end, the Ore Mountains are broken off by a southeast to northwest-trending downfaulted zone, in which the Elbe has been able to excavate the Dresden Basin in Cretaceous clays. Here is an unexpected island of warmth in Central Germany; on the loess-covered slopes grow market garden crops, fruit trees and even vines. In this attractive situation *Dresden* (508) was selected after the Reformation as the capital of Saxony. Its incomparable Baroque buildings, damaged by bombing in 1945, are being carefully restored, but the town has not recovered its prewar population. Dresden is now a mere *Bezirk* capital, but is the principal East German centre for scientific education and research, especially in the atomic field. Its industries lie away from the historic centre of the town, and depend on a skilled labour force and advanced technology. Typical are precision engineering, optical and photographic industries. The agricultural richness of its environment made it a centre of food and tobacco industries, out of which has developed the manufacture of food-processing and food-packing machines. As elsewhere in East Germany, the heavier type of industry has developed more recently. Dresden makes large electrical motors and hydro-electric generators, as well as more delicate electrical equipment for scientific and medical purposes. It is the most important German Elbe port above Magdeburg.

The upstream limit to the Dresden region is set by *Pirna*, with pulp, rayon and glass industries. At the downstream limit of the basin the Elbe narrows, and is dominated by the castle of *Meissen*, one of the great bastions of German power in the period of eastern colonization. The town is famous for its porcelain industries, based on local kaolin, which produce the Dresden shepherdesses which are still a reliable earner of foreign currency. The part of the Ore Mountains bordering Dresden has optical and precision industries. *Freital*, some miles to the west on a worked-out coalfield, makes special-quality steels and does some of the preliminary processing of uranium ore.

Eastwards from the Dresden Basin stretches the granite plateau of *Upper Lusatia*, bearing a dense population in small towns and industrialized villages, mainly engaged in the textile industry. *Zittau* also makes commercial motor vehicles and buses, *Gölitz* (89) diesel railcars and other rolling stock. The brown-coal deposits between the two towns are worked for electricity generation under co-operative agreements between East Germany, Poland and Czechoslovakia.

THE SAXON LOWLAND

The Land. Between the Saxon Hills and the Harz an embayment bites deep into the northern fringe of the Central Uplands. In Tertiary times, this was filled with hundreds of feet of sands, gravels and clays, together with seams of brown coal. The Tertiary rocks were in turn covered by deposits of the two earliest glaciations, and then by a thick sheet of loess. The even surface of this Saxon Lowland is today broken only by the incised flood plains of the rivers.

The loess soils, approaching black-earth nature in the northwest, have attracted farmers since Neolithic times. Clear through the Lowland ran the historic frontier between German and Slav on the Elbe–Saale line, so that settlement types, although predominantly nucleated, are very varied. Hamlets and round villages, with irregular field systems, probably indicate the survival of Slav peoples under German influence. These are intermixed with the planned street villages (*Strassendörfer*) and long-green villages (*Angerdörfer*), which were originally associated with regular open-field systems (Fig. 9). Unenclosed arable fields still predominate today, growing wheat, barley and sugar beet. There is very little woodland, and grassland is restricted to the flood plains; the high cattle population is mainly housed under cover and stall-fed.

The Central German Brown-Coal Field. Under the rich loess soil there are also mineral riches; potash and salt around the Harz, and seams of Tertiary brown coal varying between 10 and 20 m/30 and 60 ft in thickness. The coalfield lies mainly between the Saale and Mulde rivers, with important extensions in deep troughs westwards beyond Halle and northwestwards into the Harz. Hitherto this field has provided about two-thirds of East German output, but it has only 20% of remaining resources, so that its share is falling as other areas are developed. The Eocene and Miocene coal is suitable for distillation and hydrogenation, and the resultant products are

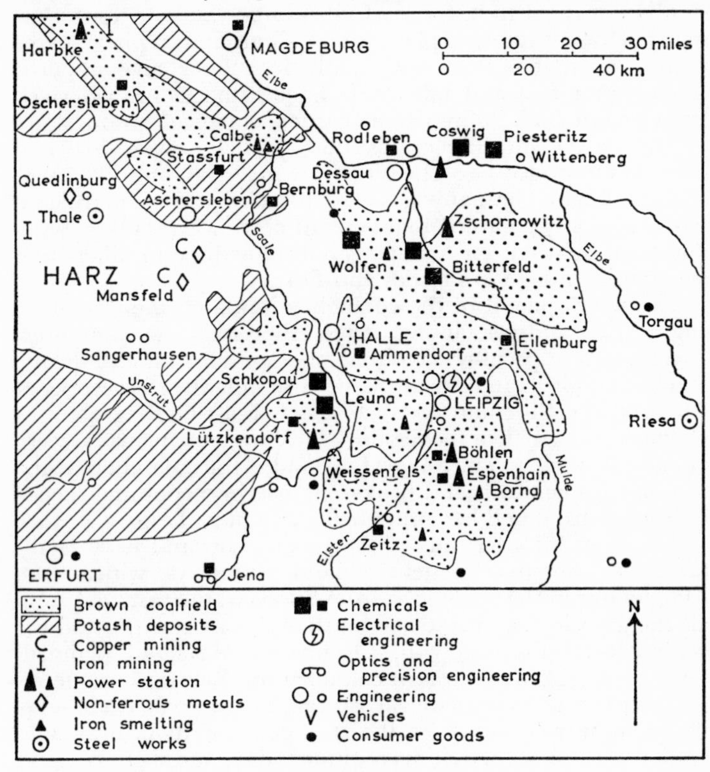

FIG. 58. The Central German brown-coal field.

the basis of chemical processing in the giant Leuna chemical plant and the adjoining Schkopau synthetic rubber plant. Poorer quality coal, which occurs especially in the northeast of the field, is used for the generation of electricity, required in enormous quantities, notably by the Bitterfeld electrochemical plant. Other major chemical plants of the field are at Wolfen (dyestuffs, photographic film, synthetic fibres), Piesteritz (nitrogen fertilizers, phosphorus) and Coswig (sulphuric acid). It will be apparent that the chemical plants are attracted to the rivers that fringe the field, which provide process water and permit the disposal of effluent.

The chemical industry is of vital importance to East Germany. Home-produced plastics and aluminium replace scarce metals, synthetic fibres and synthetic rubber save imports. Even motor fuel and lubricants have hitherto been derived from brown coal. As an export earner, chemical products are second only to machinery. By the 1960s, however, coal had become outmoded as a chemical raw material, and like other countries East Germany has had to change to a petroleum base. A greatly enlarged Leuna plant now receives oil by pipeline from Schwedt for making the intermediate products that eventually emerge as plastics and fibres.

The development of the coalfield stimulated the growth of engineering and vehicle industries. After 1945 the communist government especially favoured the manufacture of heavy machinery for its industrial plans; it rebuilt the steel-works at Riesa on the Elbe and installed a new blast-furnace plant at Calbe, in the north of the region. Many engineering works were greatly expanded. The Saxon Lowland is thus mainly devoted to mining, chemicals and heavy engineering; consumer goods industries are much less prominent, except at Leipzig.

The even loess terrains of the Saxon Lowland have facilitated the easy development of land routeways, which from Magdeburg in the northwest, from Silesia in the east, and from all the gaps in the hills to the south and west converge on the central town of *Leipzig* (596). Originating as a small 'planned' town in the German eastern colonization, Leipzig became renowned throughout medieval Europe for its great trade fairs, its fur industries and, from the 16th century, its printing and book trade. These activities continue today, and there is a very varied group of metal processing, engineering, vehicle and electrical industries.

Further west, *Halle* (276) on the Saale is the chief centre of the brown-coal and chemical industries, and builds mining and other machinery. *Dessau* (96) was known before the war for its vehicle and aircraft industries; more recently, it has been developed as a centre of heavy engineering. Near-by *Köthen* has a very similar industrial history.

Politically, the Central German brown-coal field is divided into the two *Bezirke* of Halle and Leipzig, with a combined population of 3·5 millions, at a density of about 250 to the sq. km/65 to the sq mile. Here is no dense and continuous conurbation, as in the Ruhr, but a scatter of towns and workers' housing estates in what is still one of the richest farming regions in Germany. Even before the growth of modern industry, trading routes from all Central Germany focused on the Saxon Lowland and Leipzig. Today, as the major source of power, chemicals, plastics and textile fibres for the older industries on its upland rim, the Saxon Lowland is even more the nucleus that gives Central Germany its economic unity.

THE MAGDEBURG REGION

The loess lands of the Saxon Lowland continue northwestwards into the Harz Foreland, which provides a fertile and early-settled region, and an historic routeway, situated between the Harz and the sandy plain to the north. Town growth was naturally early in such circumstances; today *Halberstadt*, *Quedlingburg* and *Aschersleben* still retain small metal-processing and engineering industries based initially on the mining of the Harz. The semi black-earth soil developed on the loess plains has also enabled the region to become a major sugar producer. Southeast to northwest-trending synclines also contain an extension of the Central German brown-coal field, which here just crosses the frontier into West Germany.

Magdeburg (268), situated at the point where the Foreland routeway reaches the Elbe, was the greatest German fortress of the Elbe–Saale frontier with the Slavs, and the sally-port for the eastern colonization. Today the town is still a major crossing point of routes by road, rail, river and canal. The agricultural riches of the region, together with the possibility of the import of bulk raw materials by the Elbe, have made Magdeburg a major centre of food processing, especially of sugar refining and milling, and also of fertilizer manufacture. It is also one of East Germany's foremost towns for the manufacture of mining machinery, machine tools, marine diesel engines and heavy industrial equipment of all kinds. Its Elbe boatbuilding yards produce barges and ocean-going tugs. Magdeburg is the main point of entry from the west into the sandy lowland of Brandenburg, the region to which we now turn.

Chapter 20

BRANDENBURG AND MECKLENBURG

The lowland of Brandenburg and Mecklenburg forms the eastern portion of the much larger Northern Lowland of Germany. In almost every detail, its relief is the work of the glaciers of the concluding phase of the Ice Age. A series of terminal moraines can be traced, swinging southeastwards from the Schleswig-Holstein peninsula to the Oder and Neisse, beyond which they pass into the territory occupied by Poland in 1945. The moraines give the basis for a division of the country into four northwest to southeast-trending belts: the Southern Heathlands, the Brandenburg Urstromtal Region, the Mecklenburg Lake Plateau and the Mecklenburg Coastal Lowland.

This eastern part of the Northern Lowland has a more extreme continental type of climate than the rest of Germany. Rye and potatoes are the characteristic crops, rather than wheat, especially as the glacially derived soils are generally sandy. The potatoes nourish a very high pig population. Large stretches of the poorest land are covered by heathland or coniferous forest plantations.

THE SOUTHERN HEATHLANDS

The outermost terminal moraines are the product of the older Warthe ice sheet (pp. 27–8). They have been much more eroded than the later moraines to the north, and any associated lakes have long been filled by peat and silt. The actual terminal moraine ridges run across sandy plateau blocks, the soils of which are generally podsolized through long leaching.

Altmark-Fläming. The westernmost of the heath blocks is the Lüneburg Heath, in Lower Saxony (Chap. 16). This is continued southeastwards in the *Altmark*, the country contained within the great bend of the Elbe above Magdeburg. The

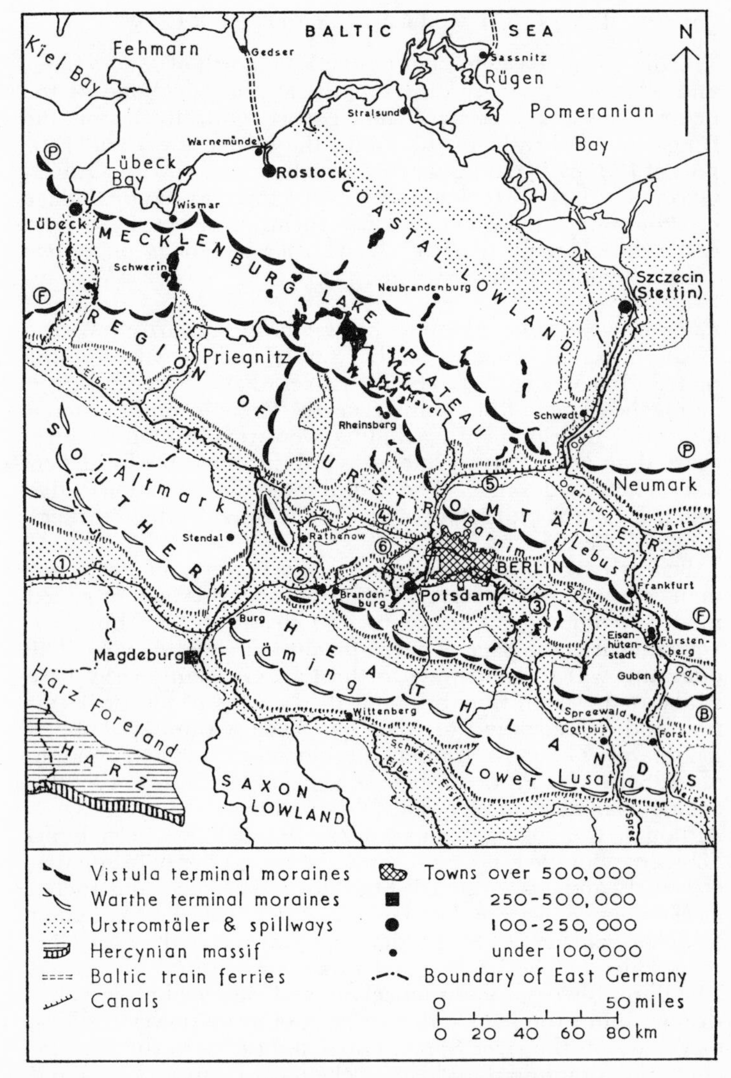

FIG. 59. Brandenburg and Mecklenburg.
Vistula moraine stages: (B) Brandenburg; (F) Frankfurt; (P) Pomeranian.
Canals: (1) Mittelland; (2) Elbe-Havel; (3) Oder-Spree; (4) Havelland; (5) Oder-Havel; (6) Paretz-Niederneuendorf by-pass.

Warthe moraine ridge is cut by the Elbe north of Magdeburg, and then continues southwestwards as the backbone of the heavily forested *Fläming Heath*. Towns naturally lie on the fringes of the heath; in the south, the bridge town and Elbe port of *Wittenberg* has been progressively drawn into the Central German industrial region, but is best known as the birthplace of Protestantism. Luther and Melanchthon lie buried in the castle church, to the doors of which Luther nailed his ninety-five Theses against Indulgences in 1517.

Lower Lusatia. The Fläming passes southeastwards into the Lower Lusatian Heath, another sandy and heavily forested plateau block (Fig. 60). The rivers Neisse and Spree cut right across the plateau from south to north. There is some scattered industrial development, including wool textile manufacture, centred on *Forst*. Pottery and glass industries use the local Tertiary clays and sands. The main route and administrative centre is *Cottbus* (76), at a crossing of the Spree on the northern fringe of the plateau.

Beneath the sands of Lower Lusatia lie 60% of East Germany's brown-coal reserves. Until the 1950s this field provided moderate amounts of briquettes and electric power, but from 1953 onwards the pace of development increased sharply. The dual aim was to contribute to the East German energy base while at the same time bringing the benefits of industrialization and urbanization to what had been a thinly-populated heathland. The most dramatic development was the founding of the Schwarze Pumpe *Kombinat*, a group of plants to produce coking coal, electricity, gas and by-products from brown coal. Although the coking plants appear not to have been built, Schwarze Pumpe is nevertheless a major supplier of briquettes, electricity and gas. A 'socialist new town' has been constructed at *Hoyerswerda* to serve the plant. An older coal-chemical plant at Schwarzheide is being redeveloped as the main East German source of herbicides and other agricultural chemicals. The diminished emphasis on coking and chemical projects has thrown into prominence the erection of large power stations, especially on the river Spree. Other industries in the area include the aluminium and electrochemical plant at Lauta and the Lauchhammer heavy machine plant, which makes the giant excavators used in the open brown-coal pits.

THE BRANDENBURG URSTROMTAL REGION

To the north of the Fläming and Lusatian heathlands we cross a series of terminal moraines which mark stages in the retreat towards the Baltic of the last (Vistula or Würm) ice sheet. Here the glacial drift is still fresh; erosion has had far less time

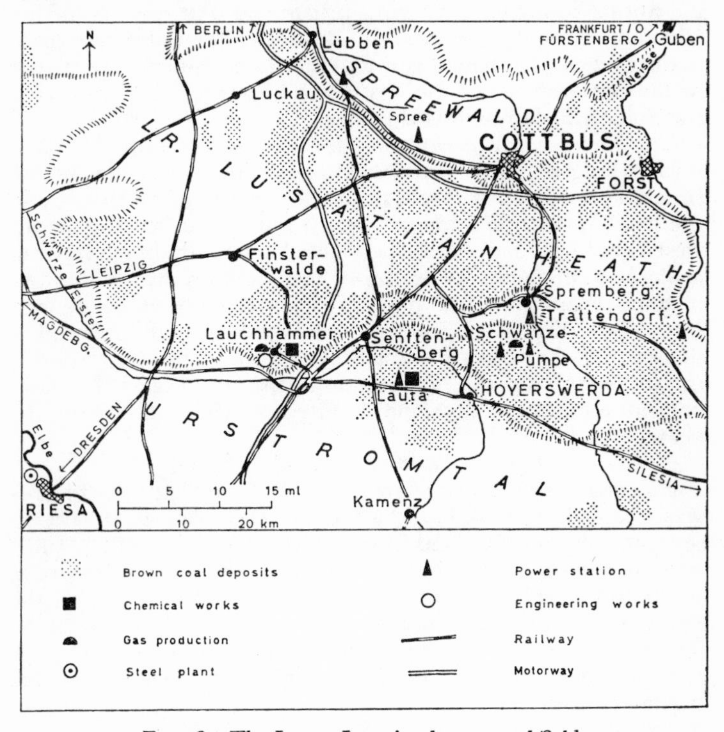

FIG. 60. The Lower Lusatian brown-coal field.

to do its work of destruction than in the Warthe moraine belt to the south and west. The chaotically tumbled boulders and clay of the terminal moraines form ridges rising to 180 m/600 ft, swinging in great arcs across the country. North of each terminal moraine the decaying ice left behind a sheet of boulder clay, with a hummocky surface holding up many lakes. To the south, water from the melting ice deposited coarse gravel cones, grading into sheets of sterile outwash sand, most unfavourable to agriculture.

The great characteristic of Brandenburg, however, is the association with the moraines of great ice-margin trenches or *Urstromtäler* (p. 28). There is a series of these trenches, swinging across country, each lying just to the south of one of the Vistula terminal moraines. In Brandenburg there are three main *Urstromtäler*, which run together in the northwest, owing to the convergence of the Vistula moraines as they approach the Schleswig-Holstein peninsula.

The present rivers follow the *Urstromtäler* only in part, meandering as misfit streams within them for a time, before breaking northwards through the moraine ridge on the way to the sea. The combination of approximately southeast to northwest trending *Urstromtäler* intersected by south–north flowing rivers has cut the drift country of Brandenburg into a number of semi-rectangular low plateau blocks separated by depressions. It is this association of low plateaus and intervening depressions that gives Brandenburg its individuality, and distinguishes it from the heathlands to the south, and the more continuous ground moraine country of Mecklenburg to the north.

The Low Plateaus. Each plateau block consists ideally of outwash sands in the south and a boulder clay plain in the north, separated by the jumbled hills of the terminal moraine. Initially, all the blocks were covered by a mixed forest of dry oak, birch and pine, the oak and the birch predominating on the boulder clay and terminal moraines, the pine on the sands. The boulder clay areas have been cleared for agriculture and their loamy sand soils produce rye for bread, and potatoes for human consumption, for distilling into alcohol and for feeding to pigs. Cattle have to be fed on roots and fodder crops, as the low rainfall and sandy soil prevent the growth of good grass. The outwash sands provide even poorer soils and are mainly covered by dark, monotonous pine plantations.

The Urstromtäler. The glacial sandy outwash that covers the floors of the *Urstromtäler* does not normally provide fertile soils, especially as a high water table has encouraged the development of marsh and peat bog. When drained, such areas provide pasture and meadow, which are otherwise scarce in this land of low rainfall and sandy soil. The peaty soils are also excellent for market gardening, especially in the Spreewald and in the Oderbruch, the great vegetable garden for Berlin. The existence of the *Urstromtäler* has made easy the construction of a network of canals connecting the Oder and Elbe through the site of Berlin. The 1,000-ton Elbe–Havel canal continues the Mittelland canal from the Elbe north of Magdeburg to the Havel lakes, through which barges can make their way to the western outskirts of Berlin. This route is continued southeastwards by the 600-ton Oder–Spree canal to the Oder at Fürstenberg. Alternatively, the Havel lakes can be followed northwards through Spandau to the 600-ton Oder–Havel (Hohenzollern) canal, which uses the northernmost of the *Urstromtäler* to reach the Oder and provides a waterway to Stettin, now in Polish hands.

Farm and Village in Brandenburg. Brandenburg is the creation of the German eastern colonization. This was not just military conquest, but the carefully planned settlement of peasants from the overcrowded villages of western Germany in the new land. The low plateaus were soon cleared and covered by the typical planned village forms of the eastern colonization, the long-street village (*Strassendorf*) and the long-green village (*Angerdorf*). Although the farmers brought the traditional open-field agriculture with them, this, too, was rigidly planned. Normally in each of the three fields all of the strips ran parallel, in orderly fashion, from one side to the other. The further east the settlement went, the more organized, standardized, the village and field forms became (Fig. 9).

The *Urstromtäler* have a different history. Here the original Slav population had lived, fishing, wildfowling, collecting honey, pasturing their beasts in the forest and practising a primitive shifting population. The Wends of Lower Lusatia have managed to preserve their language and customs to this day, sheltered in the Spreewald swamps, where movement is possible only by boat. They are now cherished as East Germany's only national minority. The *Urstromtäler* were not suited to the large open-field village; instead, hamlets and orderly small villages were associated with irregular field systems.

The peasants who so laboriously cleared the new land in the

east were attracted by promises of personal freedom from feudal restrictions. These rights they gradually lost with the growth in power of the landowning classes, the Junkers, until the peasants were reduced to serfdom. At the same time, their land was increasingly swallowed up by the great spread and expansion of the large estate farm (*Gut*). This was a world of its own, with manor house set in ornamental grounds, its quadrangle of barns, stables and byres, with cottages for its workers, perhaps a light railway to bring in the crops from the immense fields, perhaps a rural industry, like a distillery. At the end of the war land reform split the great estates into 5–8 ha/12–20 acres plots for distribution to small farmers, farm labourers and refugees. Now all is changed once more: collectivization has caused the regrouping of holdings into large units once more. The *Gut* buildings have resumed their former function as the headquarters of the new 'Agricultural Producer-Cooperatives', and the manor house is frequently a cultural centre for leisure activities and political education.

Town and Industry in Brandenburg. The towns of Brandenburg were no less carefully planned than the villages. They were sited in strategic positions at route centres, especially at points where the overland routes, which kept to the low plateaus, had to descend into a swampy valley to make a river crossing. Some, like Brandenburg itself, were built on the sites of Slav settlements, others on completely new sites selected as convenient administrative market and defence centres for the inhabitants of a group of surrounding villages. Like the East German villages, the towns have a much more regular town plan than in the west (Fig. 14).

The principal towns are sited on the west–east lines of medieval advance. One route began at *Stendal* in the Altmark and crossed the Havel at *Rathenow*, a centre today of optical industries. The Havel was crossed again at the fortress town of Spandau and the route continued through Berlin to the Oder at Frankfurt.

A second route left the bridgehead town of Magdeburg and made its way northwestwards to the towns which lie among the Havel lakes below Berlin. Here *Brandenburg* (91) has the largest of East Germany's steel works, well placed to receive scrap from Berlin, and to supply steel for further processing in the engineering works of the city.

Nearer to Berlin lies *Potsdam* (111). From the middle of the 17th century, the rulers of Brandenburg-Prussia had a palace here, where they could live among the lakes and forests, and yet be near Berlin. Potsdam is particularly associated with Frederick the Great who, despising the German language, gathered about him there a band of French-speaking writers and philosophers, including Voltaire himself. It was no doubt Potsdam's association with Prussia's military glories that caused it to be selected in 1945 as the headquarters of the Russian occupation. There are large motor and locomotive works, and other engineering industries tributary to Berlin.

From Potsdam, the medieval routeway crossed the Spree at Berlin, and reached the Oder at *Frankfurt-on-Oder* (59), situated at a point where the valley narrows to break through one of the Vistula moraines, giving an easy crossing. The railway yards and rail bridge south of Frankfurt are the principal interchange point for goods moving by land between East Germany and the U.S.S.R. Although made a *Bezirk* capital, Frankfurt has lost much former importance as an administrative centre, garrison town and central place, owing to the formation of the new boundary on the Oder. As part of efforts to industrialize the eastern areas of the DDR, Frankfurt was selected as the site of an important semi-conductor plant.

South of Frankfurt the Havel–Spree canal reaches the Oder at *Fürstenberg*. This was the location selected for a large iron and steel plant, which was to make up for supplies formerly received from West Germany, using Russian ore and Polish coking coal. Construction began in 1950, but was stopped after completion of the blast furnaces, owing to a change in economic policy. The steel works and rolling mills to complete the project were added only in the late 1960s. Alongside the works was built a planned 'socialist new town', originally called 'Stalinstadt', now *Eisenhüttenstadt* (38). Thanks to these developments, population has risen markedly in the last twenty years, contrary to the general trends in Brandenburg (Fig. 24). This is in conformity with DDR official policy for the eastern areas, which is also reflected in the selection of *Guben* further south as the location of a synthetic fibres plant.

The postwar *Land* Brandenburg had a population in 1946 of just under 2·6 millions. In the political reorganization of 1952 it was divided, the territory going mainly to the new *Bezirke* Cottbus, Frankfurt and Potsdam.

MECKLENBURG

The Mecklenburg Lake Plateau. Beyond the northernmost *Urstromtal* of Brandenburg the two most recent of the Vistula terminal moraines run close together, forming the Mecklenburg Lake Plateau, a southeast–northwest trending belt of confused, glacial country. The two moraines are so recent that erosion has not had time to destroy the freshness of the glacial forms, and drift mounds pound back the thousands of lakes from which the region derives its name. Other narrow, approximately north–south, lakes were carved by meltwater moving beneath the ice sheet.

The land-use pattern is very varied, closely reflecting the composition of the underlying drifts. The sandy boulder clay has been only slightly leached during the relatively short period that has passed since its deposition, and so provides fertile soils. Except on the steeper slopes, the original beech forests have been cleared and replaced by arable fields growing wheat and sugar beet. The many marshy hollows in the drift have been drained for meadows, while the patches of outwash sand are devoted to rye and potato fields or pine plantations.

Mecklenburg Coastal Lowland. North of the Lake Plateau, there are no more continuous terminal moraines. The drift consists almost solely of boulder clay deposited directly from the decaying ice sheet; the outwash sands which ruin such large areas to the south are rarely found here. The sandy clay is little leached, and provides fertile soils. This is the agricultural heart of Mecklenburg, producing rich crops of wheat and sugar beet.

After the withdrawal of the ice, the coast of Mecklenburg had an irregular outline, formed by promontories and islands of boulder clay with intervening drowned depressions or *Bodden*, similar to the *Förden* of Schleswig-Holstein. Marine erosion since then has somewhat smoothed the outline of the coast, building up beach bars across the *Bodden*. The existence of these barriers has hampered port development.

These conditions are repeated on a smaller scale in the large island of Rügen, except that the underlying Secondary rocks of the North German Lowland come to the surface here in small Cretaceous inliers. These have been eroded by the sea to form chalk cliffs, a unique feature of the German coast.

The chalk is a major source of lime, which is not easily available in the Northern Lowland.

Rural Settlement. The village types of Mecklenburg seem always to have been small and irregular, contrasting with the planned forms of Brandenburg to the south. Possibly the German settlers, coming mainly from Lower Saxony, brought a tradition of settlement in small villages akin to the Drubbel (Fig. 8). More and more, too, the peasant village gave place in Mecklenburg to the large estate farm or *Gut*, with its spacious buildings and immense fields. Mecklenburg was more dominated by the estate farm than any other part of Germany; by the 20th century half the land was held in units of 200 ha/500 acres or more.

Now the pattern of ownership, and in part of settlement, has changed once more. Land reform destroyed estates of over 100 ha/250 acres; the great fields were cut once more into strips for small peasant farmers, which in turn were regrouped when collectivization created the new 'Agricultural producer co-operatives'.

Industry and Towns in Mecklenburg. As part of the efforts to bring a more balanced economy to the northern part of the DDR most of the small towns of Mecklenburg have received some industrial development, especially in the form of new or extended sugar and food-packing plants. *Schwerin* (92), a former princely capital attractively situated on the lake of the same name, has been made a *Bezirk* capital and is being built up as a more substantial centre. Formerly industrial development was discouraged, but it now has plants for making agricultural machinery and cranes, and for plastics processing. It has also received a large cable plant, as part of the effort to decentralize the East Berlin electrical industry. *Neubrandenburg*, a classic example of a planned town of the German colonization (Fig. 14), is also developing as a *Bezirk* capital in a formerly rustic area.

During the period since 1945 the ports of the Baltic coast have been considerably developed with the object of replacing Stettin, lost to Poland, and Hamburg in West Germany. The approach channel and port facilities at *Wismar* (55) have been extended, and this port also possesses one of the main East German shipyards. Further east *Stralsund* (69) has a poorer approach and has expanded less. On Rügen *Sassnitz* has a fish processing plant and is the terminal of the ferry to Trelleborg in Sweden. The biggest changes have been at *Rostock* (184), which with its outport of Warnemünde has been developed into East Germany's ocean port by the creation of new dock basins in the Breitling, the Warnow estuary. In 1966 traffic exceeded 6 million tons a year for the first time. Rostock and Warnemünde are important shipbuilding centres. The building of marine diesel engines and fish processing are also important. Warnemünde is the terminal for the ferry to Gedser in Denmark.

Away to the east, on the Oder, the latest industrial development is the creation of an oil refinery, fertilizer plant and paper plant at *Schwedt* (23), on the Oder at the terminus of the oil pipeline from the U.S.S.R. The little town is now growing rapidly as blocks of flats are built for the industrial workers.

Land Mecklenburg was extended in 1945 by the addition of the western parts of Pomerania, which had not been seized by the Poles. Owing to the influx of refugees, the population was over 2 millions in 1946, compared with 1·4 millions in 1939. Mecklenburg was divided in 1952 into the districts of Rostock, Schwerin and Neubrandenburg, and population has declined as people have moved out of this predominantly rural area.

Chapter 21
BERLIN

THE CITY BEFORE 1945

The nucleus of Berlin lies in Brandenburg's central *Urstromtal*, at a point where the Spree can be crossed not only by north–south routes but by the main west–east land route from Magdeburg on the Elbe to the Oder at Frankfurt (pp. 306–7). Medieval Berlin was much less important than near-by Brandenburg, and consisted of two separate settlements, Kölln on an island of the Spree, and Berlin itself to the east across the river. Although the site is a reasonably good one, it has none of the natural advantages of, for example, Frankfurt-am-Main, Cologne or Magdeburg. It is not on one of Germany's major rivers, not in a particularly fertile countryside, not near important raw materials. It was not even centrally placed in pre-war Germany, certainly not in the Germany of 1945. The rise of Berlin was determined by its selection in the 15th century as the residence of the Hohenzollern rulers of Brandenburg, and then by the rise of Brandenburg-Prussia to predominance within a united Germany.

Berlin's Economy. In 1871, when Germany was unified under Prussian dominance, Berlin had a population of 914,000. By 1900 the figure had reached 2·7 millions, and by 1943 a record total of nearly 4·5 million people lived in the 340 square miles of Greater Berlin. The primary function of Berlin until 1945 was to act as the capital of Germany and of its largest *Land*, Prussia. To the seat of government were naturally attracted the headquarters of the banks, insurance companies and other financial institutions and offices of firms from all over Germany. Great department stores also drew buyers from far beyond the bounds of the city. Naturally the capital was an important cultural centre, with the Friedrich Wilhelm (now Humboldt) University, libraries, museums, theatres and concert halls.

In addition, Berlin was a major industrial region in its own right. This was not because there were any advantages of access to local fuel or raw materials, but because the city itself was a vast market, had well-developed communications to the rest of Germany and could offer to the industrialist a pool of labour accustomed to industrial work. The electrical industry alone, with such great firms as Siemens and AEG, was responsible for half Germany's output. The clothing industry

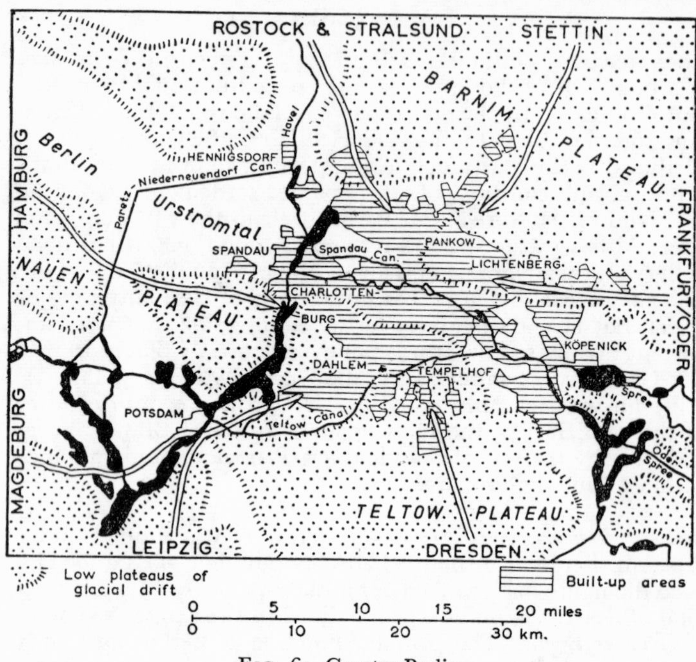

FIG. 61. Greater Berlin.

was also characteristic, especially the manufacture of women's clothing, close to the centre of fashion. The printing industry was related to Berlin's newspaper and publishing activities. Other important industries were machine tool construction, precision engineering, vehicle building and fine chemical production.

URBAN REGIONS

Central Berlin. Berlin today is bounded to the west and east by belts of lakes: in the west by the Havel lakes in the neighbourhood of Potsdam and Spandau, in the east by the lakes of the Dahme–Spree confluence in the neighbourhood of Köpenick. The two lake regions are linked by the southeast–northwest course of the *Urstromtal*, followed by the Spree. Although the heart of Berlin lies within the *Urstromtal*, the suburbs have climbed onto the fringes of the Barnim Plateau to the north and the Teltow Plateau to the south. The nucleus of the city before the Second World War was provided by the twin towns of Berlin and Kölln, which, like the city of London, still kept their narrow, congested streets until their destruction from bombing. From the middle of the 19th century the inhabitants began to move away to the suburbs, as the old dwelling houses of the 17th and 18th centuries gave way to the shops, offices and warehouses characteristic of a modern city centre.

The palace of the Electors of Brandenburg was established on the Spree Island just to the northwest of the town of Kölln. Westwards from the Palace developed the official quarter, the 'west end' of Berlin. Its axis was the wide processional way of the Unter den Linden, which passed under the triumphal arch of the Brandenburger Tor and continued westwards through the Tiergarten as the Charlottenburger Chaussee. North of the Unter den Linden were the university buildings; south of it the government quarter, where ministries, embassies and legations were grouped on the Wilhelmstrasse, the Whitehall of Berlin. The banking, financial and business quarter, and also the newspaper offices, lay between the Wilhelmstrasse and the old city. Here, too, was the centre of the fashion trade. The old city and this official quarter together made up the core of Berlin. The outer edge of this heart area was approximately marked by the line of roads and squares which succeeded the pallisade with gates erected in 1737 as a police and customs boundary to the city.

The 19th-Century Residential Ring. With the establishment of Berlin as capital of a united Germany in 1871, the city grew rapidly. North, east and south of the administrative and commercial core there grew up densely peopled residential districts.

In a characteristically German spirit of order, this growth was rigidly planned, with a regular grid-iron pattern of wide roads separating large square building blocks. The roads were lined with uniform four- or five-story tenement houses, the monotonous, airless, barrack-like dwellings (*Mietskasernen*) characteristic of working-class Berlin. The interior of each block

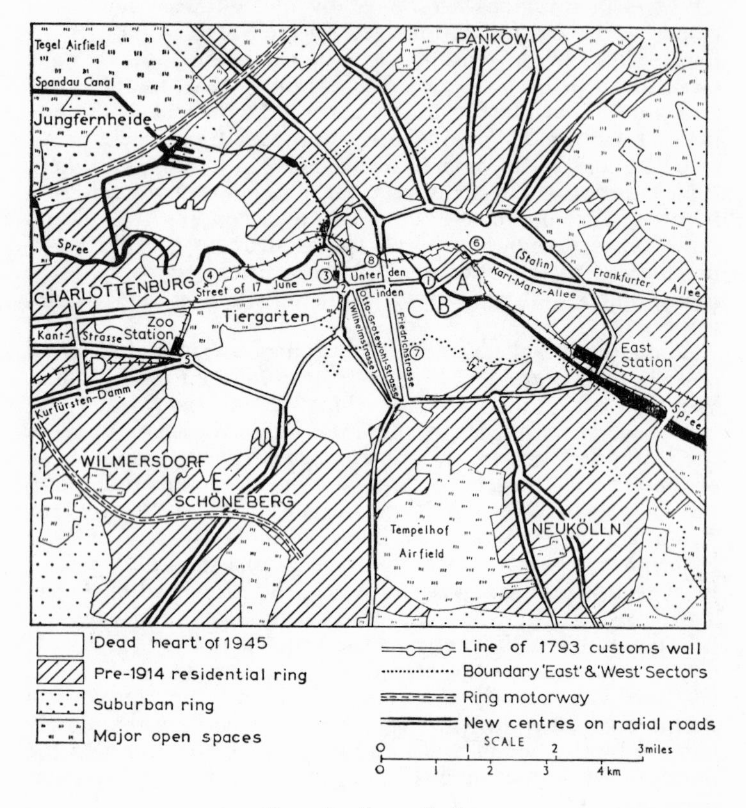

FIG. 62. Inner Berlin.

(A) medieval Berlin; (B) medieval Kölln; (C) government quarter; (D) new commercial centre of West Berlin; (E) new administrative centres of West Berlin; (1) former Berlin Palace; (2) Brandenburger Tor; (3) Reichstag (Parliament); (4) new Hanse district; (5) Kaiser-Wilhelm memorial church; (6) Alexanderplatz; (7) Checkpoint Charlie; (8) Friedrichstrasse Station.

was a maze of courts lined with more tenements, but also containing much of Berlin's industry.

The tenement ring was broken in the west by the open space of the Tiergarten, around which, more especially to the south, expensive villas and foreign embassies were built. Only west of the Tiergarten, in Charlottenburg and Schöneberg, did the more dense development resume, this time in the form of middle-class apartment blocks. After 1900, the Kurfürstendamm in Charlottenburg began to develop as a distinct entertainments district, with theatre, cinemas and cafés.

The Outer Suburban Ring. Beyond these continuously built-up central quarters is an outer ring of much more open and more varied buildings. It is here that the larger concentrations of Berlin industry are found, many of the firms having moved out from the congested central quarters. Favoured locations for industry include the Havel lakes in the west from Potsdam through Spandau to Hennigsdorf, the Dahme–Spree lakes in the east from Wildau to Köpenick, and the southeast–northwest course of the Berlin *Urstromtal* between the two. Other sites are on the inner ring railroad, and on the lines radiating beyond it.

The industrial sites have groups of workers' houses near by, including carefully planned housing estates like *Siemensstadt*, attached to the Siemens electrical works. In the west, *Spandau* was formerly an independent town, fortified to guard the crossing of the Havel, but is now an industrial and residential suburb of Berlin. *Köpenick* in the east is another small town swallowed in Berlin's growth.

This belt is diversified by lakes and forests, which make up the characteristic landscape of outer Berlin. On weekends and holidays in summer the lakes are nearly solid with sailing craft, the beaches crowded with thousands of browning Berliners. Among the lakes and forests stand the modern villas of the more exclusive outer suburbs such as Dahlem, while the humbler folk find their air and exercise in working on the allotment gardens (*Laubenkolonien*) which cover wide areas between the various suburbs.

COMMUNICATIONS OF PREWAR BERLIN

The waterways approaching Berlin from West and East, the Elbe–Havel and Oder–Spree canals, are linked across Berlin by the Spree river itself and by the Teltow canal from Grunau to Potsdam. Below Berlin, the Spandau canal gives a more direct approach for northbound traffic to the Oder–Havel (Hohenzollern) canal to Stettin (Fig. 61).

The main railway lines were brought into termini situated on the ring road, mentioned above, which was the approximate outer barrier of the city before the railway age. City rail traffic is carried on the *Stadtbahn* (S-Bahn), a mainly overground system serving the suburbs, and the underground railway (U-Bahn). The S-Bahn provides a complete inner rail ring, but the outer belt line was incomplete before the war. Berlin was also the main centre of the motorway system. A ring motorway encircled the southern, eastern and northern outskirts of the city, and from this Germany's principal motor highways diverged.

BERLIN SINCE 1945

It is scarcely possible to imagine what life must have been like in Berlin when, at the end of April 1945, after years when British bombers by night and American bombers by day had blasted the buildings and made the streets run with fire, the Russian armies began to fight their way into the city. In the *Führerbunker* beneath the ruins of the marble Chancellery that he had built, Adolf Hitler continued to direct what remained of his troops, sending orders to armies that no longer existed to speed to the relief of the capital. With Russian shells falling on the Chancellery, the former master of the German Third *Reich* and of all Europe took his own life.

By this time, the population of Berlin had fallen to only 2·9 millions. Bombing or shelling had destroyed 40% of all living accommodation, and many of the dwellings that remained were in a shattered or hastily repaired condition. Ten square miles of the centre of Berlin, including the administrative and commercial quarters, lay in ruins, forming a 'dead heart' to the city. The remaining inhabitants took refuge in patched-up holes in the ruins, in suburban villas or in shacks on the allotments.

Industrially also, Berlin suffered heavily, partly as a result of the bombing, but mainly owing to Soviet dismantling of equipment for reparations. It is believed that about 75% of total industrial equipment was destroyed or removed, including practically all the West Berlin electrical and machine tool plants. The economic damage was increased through the loss of nearly all the functions of a capital, whether of Prussia, which no longer existed, or of a Germany which was now divided into zones of military occupation.

A DIVIDED BERLIN

In the long run, however, the greatest difficulties came from the division of Berlin into sectors of occupation for Britain, France, the U.S.A. and the U.S.S.R. In theory, Berlin, like Germany itself, was to be governed as a unit. In practice, in Berlin as in Germany as a whole, the Russian-occupied area and the 'western' areas increasingly went different ways. The dividing lines were finally hardened in 1948, when West and East Germany adopted separate currencies. From then onwards, a political and customs frontier ran around West Berlin, separating it from the eastern third of the city and from the surrounding countryside. Indeed, for just under a year from June 1948 West Berlin was fully blockaded, and every scrap of food or piece of coal consumed had to be flown in by the 'Berlin Air-Lift'.

The situation created by this division of Berlin was fantastic. It was as if England were divided into the territory of two hostile governments, one based in the West Country with a detached area in the Western districts of London, and another holding the Eastern counties and Central London as far west as Marble Arch, where police and customs would have established check points. The Bank of England, the Stock Exchange and the large department stores would be in Kensington High Street, so forming the nucleus of the Western sector. The bombed ruins of Buckingham Palace would be cleared away and turned into a parade ground for political demonstrations, with the Mile End Road turned into a spectacular processional way.

Just this happened in Berlin. At the boundaries between the western and eastern sectors bus and tram routes stopped; passengers wishing to travel further had to alight and walk past the East German check points. The S-Bahn and underground railways continued to function, but several of the main-line termini were left derelict, with grass-grown tracks, because the lines leading to them pass through West Berlin, and traffic has been diverted to East Berlin stations. The East (Schlesischer) Station has been made into the main terminus for East Berlin, while trains from West Germany use the suburban Zoo station.

Then in 1961 the continuing drain of East German refugees through West Berlin led to the closing of the sector boundary to East Germans and Berliners by the building of the Berlin Wall, reinforced by belts of barbed wire, searchlights and armed guards ordered to shoot to kill. The underground railway systems were separated, but one rail crossing through the Friedrichstrasse station was retained. Through this check point, or through the limited road access points like the well-known 'Checkpoint Charlie' West Germans and foreigners could enter East Berlin after lengthy formalities. The Berliners themselves could expect only occasional day passes to visit friends and relations, even though they might live only in the next street of the divided city.

The Rebuilding of Berlin. The boundary between the east and west sectors of Berlin runs through the dead heart of the city. It cuts streets that were formerly crammed with traffic, discouraging the rebuilding of the former central administrative and business district, much of which still lay in ruins years after the end of the war. Instead, a series of new centres has developed on the roads radiating outwards through the 19th-century residential districts. The suburbs are now of greater importance than the heart.

In West Berlin, the Kurfürstendamm and the neighbourhood of the Kaiser-Wilhelm memorial church now form the undisputed hotel and amusement district, and also the site of many of the head offices of the major banks and insurance companies. The West Berlin City Hall is in Schönlberg, other administrative buildings in Wilmersdorf. In the garden suburb of Dahlem are the new Free University of Berlin and many museums. The Hanse district, north of the Tiergarten, has been rebuilt in the most spectacular modern style.

So far as possible, rebuilding takes the form of blocks of flats widely spaced in grass, instead of the continuous street façades and gloomy interior courts of the period before 1914. Berlin has always been a surprisingly green city, but the open spaces were unevenly distributed, with few breaks in the urban mass between the Tiergarten at the centre and the forests and lakes on the outskirts. Wartime destruction has given an opportunity to run a series of interconnecting open spaces through the built-up area, leading out towards the countryside. The underground railways that were built to focus on the old city centre have been intercepted by a new north–south link through the Zoo station, and work has begun on a circular urban motorway to keep traffic out of the Charlottenburg area. Now attention is turning from rebuilding to redevelopment. The 19th-century *Mietskasernen* areas north and south of the old central area present a particularly difficult problem. It is clearly wrong that people should live huddled in lightless courts next to chemical plants or over a printing works, yet to move them out to the suburbs would break up a living community. It is not any easier to move the industry, which typically consists of small clothing firms, furniture and small component manufacturers, and wholesalers, all closely interlinked with other firms in the same district.

East Berlin has the advantage of not being cut off from its surrounding countryside and of still performing the functions of a capital, although for 17 millions rather than the 70 millions ruled from the Berlin central area before 1945. The show piece of East Berlin reconstruction in the earlier postwar years was the Stalin (formerly Frankfurter, now Karl-Marx) Allee, a wide processional way rigidly lined by continuous blocks of flats heavily ornamented in the approved Moscow style of the period. The Stalin Allee was deliberately created as a backcloth for official demonstrations, and was intended to lead marchers down to pass before the saluting base in the Marx-Engels-Platz, itself created as the local equivalent of Red Square by the symbolic demolition of the former royal palace.

East Berlin includes the former central area of undivided Berlin, which however is surrounded on three sides by the western sectors, and so is not easy of access. Perhaps understandably rebuilding has been slow, although the State Opera and other historic monuments have been painstakingly restored. When large-scale rebuilding of government offices and other public buildings began in the mid-1960s activity centred on what had been medieval Berlin, between the Marx-Engels-Platz and the Alexanderplatz. The old government centre on the Wilhelmstrasse (now Otto-Grotewohl-Strasse), with the site of Hitler's Chancellery and the *Führerbunker*, was left as a wilderness on the sector boundary.

Population since 1945. The total population of Berlin had recovered to 3·2 millions by the first postwar census in 1946. It has fluctuated at just above this level ever since, with a slight tendency for East Berlin to decline over the years, and for West Berlin marginally to increase. Unfortunately the bare figures conceal serious deficiencies in population structure. West Berlin in particular is an ageing city; the proportion of pensioners is more than twice as great as in West Germany, and there is a large female surplus. Retirement is draining the labour force of thousands of workers a year, and these are not being replaced by the immigration of young people, who prefer the greater freedom of movement of West Germany. Even the total population seems likely to decline in future, as an increasing excess of deaths over births will hardly be compensated by immigration.

THE ECONOMY SINCE 1945

West Berlin. Recovery has been hampered by the loss of capital functions, which before the war brought Berlin as much income as the sale of the products of its factories. Something of the lost income and the lost prestige has been made up by attempts to develop Berlin as a centre for international congresses and by encouraging the tourist traffic. Basically, however, the attempt to provide a proper living for the people of Berlin has been by the development of industry, backed by massive West German financial assistance, both in the form of grants and in the form of contracts for the supply of goods.

There are many difficulties facing West Berlin industry. Food, fuel and materials must be hauled over 160 km/100 miles of East German territory, and nearly all the finished products sent back to West Germany for sale or export. East Germany supplies some bulky commodities like brown coal and gravel, but trade is very small. Political uncertainty tends to discourage industrialists who, like the great AEG and Siemens electrical firms, maintain their Berlin plants while reserving their expansion for West Germany. Nevertheless output had exceeded the prewar level by the mid-1950s and continued to rise steadily thereafter.

Even more than before the war, West Berlin concentrates on valuable products needing highly skilled labour, which can stand the high transport costs inherent in the 'island' situation. The manufacture of electrical equipment still leads, followed by food, drink and tobacco industries, which largely serve Berlin's own population. Then come clothing, a traditional Berlin industry which has migrated out of the eastern sector, machine building and the pharmaceutical industry.

East Berlin. Not being on a political 'island' like West Berlin, East Berlin industry stands in a much more normal relationship to its surrounding East German hinterland. As in West Berlin, industries concentrate on valuable and complex products needing highly skilled labour. Machinery and equipment made in East Berlin are essential for the fulfilment of the industrial plans, not only of East Germany, but of the whole Communist world. As in West Berlin, about a third of industrial output consists of electrical and electronic equipment; East Berlin is the principle DDR centre for this industry. Food, drink and tobacco industries come next, as in West Berlin, and again serving mainly local needs. Machine production and the reorganized clothing industry are also important. The chemical industry is represented by branches such as pharmaceuticals and photographic materials. Finally the printing industry has a greater relative importance in East Berlin as a capital and main press centre than it now has in West Berlin.

The 'Island' of West Berlin and East Germany. In the years after 1945 the East German government did all it could to seal off West Berlin and minimize the considerable inconvenience of having a politically-independent 'island' established at its most important communications node. A partial road by-pass already existed in the form of the incomplete *Berliner Ring*, the starting-point of the prewar motorway system. Nevertheless the road journey from central Berlin to, say, Potsdam, avoiding West Berlin is an extremely time-consuming and inconvenient one. The railways that formerly ran from East German territory through the western sectors to central termini have also been beheaded by a new circular line and led into the East Station. The one exception is the international line from western Europe to Warsaw and the U.S.S.R., which still runs through the heart of the city from the Zoo station to the East Station. A partial by-pass for water traffic has also been provided by the construction of the Parotz–Niederneuendorf canal west of the city.

In spite of all these measures, the situation remains a difficult and uncertain one, and the curious existence of the 'foreign body' of West Berlin must be a constant irritation to the DDR government. All that can be said is that the apparently unstable settlement of Berlin, like the division of Germany itself, survived without a major conflict for a longer period than did the Germany of the Versailles settlement after the First World War.

SUGGESTIONS FOR FURTHER READING

F. FRIEDENSBERG, 'The geographical elements in the Berlin situation', *Geographical Journal*, 133, 1967, pp. 137–47.

INDEX

Where references to a topic appear on more than one page, the principal reference (if any) is indicated by bold type. Figure references are given in italic type. (W) indicates that the references following relate to West Germany, (E) that they relate to East Germany.